To DAD
6/16/74
love
Joe & Mimi

GERMAN TANKS OF WORLD WAR II

GERMAN TANKS OF WORLD WAR II

The Complete Illustrated History of German Armoured Fighting Vehicles 1926-1945

by

Dr. F. M. von Senger und Etterlin

Translated by

J. Lucas
Imperial War Museum, London

Edited by

Peter Chamberlain and Chris Ellis

Galahad Books • New York City

Published by Galahad Books, a division of A & W
Promotional Book Corporation, 95 Madison Ave-
nue, New York, N.Y. 10016, by arrangement with
Stackpole Books, Cameron and Kelker Streets,
Harrisburg, Pa. 17105.
Library of Congress Catalog Card No.: 73–81666
ISBN: 0–88365–051–7

Contents

Inventory of Armoured Vehicles and Key to Illustrations

This inventory lists all German Armoured Fighting Vehicle prototypes, production models and their variants developed between 1926 and 1945. It also provides a key to the illustrations by listing the numbers of both the scale diagrams and the plates plus the page on which technical data is tabulated. The text follows the same sequence.

Sd Kfz number		Plate number diag	Plate number photo	Spec page no
	PANZERKAMPFWAGEN (Includes Flame Throwers, Armoured Command Vehicles, Armoured OP Tanks, Reconnaissance Tanks)			
	Grosstraktor		10	
	le Traktor		9	
	LKA 1 (Krupp) (LaS)		11	
101	Pz Kw I, Ausf A	12	13	194
	Pz Kw I, Ausf B	14	15	194
	Pz Kw I, Ausf C VK 601 (Krupp)		17	
111	Kl Pz Bw		16	194
	Pz Kw I nA verst VK 1801 (Krupp)		18	
	LKA 2 (Krupp) (LaS 100)		20	
121	Pz Kw II Ausf a 1, a 2, a 3, b		21	
	Pz Kw II Ausf c		22	
	Pz Kw II Ausf A B		23	
	Pz Kw II Ausf C	19		
	Pz Kw II Ausf D	24	25	194
	Pz Kw II Ausf E	24	25	194
	Pz Kw II Ausf F to J		26	194
	VK 1601 (D) (Pz Kw II nA verst)		29	
	Berge Pz auf Fgst Pz Kw II nA (VK 1601)		31	
	VK 1602 (D) ("Leopard", le)		33	
	VK 901 (Pz Kw II nA)		30	
	VK 1301 (Pz Kw II nA)		32	
	VK 1303			
123	Pz Spw "Luchs" (Pz Kw II Ausf L)	27	38	194
	"Leopard", schwer, 7·5 cm KwK 41			
122	Pz Kw II (Flamm)			
	Pz Kw 35(t) (LTM 35)	34	35	206
	Pz Kw 35 S(t)		202	
	Pz Kw 38(t) (TNHP-S)	37 116	36	206
140/1	Aufkl Pz 38(t)			
	Flamm Pz 38(t)			
	Pz Kw 39 H(t)		203	
	Aufkl Pz T 15 (Skoda)			

Sd Kfz number		Plate number diag	Plate number photo	Spec page no
	Pz Kw T 25 (Skoda)			
	MKA Zugführerwagen (ZW) (Krupp)		38	
141	Pz Kw III Ausf A		39	194
141	Pz Kw III Ausf B		40	194
141	Pz Kw III Ausf C		40	194
141	Pz Kw III Ausf D		41	194
141	Pz Kw III Ausf E		42	194
141	Pz Kw III Ausf F		44	196
141	Pz Kw III Ausf G		44	196
141	Pz Kw III Ausf H	43	44	196
141/1	Pz Kw III Ausf J		46	196
141/1	Pz Kw III Ausf K			
141/1	Pz Kw III Ausf L		47	196
141/2	Pz Kw III Ausf M	50	48	196
266–68	Pz Kw III Ausf N–O		51	196
	Pz Bw III (ohne KwK)			
266–68	Pz Bef Wg III Ausf H		45	
	Pz Bw III Ausf K (mit KwK)			
143	Pz Beob W III			
141/3	Pz Kw III (Flamm) Ausf M		49	
	Pz Kw III nA			
	Bataillonsführerwagen (BW)			
	VK 2001 (Rh)		54	
	VK 2001 (D)			
	VK 2001 (K)	52		
	VK 2001 (DB)			
	VK 2002 (MAN)	53		
161	Pz Kw IV Ausf A		55	196
161	Pz Kw IV Ausf B		58	196
161	Pz Kw IV Ausf C		58	196
161	Pz Kw IV Ausf D	57	56	196
161	Pz Kw IV Ausf E		59	196
161	Pz Kw IV Ausf F 1		60	196
			66	
161	Pz Kw IV Ausf F 2	62	61	196
161/1	Pz Kw IV Ausf G			198
161/2	Pz Kw IV Ausf H	64	63	198
161/2	Pz Kw IV Ausf J		65	198
161/2	Pz Kw IV Ausf K			
	Pz Kw IV mit 2 × 7·5 cm LG		67	
	Pz Kw IV als Bw Ausf H			
	Pz BeobW IV			
	Pz Kw IV nA			
	Pz Kw III/IV		68	

Sd Kfz number		Plate number diag	photo	Spec page no
	Nb Fz (Pz Kw V) (Rheinmetall)		69	
	Nb Fz (Pz Kw VI) (Rheinmetall)		70	
	Durchbruchswagen 1 (Henschel)			
	Durchbruchswagen 2 (Henschel)			
	VK 6501 (H) (SW) (Pz Kw VII)	71		
	VK 3001 (H)	73		
	VK 3001 (P) (Porsche-"Leopard")		72	
	VK 3002 (MAN)			
	VK 3002 (DB)		74	
171	Pz Kw "Panther" Ausf D	75 / 84–5	76	198
171	Pz Kw "Panther" Ausf A	75	83	198
171	Pz Kw "Panther" Ausf G		77–9	198
	Pz Kw "Panther" Ausf F			
	Pz Kw "Panther" II			
	Pz Kw V 7·5 cm KwK L/100			
267–68	Pz Bw "Panther"		80	
	Pz BeobW "Panther"		81	198
	Minenräum Pz Wg "Panther"			
	Räumschaufel Pz Wg "Panther"			
	VK 3601	86		
	VK 3602			
	VK 4501 (H)	87		
	VK 4501 (P) (Porsche 102)	88	89	
	Pz Kw "Tiger I" Ausf E	90	91–3	200
181	Pz Bef Wg "Tiger I" Ausf E			
267/8	VK 4502 (P) (Porsche 180)	96		
182	VK 4503 (H)			
	Pz Kw "Tiger II" Ausf B (Turm aA)		97	200
	Pz Kw "Tiger II" Ausf B (Turm nA)	94	95	200
	E 5, E 10, E 25, E 50, E 75			
	E 100	99	100–1	200
	VK 7001 (K) ("Löwe" oder "Tiger-Maus")	99	100 / 98	
	"Maus I & II" (Porsche 205)	102 / 105	106 / 108	200
	STURMPANZER			
142	StuG III für 7·5 cm StuK	109	110	202
142/2	StuG III für 10·5 cm StuH 42		111	202
	Sturm IG 33 mit Fahrgest. Pz Kw III			
166	Sturm Pz IV "Brummbär" für 15 cm StuH 43 (Sturm Pz 43)	112	113	202
	Sturmhaubitze 10·5 cm III/IV			
	Sturmmörser 38 cm RW 61 "Sturmtiger"	114	115	202
	JAGDPANZER			
	Jgd Pz 38 "Hetzer"	117	118	202
	Jgd Pz 38(d)			
142/1	StuG III für 7·5 cm StuK 40 L/43 & 48	116 / 120	121 / 122	
162	Jgd Pz IV für 7·5 cm PaK 39	116 / 123	124	
163	StuG IV für 7·5 cm StuK 40	116	127	
162/1	Jgd Pz IV für 7·5 cm StuK 42		126	202
162	Pz IV (lang) für 7·5 cm KwK 42		125	
	le Pz Jg III/IV			

Sd Kfz number		Plate number diag	photo	Spec page no
173	"Jagdpanther" für 8·8 cm PaK 43/3	128	129	202
194 s	sPz Jg "Tiger" (P) "Elefant" für 8·8 cm PaK 43/2 oder StuK 43/1	130	131–3	202
	Pz Jg "Panther" mit 12·8 cm PaK 80 E 25 (Porsche)	140		
186 s	"Jagdtiger" für 12·8 cm PaK 44 (Henschel)	135 / 136	135 / 136	202
	"Jagdtiger" für 12·8 cm PaK 44 (Porsche)		139	202
	FLAKPANZER			
	"Kugelblitz" mit 3 cm 103/38	268	269	
	"Kleiner Kugelblitz" 38(d)			
	SCHÜTZENPANZER (Personnel Carriers)			
250/1	le SPW	145	144	208
250/2	le Fernsprech Pz Wg	151		
250/3	le Fu Pz Wg			
250/4	Luftschutz Pz Wg			
250/5	le Beob Pz Wg			
250/6	le Mun Pz Wg			
250/7	le SPW—8 cm GrW	146		
250/8	le SPW—7·5 cm K 37	148	147	
250/9	le Pz Spw (Halbk) 2 cm	152	153	
250/10	le SPW—3·7 cm PaK	150	149	
250/11	le SPW sPz B 41			
250/12	le Schützen-Messtrupp Pz Wg			
	HL kl 3 (H) (Prototyp) 3·7 cm Kanone (1935)		143	208
	HL kl 4 (H) (Prototyp) 7·5 cm Kanone (1936)		141 / 142	208
251/1	mit SPW	156	155 / 160	208
251/2	mit SPW 8 cm GrW	159		
251/3	mit Fu Pz Wg			
251/4	mit SPW—IG-Mun			
251/5	mit SPW—Pi			
251/6	Kdo Pz Wg			
251/7	mit Pi Pz Wg			
251/8	mit Kranken Pz Wg			
251/9	mit SPW—7·5 cm K 37	161	162	
251/10	mit SPW—3·7 cm PaK	163	164	
251/11	mit Fernsprech Pz Wg			
251/12	mit Messtrupp- und Geräte Pz Wg			
251/13	mit Schallaufnahme Pz Wg			
251/14	mit Schallauswerte Pz Wg			
251/15	mit Lichtauswerte Pz Wg			
251/16	mit Flamm Pz Wg			
251/17	mit SPW 2 cm			
251/18	mit Beob Pz Wg			
251/19	mit Fernsprech-Betriebs Pz Wg			
251/20	mit SPW—Infrarotscheinw: "Uhu"		165	
251/21	mit SPW—1·5 od 2 cm Drilling		166	
251/22	mit SPW—7·5 cm PaK 40		167	
	mit SPW—28 cm Wurfrahmen	157	158	
252	le gp Mun Trspt Kw		154	
253	le gp Beob Kw			
254	mit gp Beob Kw auf RK 7 (Saurer)		278	
	H Kp 606 (1941/42)		168	208
	SPW auf Fahrgestell 38(t)			
	PANZERSPÄHWAGEN (Armoured Cars)			
13	MG-Kraftwagen (MG)	174	175	

Sd Kfz number		Plate number		Spec page no
		diag	photo	
14	MG-Kraftwagen (Fu)			
221	le Pz Spw MG	176	177	
222	le Pz Spw 2 cm	181	182	204
222	le Pz Spw 2·8 cm Pz B 41		180	
223	le Pz Spw (Fu)		179	204
231	sPz Spw 6-Rad 2 cm		183	204
232	sPz Spw 6-Rad (Fu)	184	185	
231	sPz Spw 8-Rad 2 cm	188	187	204
			190	
232	sPz Spw 8-Rad (Fu)		191	
233	sPz Spw 8-Rad 7·5 cm StuK L/24		189	
234/1	sPz Spw 8-Rad 2 cm (Tp)	194	193	204
234/2	sPz Spw 8-Rad 5 cm KwK 39 "Puma"	195	196	204
234/3	sPz Spw 8-Rad 7·5 cm KwK 37	197		
234/4	sPz Spw 8-Rad 7·5 cm PaK 39		198	
260	Kl Pz Fu Wg			
261	Kl Pz Fu Wg		178	
263	Pz Fu Wg 6-Rad		186	
263	Pz Fu Wg 8-Rad		192	
204 (f)	Panhard 178 (P 204 (f))			206
	Pz Spw Trippel Schildkröte I			
	Pz Spw Trippel Schildkröte II			
	Pz Spw Trippel Schildkröte III			
	Pz Spw RK (Ausf A) (Saurer)			
	Daimler-Benz ARW/MTW 1	170 / 171		
	Daimler-Benz G 3 (p)	173		
	Büssing NAG ZRW	172		
	PANZERJÄGER (Tank Destroyers)			
	3·7 cm PaK 35/36 auf Inf Schlepper UE (f)		206	
	4·7 cm PaK (f) auf Gw LrS (f)		207	
101	4·7 cm PaK (t) auf Pz Kw I Ausf B	199	200	206
	4·7 cm PaK (t) auf Gw Renault R 35 (f)		204	
	7·5 cm PaK 39 auf Gw II, Marder II		212	
135	7·5 cm PaK 40 L/48 auf Gw LrS (f)		205	
	7·5 cm PaK 40 L/48 auf Gw FCM (f)		208	
	7·5 cm PaK 40 L/48 auf Gw Hotchkiss (f)		209	
131	7·5 cm PaK 40/2 auf Pz Jg II Ausf A–C "Marder II"	210	211	
132	7·5 cm PaK 40/2 auf Pz Jg II Ausf D & E			
132	7·62 cm PaK 36(r) auf Pz Jg II Ausf D & E		213	
138	7·5 cm PaK 40/3 auf Pz Jg 38(t) Ausf H "Marder III"		215	
138	7·5 cm PaK 40/3 auf Pz Jg 38(t) Ausf M "Marder III"	214	216 / 217	206
139	7·62 cm PaK 36(r) auf Pz Jg 38(t)		218	
	8·8 cm PaK 43 auf Pz Jg 38(t)		219	
164	8·8 cm PaK 43/1 auf Pz Jg III/IV "Nashorn" (früher "Hornisse")	223	222	206
	8·8 cm PaK 43/1 auf Rheinmetall-Borsig-Ardelt Waffentr 38(d) (Prototyp)		220	

Sd Kfz number		Plate number		Spec page no
		diag	photo	
	8·8 cm PaK 43/1 auf Krupp/Steyr Waffenträger 38(d) (Prototyp)		221	
	12·8 cm K 40 auf VK 3601 (H)		224 / 225	
	7·5 cm PaK 40/1 auf RSO		277	
	ARMOURED ARTILLERY AND INFANTRY GUNS			
101	15 cm sIG 33 auf Pz Kw I Ausf B		226	
	15 cm sIG 33 auf Pz Kw II	227	228	
	15 cm sIG 33 auf Pz Kw II (verlängert)			
138/1	15 cm sIG 33 auf Gw 38(t) (vorvers Motor)	229	230	
138/1	15 cm sIG 33 auf Gw 38(t) (rückvers Motor)		231	
124	10·5 cm leFH 18/2 auf Gw II "Wespe"	232	233	206
	10·5 cm leFH 18 auf Gw 39 H (f)	234	235	
	10·5 cm leFH 18 auf Gw LrS (f)			
	10·5 cm leFH 18 auf Gw 35 R (f)			
	10·5 cm leFH 18 auf Gw B 2 (f)			
	10·5 cm leFH 18 auf Gw FCM (f)		236	
	10·5 cm LG 2540 auf Sf VK 302 (Borgward)		276	
	s 10 cm K 18 auf Gw IV a		238	
135/1	15 cm sFH 13/1 auf Gw LrS (f)		237	206
165	15 cm sFH 18/1 auf Gw III/IV "Hummel"	243	242	
	54 cm Mörser "Karl" (Gerät "041")		248	
	60 cm Mörser "Karl" (Gerät "040")	247 / 249 / 250		206
	PANZERFLAK (Armoured Anti-aircraft Guns)			
140	Flakpanzer 38 (2 cm)	252	253	
	Pz Kw IV—3·7 cm Flak 43	261	260	
	Pz Kw IV—2 cm Flakvierling 38	259	258	
	2 cm Flakvierling 38 auf Pz IV/3 "Wirbelwind"	255	254	
	3·7 cm Flak 43 auf Pz IV "Ostwind"	257	256	
	3·7 cm Flak 43 auf SWS	263	262	
	3 cm Flakvierling 103/38 "Zerstörer 45"			
	3·7 cm Flakzwilling 43 Sf IV			
	3·7 cm Flakzwilling 44 Sf IV "Ostwind II"			
	3·7 cm Flakzwilling 341 Sf V "Coelian"			
	8·8 cm Flak 37 Sf (Prototyp)	264	265 / 267	
	8·8 cm Flak 41 Sf V		270	
	PANZERWERFER (Armoured Rocket Projectors)			
4/1	15 cm Pz W 42 (Zehnling) auf "Maultier"	271	272	
	15 cm Pz W 42 (Zehnling) auf SWS	275	274	
	Panzerwerfer auf Halbketten-Fgst Somua		273	

Sd Kfz number		Plate number		Spec page no
		diag	photo	
	WAFFENTRÄGER (Weapons Carriers)			
	Einheitswaffenträger Grösse I für 10·5 leFH 18/40 (Ardelt)	279		
	Einheitswaffenträger Grösse I für 8·8 cm PaK			
	Einheitswaffenträger Grösse II für 12·8 cm K 81	280		
	Einheitswaffenträger Grösse II für 15 cm sFH 43	281		
165/1	10·5 cm leFH 18/1 auf Gw IVb "Heuschrecke" (Prototyp)	240	239 241	
	10·5 cm leFH 43/35 "Grille 10" (Krupp)		244	
	15 cm sFH 43 "Grille 15"			
	12·8 cm K 43 "Grille 15"		245	
	17 cm K "Grille 17/21"		246	
	21 cm Mrs "Grille 17/21"		246	
	Gerät 5—1026 10·5 cm leFH 43 (Sf) (Kp I)			
	Gerät 5—1027 10·5 cm leFH 43 (Sf) (Kp II)			
	Gerät 5—1028 10·5 cm leFH 43 (Sf) (RhB)			
	Gerät 5—1211/2 12·8 cm K 43 (Sf) (Kp I & II)			
	Gerät 5—1213 12·8 cm K 43 (Sf) (RhB)			
	Gerät 5—1528 15 cm sFH 43 (Sf) (Kp I)			
	Gerät 5—1529 15 cm sFH 43 (Sf) (Kp II)			

Sd Kfz number		Plate number		Spec page no
		diag	photo	
	Gerät 5—1530 15 cm sFH 43 (Sf) (RhB)			
	FUNKLENKPANZER (Radio-controlled Tanks)			
301	Explosive charge layers or carriers, mine clearers or Funklenkpanzer B IV A to C	284	285	
304	Funklenkpanzer NSU "Springer"			
	SCHLEPPER (Tractors)			
	7·5 cm PaK 40/1 auf Gw Lorraine Schlepper (f)		283	
	le Wehrmachtsschlepper (le WS)		169	208
	s Wehrmachtsschlepper (SWS)	287	286	208
	Mörserzugmittel 35(t)			
	Zugkraftwagen 35(t)			
	Schlepper III			
	SONDERPANZER (Special Variants)			
	Bergepanzer I			
	Bergepanzer "Luchs"		119	
	Bergepanzer 38(t), III, IV			
179	Bergepanzer "Panther" Ausf A		82	
	Mun Pz I II, III			
	Mun Pz IV		251	
	Munitionsträger GW III/IV			
	Pz Kw IV Brückenleger			
	Pz Kw IV Inf Sturm-Steg		283	
	Minenräumpanzer "Räumer"	282	283	

Preface

Under its original title *Die deutschen Panzer 1926–45* this famous book by Dr. F. M. von Senger und Etterlin has long been regarded as the standard work on German tanks and armoured vehicles, and it is certainly one of the most comprehensive books ever produced on the AFVs of any nation.

There have been three editions of the German book, each time revised and expanded with additional material, and with additions to the data by Dipl. Ing. F. Kosar. Contributions to the text are by Ing. W. J. Spielberger, a noted authority on German tanks who was closely involved with the engineering and development side of German armoured vehicles during World War II, and also by E. Aders.

The book is appearing for the first time in a complete English language edition. The translation is by J. Lucas of the Imperial War Museum, working with Peter Chamberlain and Chris Ellis, who also contributed material about the Tiger. The English language editors have taken the opportunity to make some changes in presentation, mainly to clarify the subject for non-German readers, but also to revise and expand certain aspects of the work. In the appendices at the end of the book there are tables for converting metric weights and measures into their British and American equivalents. Extra pictures have also been included, making a total of 287.

Introduction

The armoured forces of the German Army in World War II formed the spearhead of an efficient and well-trained military machine. Their deficiencies in equipment, even in the victorious years of 1939–41, were largely compensated for by superior handling and tactics. The popular myth of Germany's great wealth of first-class equipment and numerical superiority is a legacy of her tactical successes. In nearly all the important campaigns, from the invasions of France and Flanders in 1940 onwards, German troops, tanks and guns were outnumbered by their opponents: in North Africa for instance Rommel's Afrika Korps was considerably smaller in men and materials than the British 8th Army.

The Pz Kw I to IV series was not sufficiently advanced in 1939 to equip tank battalions up to the establishment laid down by the staff. Although there was a well-planned and well-balanced production programme for this series it became necessary to improvise from the start: even the tank divisions which took part in the invasion of France in 1940 had to be brought up to effectiveness with Czech vehicles seized when Germany occupied that country. The standard Czech tank was extremely efficient and this vehicle formed the basis of many later successful German designs and adaptations in the armoured field.

When mass-production of tanks and armoured vehicles was needed most in 1940–41 German industry could not cope, and the vast proliferation of different types of SP guns and their predominance in German AFV output dates from this time. To make up losses caused by ever-increasing attrition and to equip the expanding armoured divisions it was found that mounting self-propelled guns on existing chassis was the one way to produce armoured vehicles more quickly and more cheaply than purpose-built tanks.

German advances in the field of tank technology did not stand still however. Over the period 1926–45 tank designs advanced from the tiny Pz Kw I of about five tons in weight to the mighty Maus of over 100 tons. German engineers found an answer to almost every requirement, feasible or impractical, and produced designs like the Panther and the Jagdpanther to outfight the Russian T-34 and other powerful British and American types, and monster vehicles like the Tiger II (B) and the Maus, whose sheer size and impregnability rendered them tactically almost valueless. They also designed armoured personnel carriers, weapons carriers and SP carriages that have influenced many of the post-war designs of other nations.

Nomenclature

The nomenclature adopted by the Germans for their armoured vehicles was basically simple. Since German publications and specifications are referred to throughout, all vehicles in this book are referred to, at least in each section heading, by their full German designations. Generally speaking, all subsequent references are by the German abbreviated versions of those designations. The term "Panzerkampfwagen", for example, which translates literally into English as "armoured fighting vehicle" (i.e. tank), is shortened to Pz Kw.

Each German vehicle was designated by a term descriptive of its function, followed by a number indicating the design in the series—usually a Roman numeral for German-designed equipment and an Arabic numeral for that of non-German design. In the latter case a small letter in parentheses indicated the country of origin. The designation was completed, where necessary, by an indication of the model or mark, shown by a letter. For example, Panzerkampfwagen III Ausführung E is abbreviated to Pz Kw III Ausf E. "Ausführung" is German for "model" or "mark".

Self-propelled guns normally followed the same designation form as tanks in the case of purpose-built vehicles. A simple example is Sturmgeschütz III, shortened to StuG III. The full designation however normally included a description of the weapon with which the vehicle was fitted, for example Sturmgeschütz III mit 7·5 cm StuK 40 L/48 ("mit" means "with"), and what follows is the designation of the gun. Self-propelled guns which were adaptations were usually designated with the description of the gun followed by the basic chassis on which it was mounted—8·8 cm PaK 43/1 L/71 auf GW III/IV Nashorn for example. "Auf" means "on" and GW is short for Geschützwagen, which means "gun carriage". In this example the name came last, as was usual where a name was allocated. A well-known example is Pz Kw V Panther. Where a vehicle had a name it was of course usual to use just the name as an abbreviated form of reference to the vehicle concerned.

To sum up, the way to identify German AFVs from their designation alone is to look for a type indicator or its abbreviated form first, then the design indication and finally, where there is one, the model indication. If the designation includes "mit" some reference to a gun type or a special variant is indicated, and where the designation starts with a gun calibre and designation (indicating SP equipment) the basic chassis will follow "auf GW" or "auf Sfl".

The Sonderkraftfahrzeug (literally "special purposes motor vehicle") number was normally included in parentheses at the end of the designation. It was usually abbreviated to Sd Kfz and was the prefix used for numbering vehicles in the ordnance inventory. This could be, and often was, used alone as an abbreviated form of reference to a vehicle, particularly where the full designation was long and complicated.

The text and notes in this book sometimes use this form of abbreviation only, usually where continual references to a specific type are made in any one section. Some vehicles did not have this Sd Kfz number however, and this applied particularly to captured equipment which was not adopted as a standard design.

The following list of German terms and abbreviations for basic types of AFVs is in alphabetical order.

Flakpanzer (anti-aircraft tanks) were special vehicles designed to defend armoured units against air attack. They had all-round armour protection, though often had open-topped mountings.

Funklenkpanzer (radio-controlled tanks) were vehicles operated by remote control (usually radio) and used for special missions.

Funkwagen (Fu) (wireless tanks or cars) were equipped for long-range communications.

Jagdpanzer, see Panzerjäger.

Minenräumpanzer (mine-clearing tanks) carried equipment to facilitate mine clearing.

Panzerbefehlswagen (armoured command vehicles) were AFVs with multiple wireless equipment and reduced armament, designed for the commanders of tank formations.

Panzerbeobachtungswagen (armoured OP tanks) were used to control artillery fire.

Panzerjäger or **Jagdpanzer** (Jagd) (tank destroyers) were intended specially to be used against Panzerkampfwagen and were either lighter than similarly armed Panzerkampfwagen or carried heavier armament.

Panzerkampfwagen (Pz Kw) (battle tanks) had their main armament mounted in a revolving turret and were fully-tracked vehicles intended for the main fighting role within tank formations.

Panzerspähwagen (Pz Spw) (armoured cars) were fast lightly wheeled armoured vehicles used for reconnaissance work.

Räumschaufelpanzer (dozer tanks) had shovels mounted on the front for clearing earth or rubble.

Schützenpanzerwagen (SPW) (armoured personnel carriers) were the fighting vehicles of the mechanised infantry. Numerous variants were produced for diverse specialist purposes.

Selbstfahrlafetten (self-propelled carriages) carried weapons for a number of specialist tasks. They were lightly armoured.

Sonderkraftfahrzeug (Sd Kfz) (special purposes motor vehicle) was the prefix (nearly always abbreviated) used for numbering vehicles in the ordnance inventory.

Sturmgeschütz (StuG) (assault tanks) were intended for use against infantry targets and were therefore usually equipped with a large-calibre short-barrelled gun firing high explosive shot.

Waffenträger (weapon carriers) carried weapons which could be brought into action either on the vehicle itself or could be dismounted and fired from the ground.

GERMAN TANKS OF WORLD WAR II

History and Development

Panzerkampfwagen I (Pz Kw I) and its Variants

Development

It was quite clear from the tests which were carried out during 1929 and 1930 with the "light and heavy tractors" that new ideas would have to be examined if the Army was to be equipped with effective armoured fighting vehicles. The design features for what were later to be the Pz Kw III and Pz Kw IV tanks had already been determined and, in order that there would be a suitable interim training vehicle available when military sovereignty was announced, the Army Weapons Department issued contracts in 1933 for the development of a light armoured fighting vehicle in the 5-ton class. The following firms were invited to tender: Maschinenfabrik Augsburg-Nürnberg (MAN), Nuremberg; Friedrich Krupp AG, Essen; Henschel und Sohn, Kassel; Daimler-Benz AG, Berlin-Marienfelde; Rheinmetall-Borsig, Düsseldorf.

The prototypes they produced, particularly the Krupp version, were influenced by the experience which had been gained by collaboration with the Swedish Landsverk company. Rheinmetall-Borsig based their design on experience gained from the experimental light tractor VK 31/A2 of 1928–29. After exhaustive tests the Army Weapons Department accepted the "LKA 1" type, based on the Krupp design, and selected two firms to complete the final developments—Krupp for the chassis and Daimler-Benz for the superstructure.

Krupp gave the designation "LKA/LKB" to their project, but the Army Weapons Department used the code name "Landwirtschaftlicher Schlepper" (industrial tractor) (LaS). Firms which became prominent in the manufacture were Henschel, who completed the first three prototypes during December 1933, MAN and Wegmann of Kassel, who were brought in at a later date. The first test run at Henschel's was made on 3rd February 1934. The vehicle finally produced was fully tracked, with a two-man crew (driver and gunner) and had a main armament of two MG 13s

mounted in a turret with a 360-degree traverse. The air-cooled engine (Krupp M 305) together with the oil cooler, was at the rear of the vehicle. The M 305 was a four-cylinder horizontally opposed 3·5 litre engine, which produced 57 hp at 2500 rpm. From the engine the drive was through a dry two-disc main clutch to the ZF Aphon FG 35 five-speed gearbox. Final drive was through a bevel, a clutch-and-brake steering mechanism and a traverse shaft to the front sprockets.

As an experiment a few vehicles were fitted with the air-cooled Krupp M 601 diesel engine which was almost identical in size but produced 45 hp at 2200 rpm, which was insufficient. The tests were consequently discontinued. Strangely enough it was not until late in 1939, with the Tatra diesel Type III, that any further attempt was made in Germany to produce an air-cooled diesel engine for armoured fighting vehicles.

The suspension, consisting of bogie wheels, beam and return rollers, was secured to the hull by bolts and quarter elliptic springs. This vehicle had a prominent trailing idler wheel. The whole 5·4 ton vehicle had an armoured thickness of 15 mm and was proof against penetration by steel-cored small arms ammunition.

Production

Under the designation of "I A LaS Krupp" quantity production began at Henschel's during July 1934. The complete contract was for 150 machines.

Completed vehicles were handed over to the Army under the stores description "Pz Kw (MG) (Sd Kfz 101) Ausf A", and formed the nucleus of the vehicle strength of the armoured units. The machines delivered for troop trials soon proved that the engine fitted did not always meet the demands made upon it.

Improvements became necessary and a modified design quickly appeared with the type description "I B LaS May". Basically this type differed only in the Maybach, six-cylinder NL 38 TR water-cooled

engine which was fitted. To accommodate this larger
engine it was necessary to increase the length of the
engine compartment and therefore the hull. This, in
turn, was only made possible by the addition of a pair
of extra road wheels. In order not to affect the
vehicle's manoeuvrability, the idler wheels at the
rear were raised so that there was no increase in the
length of track actually in contact with the ground.
The combat weight of the vehicle was increased to
approximately six tons. The considerably more
powerful engine increased the power-to-weight ratio
and, despite the increased total weight, a maximum
speed of 40 kph was attained. The technical and
tactical characteristics remained unaltered and an
improved transmission was put in (ZF Aphon FG 31).
The vehicle was issued to the Army in 1935 and
received the official description "Pz Kw I (MG) (Sd
Kfz 101), Ausf B", ref D 650/4 of 23rd February
1938.

By 1939 the contractors produced about 1500 of
these vehicles and construction of the chassis continued until 1941. Henschel produced the bulk of the
output from 1935 to 1937, and Wegmann were also
engaged in assembly from 1935 onwards. The main
manufacturer of the superstructure components was
the Deutsche Edelstahlwerke AG in Hannover-
Linden, and this firm produced the following totals
of vehicle parts for the Pz Kw I building programme.

	hulls	superstructures	turrets
1933	31	—	—
1934	337	54	54
1935	811	851	851
1936	574	565	557
1937	114	255	31
1938	—	22	—

Ceskomoravska Kolben Danek, later Böhmisch-
Mährische Maschinenfabrik, Prague, were also
engaged on the construction and conversion of these
vehicles.

Both models of the Pz Kw I were first used operationally during the Spanish Civil War. At the time of
the invasion of Poland (1st September 1939) 1445 Pz
Kw I tanks were available and, at the start of the
campaign in France, 523 Pz Kw I combat tanks were
on the strength of the armoured divisions detailed for
the attack. A statement, dated 1st July 1941, gave a
total of 843 Pz Kw Is still available.

Guderian states in his book that these tanks were
not considered suitable for combat and operations in
Poland and in France very quickly proved that
neither their fire power nor their armour was sufficient
for them to face enemy tanks. As replacement by

larger vehicles was by now more or less assured the
Pz Kw I was phased out at first slowly, but later
more quickly, so that by the end of·1941 it had dis-
appeared almost completely as a combat tank.

Further developments

In an instruction dated 15th September 1939, the
AHA/AgK/In 6 issued an order to the Army
Weapons Department for further development of the
Pz Kw I tank. It was stipulated that it should fill the
roles of a light combat reconnaissance tank and also
act as a light combat tank for the air landing troops.
The firms selected to develop this project were the
Krauss-Maffei AG of Munich for the chassis, and
Daimler-Benz for the superstructure and the turret.
Forty vehicles of the first experimental series were
ordered with a proposed delivery date of mid-July 1942.

With a total weight of about 8 tons and 10–30 mm
armour, the machine was capable of a top speed of
65 kph. The Maybach 150 hp HL 45 6-cylinder
engine was fitted. There was a two-man crew and
the armament consisted of a 2 cm EW/141, and an
MG 34 mounted in a revolving turret. The ordnance
description was "Pz Kw Ausf C (VK 601)".

On 22nd December 1939 a further contract was
issued by the Army Weapons Department for 30
vehicles of the Pz Kw I nA verst (neue Ausführung,
verstärkt) (VK 1801), with the demand for a further
development of the Pz Kw I combat tank, with the
"thickest possible armour". As before Krauss-Maffei
and Daimler-Benz were appointed to do the development work. The total weight was now between 18 and
19 tons and the armour thickness 80 mm. The
Maybach HL 45 engine gave the vehicle a maximum
speed of 25 kph. The crew consisted of a driver and a
gunner, with an armament of two MG 34s in a revolving turret. The first chassis ran on 17th June 1940
and the turret was completed at the same time. The
initial series of 30 machines was delivered but a
second and final order for 100 vehicles was cancelled.

Krauss-Maffei received an experimental contract
during March 1940 to install wireless sets (Fu 2 and
an intercom) into the VK 1801, but this project was
cancelled.

Variants

As the vehicles still on hand were obsolete as
combat tanks experiments were carried out on the
chassis of both Pz Kw I models to assess the possibility
of adapting them for other roles. Chassis of both basic
models, like those of other obsolete AFVs, were used
in driving schools as well as being utilised for supply
purposes.

At the outbreak of war there was already in service an ammunition tractor based on the chassis of Pz Kw I, Ausf A, developed and built by Daimler-Benz. This armoured supply vehicle, officially designated "Pz Kw I (A) Munitions-Schlepper (Sd Kfz 111)", had a height of only 1·4 metres. Frontal armour was 15 mm thick. At the sides and the rear it was 13 mm thick. There was a crew of two. These vehicles were produced, as were the self-propelled gun variants which will be described later, from conversions of redundant fighting vehicles.

From 1940 some Mark Is, with superstructure removed, were issued to tank maintenance and repair units and used in place of the Zg Kw 1-ton tractor. As the engine of the Model A was not powerful enough all other conversions were mounted on the chassis of the Model B.

By 1939 Alkett in Berlin-Spandau had produced the first anti-tank vehicle, which was intended to be a prototype of future developments. It consisted of a 4·7 cm Czech anti-tank gun mounted on a turretless version of the tank and the gun was protected on three sides with armour. The weapon had a barrel length of 2040 mm (L/43·4), and it could be traversed only 15°. This equipment was issued to the troops with the description 4·7 cm PaK (t) (Sfl) auf Pz Kw I Ausf B, and 132 were still on the strength on 1st July 1941. The combat weight was 6400 kg and the crew consisted of three men. The overall height was 2250 mm and 86 rounds of ammunition were carried. After the Russian campaign had begun it was found that these vehicles were only of limited value due to their light armament and armour, but they rendered useful service as stop-gap equipment, particularly in Africa.

At about the same time Alkett produced another self-propelled gun version which carried the type 33 15 cm heavy infantry gun (schwere Infanterie-geschütz). This weapon, complete with carriage and wheels, could be mounted on the Pz Kw I Ausf B chassis and could be enclosed on three sides with a 10 mm armoured shield. This solution, however original it may have been, produced a vehicle with a very high silhouette of 3·35 metres. The chassis was overloaded, as the weapon alone, ready for action,

weighed 1750 kg. With a four-man crew the combat weight was about 8·5 tons. This machine was used in both the Polish and French campaigns and gave useful high-angle support fire for armoured assaults. The few which went into service were designated "15 cm sIG 33 auf Pz Kw I Ausf B" and were also known as "GW (Geschützwagen) I für 15 cm sIG 33". Thirty-eight were converted.

Many attempts were made to produce radio-controlled tanks and explosive charge layers, using the obsolete chassis of the Pz Kw I as the carriage. Of these little known experiments information is available only on the "Ladungsleger I" (Explosive Charge Layer I). A contract dated 9th May 1940 was given to Waggonfabrik Talbot of Aachen to construct a vehicle able to place in position an explosive charge weighing 75 kg by means of an extending arm fitted to the Pz Kw I. This arm, mounted on the vehicle roof, was 2 metres long when retracted and could be extended to 2·75 metres. However, the experiments did not progress beyond prototype stage.

Efforts to supply an armoured command vehicle to tank formations resulted in the production of the "kleine Panzerbefehlswagen" (small command tank) (Sd Kfz 265) during the years 1936/38. This vehicle based on both Model A and B chassis, was developed and built by Daimler-Benz. Approximately 200 of the three differing types "1 kl B" "2 kl B", and "3 kl B" were produced. Some were fitted with a small rectangular revolving turret, but most had the much better known rigid full-width superstructure. The combat weight was 5880 kg. There was a machine gun for self-defence, and a three-man crew. The wireless equipment consisted of an Fu 6 and Fu 2 set. Super-structures were supplied, once again, by Deutsche Edelstahlwerke. At the start of the French campaign in 1940, 96 of these vehicles were in service with the troops.

It is interesting to note that the idea of developing a two-man tank was revived towards the end of the war. Existing data shows that Weserhütte AG of Bad Oeynhausen were engaged in designing a VK 301, while Büssing-NAG were busy with plans for a VK 501. But at the end of the war both vehicles were still in the design stage.

Panzerkampfwagen II (Pz Kw II) and its Variants

Development

Guderian's *Panzer Leader* gives some background information on the development of the Pz Kw II. Thus as the completion of the planned types of tanks (Pz Kw III and IV) was delayed longer than had been originally anticipated, General Lutz decided on a further stop-gap model. This was the Pz Kw II, supplied by MAN, and equipped with a 2 cm automatic cannon and a machine gun.

In July 1934 the Weapons Department issued development contracts for a vehicle of the 10-ton class to Krupp, Henschel and MAN. Krupp went back to the Pz Kw I prototype already available and equipped this machine, designated LKA 2, with a 2 cm tank gun 30 and an MG in a revolving turret. The Henschel and MAN prototypes were of similar appearance but they differed basically from the Krupp prototype in their suspension systems.

Under the Weapons Department's camouflage name of "LaS 100" (Industrial Tractor 100), the prototypes were thoroughly tested. Development was eventually concentrated on the design submitted by MAN, and for the final development MAN were selected for the chassis and Daimler-Benz for the superstructure. Companies brought in as licensed constructors were Famo of Breslau (1936–43), Wegmann of Kassel (1935–41) and MIAG in Brunswick (1936–40).

Production

The first production vehicles, chassis numbers 20,001 to 20,025, appeared with the type designation 1/LaS 100 and were issued to the Army during 1935 with the official description "Pz Kw II (2 cm) (Sd Kfz 121)". These 7·2 ton machines with a three-man crew were fitted with a Maybach 6-cylinder high-performance engine, HL 57, which produced 130 hp at 2600 rpm. The maximum speed was 40 kph. The power transmission was transmitted via a plate clutch to a ZF 6-speed crash gearbox with final drive by a clutch steering gear to the front driving wheels. The bogies were suspended in pairs and attached to the hull by means of leaf springs and horizontal bars. Model "a1" also had a transmission shaft without reduction gears. The "a2" type appeared in the same year and a further 25 of this version were constructed (chassis numbers 20,026 to 20,050). Improvements were made in the engine compartment and in the cooling systems of these vehicles. The third type appeared in 1936 as the "a3" in a run of 50 machines (chassis numbers 20,051 to 20,100) and had improved tracks and suspension and a better cooling system. All three types had as standard a 2 cm tank gun 30 and an MG 34 in a revolving turret and their armour was 14·5 mm thick all round.

Tests showed that the engine power was not always sufficient and therefore the chassis from 21,001 onwards were fitted with the Maybach 6-cylinder engine, HL 62. By increasing the bore from 100 to 105 mm the cubic capacity was increased to 6191 cc and the engine power raised from 130 to 140 hp. At the same time the vehicle, now known as the 2/LaS 100 (Ausf "b") was fitted with new reduction gears and the tracks which became standard for the Pz Kw II tank series. The total weight had been increased to 7·9 tons. One hundred vehicles of this type were produced. From the fourth series onward the frontal armour was increased to a thickness of 30 mm. In 1937 Henschel were brought into the construction programme of the Pz Kw II tank. The "c" model also appeared in this year (designated 3/LaS 100). This vehicle already had the characteristic suspension of five road wheels suspended on quarter elliptic springs, which was retained until Pz Kw II production ceased. Chassis numbers ran from 21,101 to 23,000. All models produced thus far had a rounded nose plate, but this was replaced in subsequent vehicles by a welded squared-off front. Between 1937 and 1940 models A, B and C were produced (designated 4, 5 and 6/LaS 100). On 1st

November 1940 there were five contracts for Pz Kw IIs of which three had been placed in April and two in August 1940. Production started in December 1940.

At the outbreak of war the Pz Kw II was the backbone of the armoured divisions and at the start of the campaign against France in 1940 955 machines were available. The Army still had 1067 tanks of this type on the strength at 1st July 1941 and 860 vehicles on 1st April 1942.

Further developments

During 1938 Daimler-Benz produced the "8/LaS 138" type, which was distributed to the mechanised divisions as the "Pz Kw II (2 cm) (Sd Kfz 121), Ausf D und E"—the so called "Schnellkampfwagen" (fast fighting vehicle). While the superstructures and the turret resembled those of the Pz Kw II, this series was the first to use torsion-bar suspensions. During 1938 and 1939 nearly 250 of these machines were produced. Drive and transmission were similar to the other production models of the Pz Kw II and they achieved a maximum speed of 55 kph. The weight was 10 tons. Crew, armament and armour remained unchanged.

Following discussions with Hitler on 7th July 1941 it was decided that all future new armoured fighting vehicles should be uparmoured with spaced plates to the front in order to reduce the effect of the new hollow-charge shells. The expected increase in weight and the loss of speed was, in Hitler's opinion, to be accepted (according to Field Marshal Keitel in a despatch to the Army Command). Equally interesting is an extract from one of the meetings of the Armour Committee dated 17th July 1941. A new order from Hitler demanded that the tank arm be raised to 36 divisions. A representative of the Army General Department worked out that to raise these formations a total of 4608 Pz Kw IIs, among others, would be required. It is surprising to note that at this time the production of the Pz Kw II was still continuing, although experience of the French campaign had clearly shown that these vehicles were effective against enemy tanks only in the most exceptional circumstances.

At the end of 1940 and the beginning of 1941 the production of the final model of the Pz Kw II series appeared under the designation "7/LaS 100 (Ausf F)". These vehicles had been uparmoured in front to 35 mm and the side armour had been increased to 20 mm, raising the combat weight to 9·5 tons. The monthly production figure was scheduled to be 45 vehicles as from 1942, but because of labour short-

ages, especially at the Famo plant, considerably fewer were produced. When production ceased at the beginning of 1944 a total of only 625 machines of this type had been produced. The cost per vehicle, without armament and communications equipment, was approximately RM 50,000 (roughly £1650 or $6600 at that time).

In 1941 the AHA/AgK (Inspectorate Department 6) called for an armoured fighting vehicle of the 10-ton class with "increased speed and improved armour". A development chassis of this Pz Kw II (Ausf H and M) was delivered on 1st September 1941 by MAN. Equipped with the Maybach HL-P 6-cylinder 200-hp engine the 10·5-ton vehicle was intended to reach a speed of 65 kph. Frontal armour was to be 30 mm thick, the side and rear armour to be 20 mm, while the roof was to be fitted with 10 and the floor with 5 mm armour. Track width was 2·08 metres. There was a three-man crew, a 2 cm tank gun Type 38 and an MG 34 in a revolving turret. The start of production was scheduled for mid-1942, but the vehicle was already obsolescent by this time. Deutsche Edelstahlwerke AG of Hannover were one of the main contractors for the hulls, superstructures and turrets for the Pz Kw II construction programme and produced the following parts during the period 1936–42:

	hulls	superstructures	turrets
1936	117	147	84
1937	215	309	194
1938	308	346	432
1939	—	85	2
1940	42	118	118
1941	131	92	92
1942	148	172	54

On 18th June 1938 a contract was sent to MAN for the chassis and to Daimler-Benz for the superstructure and the turret. They were to produce the further development of the Pz Kw II with "the principal emphasis on increased speed" proposed by the Weapons Department. This vehicle was designated "Pz Kw II, neuer Art (VK 901)". The first chassis was completed by the end of 1939 and fitted with the Maybach HL 45 145 hp engine. The armour was 30 mm thick at the front and 14·5 mm at the sides and the vehicle had a total weight of 9·2 tons. Maximum speed was 50 kph. Sixty kph was attempted, but to have attained that speed it would have been necessary to fit a 200 hp engine. Such an engine later became available in the HL 66 P. The three-man crew served a 2 cm tank gun Type 38 and an MG 34, which were fitted co-axially in a stabilised mount inside the revolving turret. The pre-production series of 75 machines was begun in October 1940 and delivered. Daimler-Benz, Rheinmetall-Borsig and Skoda received a contract, dated 1st June 1942, in which it was proposed that 30 of these Pz Kw II nA machines be converted into armoured reconnaissance vehicles for armoured artillery and tank regiments. An experimental model, VK 903, with the 1303 b turret, was produced by the end of September 1942 and equipped with range-finder, locator, observation and communications equipment.

On 22nd December 1939 a second development contract was sent to MAN and to Daimler-Benz, stipulating further development of the Pz Kw II with "the main emphasis on the thickest possible armour". The designation for this machine was "Pz Kw II, nA, verstärkt (VK 1601)". An initial series of 30 machines was planned with delivery to begin in December 1940. The first chassis ran on 18th June 1940 and the first turret was completed on 19th June. A contract for the delivery of a first series of 100 vehicles was cancelled however. These vehicles too were fitted with the Maybach HL 45 150 hp engine, which gave the 16–17-ton machine a maximum speed of 31 kph. The track width was 235 cm. Frontal armour was 80 mm thick and the side armour 50 mm thick. With a crew of three there was, once again, a 2 cm tank gun Type 38 and an MG 34, in a stabilised mount.

Luchs (Lynx)

The experience gained with the two models described above, resulted in the design of the "Pz Kw II nA (VK 1301)". The Weapons Department contract called for a type similar in appearance and proportion to the VK 901. A prototype in mild steel was delivered by the end of April 1942. The combat weight was about 12·9 tons. After minor alterations had been carried out the vehicle went into production as the VK 1303. It is interesting to note that on 15th September 1939 Inspectorate 6 had asked the Army Weapons Department for a similar type of armoured reconnaissance vehicle, fully tracked and equipped with communications equipment of medium and ultra-short wave radio apparatus. Eight hundred of these vehicles were ordered straight from the drawing board, though this particular project was abandoned. The contractors were MAN for the chassis and Daimler-Benz for the turret and assembly. The original designation was "Pz Kw II (Sd Kfz 123), Ausf L", but the exclusive use of the machine in reconnaissance units caused the designation to be amended to "Panzerspähwagen II (2 cm KwK 38) (Sd Kfz 123) Luchs". This vehicle, weighing 11·8 tons, was fitted with the Maybach HL 66 P, 6-cylinder engine, which produced 180 hp and was fitted with a six-speed ZF transmission which enabled the vehicle to reach a maximum speed of 60 kph. The first 100 vehicles were armed with a 2 cm tank gun 38 and an MG 34 in a revolving turret. The crew consisted of four men. Frontal armour was 30 mm while the side armour was 20 mm thick. From vehicle No 101, the 5 cm tank gun L/60 was fitted. A further 31 vehicles of this type were built, and production ceased on 12th May 1943.

Leopard

Even after this the development of the Pz Kw II series was not finished. Referring to the VK 1601 (Pz Kw II, nA, verstärkt), mentioned above, the Army Weapons Department issued development contracts in 1941 to MIAG of Brunswick for the chassis and to Daimler-Benz for the turret and superstructure of a heavily armoured fighting vehicle for battle reconnaissance. The development was designated "Gefechtsaufklärer VK 1602 (Leopard)". It is interesting to note that the weight of the VK 1602 was laid down as about 26 tons. Proposed armour thicknesses were to be 50 to 80 mm for the turret and 20 to 60 mm for the hull. The power unit planned was a spark-ignition engine of 550 hp, which was intended to give the machine a maximum speed of 60 kph. A crew of four operated a 5 cm tank gun Type 39/1 and an MG 42 mounted in the revolving turret. The drawings for the hull were completed on 30th July 1942, those for the main chassis parts on 1st September and those for the chassis assembly on 1st November. Construction of the vehicle did not however take place, but the 5 cm turret was developed by Daimler-Benz and was later used for the improved Büssing-NAG 8-wheeled "Puma" armoured car.

Amphibious versions of Pz Kw II

In conclusion, the role of the Pz Kw II in connection with Operation Sea Lion is worthy of note. During September and October 1940 Armoured Battalion A was raised from volunteers of 2nd Panzer Regiment in Putlos and trained for the invasion of England. For this purpose the Pz Kw II was converted, using special equipment, into an amphibian. Army Testing Department 6 ordered flotation equipment from Alkett of Berlin, from Bachmann of Ribnitz and from Sachsenberg of Roslau, which would allow a speed of 10 kph and be seaworthy in a wind of force 3–4. Fifty-two of these flotation kits were ordered and they were fixed to the return rollers. The hulls were divided into three chambers by internal walls and filled with small celluloid bags. The waterproofed engine worked a small marine propeller by means of an extension sleeve, universal joint and shaft. The space between the hull and the turret was made water-tight by an inflatable rubber tube. In the water the vehicle submerged to about the top of the track covers. The turret guns were ready for action even when the vehicle was afloat. In addition there was in the Pz Kw II series a "Panzergerät 13", but details of this are not known.

Before continuing in greater detail with the many Pz Kw II variants it should be mentioned that the Pz Kw II, like the Pz Kw I used in the motorised divisions, could be transported on trucks, while trailers and flat-bed trailers were also used. The vehicles principally used for this purpose were the Büssing lorries "900" and "654", as well as the Faun type "L 900/D 567".

Variants

During 1940 some of the Pz Kw II models D and E, mentioned above, were converted into flame-throwing tanks. A development contract for this was issued by Inspectorate 6 of the Weapons Department for 90 vehicles of an initial series and was sent to MAN and to Wegmann on 21st January 1939. By 19th July 1940 16 were ready and the final nine machines were delivered in January 1942. Ninety-five "Pz Kw II (F) (Sd Kfz 122)" vehicles were in service with special tank formations on 1st April 1942. With a two-man crew and weighing 11 tons, these vehicles were fitted with two projectors, each of which moved through a 180° arc. The flame fuel supply carried was sufficient for 80 flamings, each of 2 to 3 seconds' duration, with a range of 35 metres. An MG 34 was fitted for self defence.

Self-propelled Carriages

As these vehicles did not prove very successful they became the first of the Pz Kw II series to form the basis for different types of self-propelled carriages. On 20th December 1941 the Weapons Department was ordered to construct an anti-tank (self-propelled) vehicle, using the captured Russian 7·62 cm anti-tank gun as well as the light field gun and the "LaS 138" (i.e. Pz Kw II) chassis. These machines were a wartime expedient and were given to Alkett to complete without a development contract. By 12th May 1942 a total of 150 armoured SP carriages had been turned out. An extension contract for a further 60 superstructures was issued. The continued supply of SP carriages depended however upon the delivery of

repaired Pz Kw II flame-thrower chassis. In some isolated cases German 7·5 cm anti-tank guns Type 40/2 were mounted and it is known that the Russian 7·62 cm field gun Type 296, without muzzle brake, was also used. The official designation of the vehicle was "Pz Sfl II für 7·62 cm PaK 36(r) (Sd Kfz 132) Marder II". This 11·5-ton vehicle with a four-man crew was also known as the "7·62 cm PaK (r) auf Fahrgestell Pz Kw II (Sf)" and also as the "7·62 cm 36 (Sfl) im Pz Kw II". From 1942 onward the obsolescent chassis of the LaS 100 was also used for this type of conversion. On 18th May 1942 the Minister for Arms and Armament sent a requirement (numbered 6772/42 g) to the Weapons Department for "an anti-tank gun on an SP mounting". MAN were made responsible for the development of the chassis, Alkett for the superstructure with Rheinmetall-Borsig fitting the mounting. After trials with the 5 cm anti-tank gun Type 38, which proved this weapon unsuitable, the 7·5 cm anti-tank gun 40/2 was installed. With a three-man crew this vehicle had a combat weight of 10·8 tons. On 15th June 1942 delivery of the pilot vehicles was made, followed by a production run of 1216 vehicles. The official designation was "7·5 cm PaK 40/2 auf Sfl II chassis (Sd Kfz 131) Marder II". Despite their open fighting compartment these vehicles were a most valuable aid in the anti-tank role in Russia.

A further six machines of the new version of the Pz Kw II already mentioned, were produced in January 1942, and two of these chassis were converted into light anti-tank vehicles in accordance with a Weapons Department contract of 5th July 1940 Az 73a/p Agk/In 6 (VIIIa) No 1684/40 g. The two trial pieces which arrived at the front in January 1942 had the designation "5 cm PaK 38 auf Pz Kw II Sonderfahrgestell (special chassis) 901 (Pz Sfl Ic)". Rheinmetall were responsible for the gun and the superstructure, while the alterations to the chassis were carried out by MAN. The vehicle had a total weight of 10·5 tons, frontal armour was 30 mm and side armour was 20 mm thick. There was a four-man crew. The trials were not continued, as the 5 cm PaK 38 proved ineffective against the Soviet T-34 tank.

The "Wespe" (Wasp) of 1942 was based on the LaS/100 (standard Pz Kw II) and was the best known artillery SP vehicle. The official designation was "le FH (light field gun) 18/2 auf Fahrgestell (chassis) Pz Kw II Sf (Sd Kfz 124)" and also "GW II für le FH 18". The name "Wespe" was dropped as a result of Hitler's order of 27th February 1944. The companies responsible for the development of this vehicle were MAN for the chassis, Alkett for the superstructure and Rheinmetall-Borsig for the gun. Production was carried out mainly at Famo (formerly Vereinigte Maschinenfabrik) in Warsaw.

The combat weight was 11,480 kg and the crew consisted of five men. Thirty-two rounds of light field gun ammunition could be carried. Some of the vehicles had a distinctive hull front, with a chassis armour of 18 mm in front and 15 mm at the side, while the superstructure had an average thickness of 10 mm. Six hundred and eighty-three of these vehicles were in service in 1942 with the light artillery batteries of armoured artillery battalions. These units also used the "Munitionsselbstfahrlafette auf Fahrgestell Pz Kw II" (ammunition carrier on the Pz Kw II chassis), of which 158 were built. This vehicle resembled the SP Wespe in construction, but the gun was omitted. A total of 90 rounds of 10·5 cm ammunition was carried and the crew consisted of a driver and two gunners. It was possible for the troops to adapt these vehicles as extemporised gun carriages, using suitable weapons to hand.

Other sources state that a 10·5 cm leFH 18/2 was mounted, as part of the Heuschrecke production series, on the chassis of an LaS 100 (Pz Kw II) series vehicle. The specification intended that the armament, including the turret, should be capable of being dismounted; the gun could be used as a permanent fixture. The armoured chassis could also be used as an ammunition carrier. Pictures of a wooden model of this vehicle show that the idea of lengthening the Pz Kw II chassis with an extra pair of road wheels had already been considered. This construction was actually used at a later date when the 15 cm heavy infantry gun was mounted on a Pz Kw II chassis. Although the Heuschrecke 10 was not constructed, the sIG (heavy infantry gun) 33 was installed in a normal LaS 100 (Pz Kw II) chassis from 1942 onwards. This vehicle, designated either as the "15 cm sIG 33 auf Pz Kw II (Sd Kfz 121)" or as the "GW II für 15 cm sIG 33", had a low and therefore more favourable appearance, but was heavily overloaded. In 1943 the lengthened chassis previously mentioned was adopted

for this vehicle. With a five-man crew it had a combat weight of about 12 tons.

1942 is a date of great significance in the development of SP artillery, for several interesting ideas which were produced at this time had their beginnings in the chassis of the Luchs reconnaissance tank (qv) and the Leopard (VK 1602). These were, however, never constructed.

In the spring of 1942 Krupp received a contract for a "10·5 cm field gun to be used as an armoured SP carriage". If possible the barrel of the Rheinmetall-Borsig's new light field gun Type 43 was to be used. The possibility of interchanging the Rheinmetall-Borsig and Krupp gun barrels was also to be considered. The designation of this vehicle was "Gerät 5-1027 (leFH 43 (Sfl) Kp II)". Parts of the Luchs chassis were used. Also recorded is the "Gerät 5-1026 (leFH 43 (Sfl) Kp I)", produced by Krupp. The travelling weight of this piece was 25 tons and the weight of the dismounted gun was 4·3 tons. All the vehicles in the contract were to be delivered by the middle of 1943 and were based, as were succeeding vehicles, on mechanical and chassis components of the Leopard. A contract for the "Gerät 5-1028 (leFH 43 (Sfl) Rh B)", went at the same time to Rheinmetall-Borsig, who reduced the travelling weight to 23 tons and the weight of the dismounted gun to 2·15 tons by using their 10·5 cm leFH 43L/31. To the same specification, Krupp produced the "Gerät 5-1529 (sFH 43 (Sfl) Kp II)" and "Gerät 5-1212 (12·8 cm K 43 (Sfl) Kp II)". One of each was contracted for. The proposed delivery date was to be the summer of 1943. The total weight of these vehicles was about 34 tons. The whole programme got no farther than the trials stage of individual models.

In conclusion, mention must be made of the Pz Kw II, neuer Art, verstärkt (VK 1601), which was used in isolated cases as a recovery vehicle. A bridge-laying tank on a Pz Kw II chassis remained in the design stage.

Czech types in German service

No tanks of foreign origin were as important to the German Armed Forces as these vehicles. The Pz Kw 38(t) in particular formed the basis for numerous variants which gave useful and reliable service in large numbers throughout the war.

Pz Kw 35(t)

The Pz Kw 35(t), developed by Skoda and designated "LTM 35", was used as a light tank by the Czech Army as well as being exported. Taken over by the German Army in 1939, subsequent to the occupation of Czechoslovakia, this 10·5 ton vehicle was used in 1940 by the 6th Panzer Division. On 1st June 1942 a total of 167 was still on hand. The armament consisted of a 37 mm tank gun (designated A3) and two machine guns. The riveted armour was 25 mm thick at the front and 16 mm at the sides. The 4-cylinder Skoda T 11, 8·5 litre petrol engine produced 120 hp at 1800 rpm and gave the vehicle a maximum speed of 40 kph.

The external measurements were 445×214×220 cm and a crew of four was carried. This compact vehicle was a very modern one for its time. Its range was 190 km on roads and 115 km across country. In the production of this machine Skoda successfully developed many advanced ideas in AFV construction. Basically the vehicle had the following characteristics:

1. Driving sprockets at the rear, which made it possible to keep the fighting compartment clear of the drive mechanism. This differed from German practice, which called for front drive sprockets so as to give the tracks a certain measure of automatic cleaning.
2. The power unit was kept as short as possible to leave maximum room in the fighting compartment.
3. Compressed-air-assisted transmission and steering were used in order to reduce the strain on the driver. It was however found out that the extremely low temperatures of the Eastern Front caused trouble in the compressed-air gears and steering. These units were therefore replaced by mechanical transmission parts.
4. The suspension facilitated an equal weight distribution on all bogie wheels.

Compressed-air-assisted gearchange and steering, mentioned above, noticeably reduced the physical strain imposed upon the driver. It was possible to achieve daily distances of 200 km at speeds averaging 20 to 25 kph, although maximum speed was only 40 kph. The life of the tracks and suspension was also noticeably increased. In some cases track and bogie life of between 4000 to 8000 km was achieved.

When the Pz Kw 35(t) was replaced as first-line equipment the remaining chassis were used either as "Mörserzugmittel (mortar tractors) 35(t)" with heavy artillery units or as "Zugkraftwagen (tractors) 35(t)" with a trailer capacity of 12 tons, in the maintenance sections of tank formations, either as tractors or towing vehicles. These had a crew of two.

Vehicles of the same type (LTM 35) were used in the Rumanian Army, sometimes in the Italian Army and in small numbers by the Hungarian Army, who used an improved version.

These otherwise excellent Czech vehicles did however suffer from the disadvantage of riveted construction, in which respect they fell below German design standards of the period.

Pz Kw 38(t)

The "TNHP-S" type, built from 1938 by Ceskomoravska Kolben Danek of Prague (after 1940 Böhmisch-Mährische Maschinenfabrik AG) was one of the most modern vehicles of its time. Production of this vehicle continued under German aegis after the occupation of Czechoslovakia until 1942. A report of 1st November 1940 gives the expected monthly production figures as 40 vehicles of this type. These extremely robust and reliable vehicles formed a quarter of German tank strength in the 1940–41 period and remained divisional equipment even after widespread introduction of Pz Kw III. Official German designation of the vehicle was "Pz Kw 38(t) (3·7 cm)". In 1940 228 were on the strength of the 7th and 8th Armoured Divisions for the attack in the West. On 1st July 1941 the inventory showed 763 Pz Kw 38(t), though this figure had sunk to 522 by 1st April 1942. However they were no longer pitted against Russian tanks after the end of 1941 due to inadequate firepower. The combat weight of the 38(t) was 9725 kg. Equipped with a Praga EPA 7·7-litre 6-cylinder petrol engine the vehicle reached a maximum speed of 42 kph. From chassis No 1601 the engine was uprated to 150 hp by fitting twin carburettors and increasing the revolutions (the improved engine was designated epa/AC). This type was used in a number of variants up to the end of the war. Main armament was a 3·7 cm tank gun (A7) L/40 and a 7·9 mm machine gun mounted in a turret. There was a crew of four. A Praga-Wilson pre-selector five-speed gearbox simplified the gear changing and drove the front sprocket wheels by means of a two-stage epicyclic steering gear. The chassis had four large bogie wheels on each side, fitted to the hull in pairs, on longitudinal leaf springs.

These vehicles were widely exported, as well as being constructed under licence, and were used in the armies of Sweden, Switzerland and Peru. Models A to G and S were produced.

Preliminary sketches by Krupp, dated from 1944, show the intention of mounting a Pz Kw IV turret with a 7·5 cm KwK 40 L/48 on the 38(t) chassis. This project would probably not have been feasible because of the overloading of the chassis. A further adaptation of the Pz Kw 38(t) chassis arose because the standard (and complicated) half-track chassis was not entirely satisfactory over difficult ground conditions. It was decided, from October 1943, to utilise the proven chassis of the Pz Kw 38(t), as a reconnaissance vehicle fitted with the turret of the Sd Kfz 222 armoured car. In fact 70 vehicles of this sort went into service during 1944 under the designation "Sd Kfz 140/1".

Marder (Marten) III

The demand by the German infantry for effective anti-tank weapons shortly after the start of the Russian campaign in 1941 led on 22nd December of that year to the Weapons Department's being ordered to produce a self-propelled anti-tank weapon as an interim measure. For this purpose the captured Russian 7·62 cm light field gun and anti-tank gun, as well as the chassis of the 38(t) tank were to be used. A development contract was not drawn up.

It is noteworthy that after the appearance of the Russian T-34 captured Russian guns were the only effective anti-tank weapons in the German armoury able to counter them as German-built anti-tank equipment of the period was practically useless against the new Soviet tanks. As in the case of the Pz Kw II these weapons were mounted on the basic Pz Kw 38(t) chassis with suitably modified superstructure. The gun with the complete carriage (less wheels) was fixed on top of the superstructure using a specially-fabricated mounting plate. This plate was shaped like a bridge and was fixed to the roof of the vehicle, fore and aft, by bolts. The crew (gunner and loader) were protected at the front and the sides by fixed armour consisting of an elongated movable gun shield and fixed sides. The superstructure armour was proof against steel-cored small arms fire at the front, but was weaker at the sides. In the armoured hull the driver and wireless operator's seats were arranged as in the original 38(t) tank. Behind them were on the right and left three ammunition boxes to take 24 rounds. There was a further supply of six rounds in each of the ammunition boxes on the side walls of the superstructure. The official designation of this vehicle was laid down as "Panzerselbstfahrlafette 2 für 7·62 cm PaK 36 (Sd Kfz 139)". An additional name suggested by Hitler's order of 27th February 1944 was that of "Marder III". The vehicle was also known as "Panzerjäger 38 für 7·62 cm PaK 36", reference order D 652/34 of 27th April 1942.

Production began on 24th March 1942 at the Böhmisch-Mährische Maschinenfabrik in Prague with an output of 17 vehicles per month. The estimated production target was 30 machines per month. Up to 15th May 1942 120 had been turned out and an extension contract for a further 100 vehicles was issued. Delivery totalled 20 machines in June and a further 20 in July 1942, while 30 were produced in August and in September. With an overall height of 2·5 metres and mean height of 2 metres, combat weight was 10·8 tons. A total of 344 vehicles of this type were produced.

A further contract for anti-tank vehicles, this time using the German 7·5 cm anti-tank gun 40/3, was ordered by Hitler via the Minister of Arms and Armament on 18th May 1942 (Order No 6772/42 g). Once again the basic chassis of the Pz Kw 38(t) was used but fitted with a new superstructure. The engine was still at the rear but in some vehicles had been uprated to 150 hp. The first test vehicle was delivered in June 1942. The weight was 10·8 tons and its official designation was "7·5 cm PaK 40/3 auf Sfl

38 (Sd Kfz 138)". This vehicle was also known as "Pz Jg 38, Marder III" (Reference order D 652/36 of 15th January 1943). With these vehicles, as with the SP conversions for the heavy sIG 33, which will be described later, the position of the engine in the rear of the chassis made necessary further modifications to the fighting compartment at the front of the vehicle in order to accommodate the PaK 40/3. For this reason these vehicles were very top heavy.

In later production vehicles the engine was re-positioned centrally in the chassis, which made it possible to set the fighting compartment more conveniently at the back of the hull. In addition the engine was now made much more accessible. Modified vehicles of this type, designated "Pz Kw 38(t) mit 7·5 cm PaK 40/3 (Sd Kfz 138)", were introduced from March 1943. The new arrangement on these vehicles gave them superior protection compared with the earlier Marder III and, despite the open fighting compartment, they formed the backbone of the anti-tank forces until 1944. Production ceased in May 1944 after 799 vehicles of both types had been completed.

Jagdpanzer (Tank Destroyer) "Hetzer" ("Baiter")

It was accepted from the beginning that Marder III, a converted and makeshift vehicle, could only be a temporary solution to the SP anti-tank gun requirement. Because good results had been obtained from using assault guns on the Pz Kw III chassis it was logical that the tried and tested chassis of the Pz Kw 38(t) should be used in a similar role. These considerations led to the Jagdpanzer 38 "Hetzer" (Reference order 652/63 of 1st November 1944), which became one of the most advanced anti-tank vehicles of the Second World War. This vehicle, weighing 16 tons, was in service with anti-tank battalions of infantry divisions in May 1944 and, after the end of the war, continued to be built by Skoda of Königgrätz for the Czech Army. Switzerland ordered 158 of these vehicles during the years 1946–47 and in the Swiss Army they were designated the G 13 tank destroyers. The track was strengthened and the shoe width increased from 178 to 212·3 cm. Engine revolutions were increased to 2800 rpm and this, uprating the output to 160 hp, produced a maximum speed of 40 kph. The fuel tank capacity was increased from 218 to 320 litres. With a frontal armour of 60 mm and a main armament consisting of a 7·5 cm PaK 39 L/48, these vehicles were well suited for anti-tank work. The crew of four men also had a roof-mounted machine gun with a 360° traverse for local defence.

While the vehicle was normally fitted with an ultra-short wave Fu 5 radio set, command vehicles were equipped with the Fu 8 model.

Construction of the chassis and the assembly were carried out by Böhmisch-Mährisch and by Skoda of Königgrätz, while the armour plate was supplied by Poldihütte of Komotau, Böhmisch-Mährisch, Linke-Hoffmann-Werke of Breslau and Skoda of Pilsen. A total of 1577 vehicles of this type was produced during 1944, and Skoda turned out 750 between September 1944 and May 1945. Krupp also participated in the production programme during 1944, being responsible for the installation of new main armament.

Drawing No Bz 3471, dated 24th November 1944, shows Pz Kw 38(t) fitted with the 7·5 cm L/70 (KwK 42 of the Panther tank). The gun had a side traverse of 15° each side and elevation limits of +15° to −8°. This idea, like that of trying to mount a Pz Kw IV turret on the 38(t), did not progress beyond the drawing board.

There was a flame thrower variant, designated "Flammenwerferpanzer 38(t)", almost identical in appearance to the basic "Hetzer", which had a flame gun fitted in place of the 7·5 cm anti-tank gun. The "Bergepanzer (recovery vehicle) 38", was very similar in appearance but had a slightly lower superstructure and no armament. Only a small number of these two variants were produced during 1944–45.

Further developments

The Pz Jg 38(d) was planned as a further development of the 38(t), and was intended to enter service in the German Army after 1945 as a light standard armoured vehicle. Although basically similar in appearance, this machine differed principally in the installation of the air-cooled Tatra 111 12-cylinder diesel engine, which produced 210 hp from a swept volume of 14·8 litres. The original German drawings for the vehicle, dated February 1945, envisaged the production of two marks: (a) the Pz Jg 38(d) (W 1807), with rear-mounted engine, and (b) Pz Jg 38(d) (W 1806) with engine mounted in the centre of the chassis. It was planned to install the 7·5 cm KwK 42 or the PaK L/70 in a rigid mounting. All those firms with spare production capacity as a result of the ending of Pz Kw IV production in the autumn of 1944 were to build the Pz Jg 38(d). Development of this vehicle during 1944–45 was accorded special priority. Production was to be 2000 vehicles per month, including 300 to 350 Waffenträger (weapons carriers) and a few reconnaissance vehicles.

Mention has already been made of the adaptation

of obsolete tank chassis as self-propelled gun carriages. In the case of the Pz Kw 38(t) there was a vehicle of this type in service as early as 1940 known as the "sIG 33 Fl auf Pz Kw 38(t) (Sd Kfz 138/1)", also designated "15 cm sIG 33 auf GW 38". Conversion of this vehicle was carried out by Alkett, while the armament was supplied by Rheinmetall-Borsig. As in the case of the previously-mentioned anti-tank SP carriages (Marder III) the normal tank chassis with the rear-mounted engine was adapted. An improved version of this vehicle, with the fighting compartment in the rear, was brought into service in 1942 however. The engine was relocated centrally as in the later Marder III. Chassis construction for these vehicles was carried out by Böhmisch-Mährisch while the armour was produced by Poldihütte. By 1944 a total of 370 vehicles had been produced. Designation was the same for both the early and late production types. Standard price of this vehicle (without armament) was approximately RM 53,000 (about £1750 or $7000 at that time).

With the armament omitted the same vehicles were used as ammunition carriers by the heavy infantry gun companies of Panzergrenadier Regiments. With a three-man crew (driver and two riflemen), 40 rounds of sIG 33 ammunition could be carried. A total of 102 such vehicles were completed.

Flakpanzer (Anti-aircraft Tanks)

Böhmisch-Mährisch's "Flakpanzer 38 (2 cm) (Sd Kfz 140)" came into service during October 1943 to strengthen anti-aircraft defences in the field. This 9·8 ton vehicle had a five-man crew but was poorly armed with only the 2 cm anti-aircraft gun. It was however the first attempt at producing an anti-aircraft tank. One hundred and sixty-two were produced and construction ceased in 1944. A further Pz Kw 38(t) variant which came into troop service during 1943 was Aufklärungspanzer (reconnaissance tank) 38(t) (Sd Kfz 140/1), 70 of which were built. These vehicles were intended as replacements for the four-wheeled armoured reconnaissance car (Sd Kfz 222) and the light reconnaissance armoured personnel carrier (Sd Kfz 250/9). The open turret of the Sd Kfz 222 fitted with a 2 cm KwK 38 and an MG 34 armament was mounted on the standard Pz Kw 38(t) chassis. This modification required only minor alterations to the superstructures.

One projected development of the Flakpanzer 38 was the new anti-aircraft tank "Kugelblitz". It was planned for production during 1945 using the chassis of the Pz Jg 38(d) for the purpose. Development was completed and a wooden model was built. Because of the prevailing war situation however it did not go into production. Two 20 mm Flak 38s were to be mounted in addition to the main armament of 30 mm automatic cannon 103/38. All the weapons were enclosed within a spherical revolving turret which was mounted on the turret ring of the Pz Kw IV. Elevation and traverse were controlled hydraulically by a layer, while the second man in the turret was both loader and commander. This vehicle was theoretically capable of producing an enormous volume of fire and would have given field units the anti-aircraft protection which they so badly needed.

Waffenträger (Weapons Carriers)

The idea of equipping field artillery with "Waffenträger Fahrzeugen" (literally "weapons carrier vehicles") arose as early as 1942. It was planned to produce a fully-tracked chassis, partially protected by armour, which could carry and dismount various types of guns. The use of the 38(t) and (d) chassis was considered. Although these machines have nothing to do with armoured fighting vehicles their development and production was in the hands of the tank building industry. It took two years of research to develop a fully-tracked vehicle which could meet all the requirements of the field artillery. The following characteristics were required: a fully-tracked chassis; a gun with the ability to elevate and with a 360° traverse; light armoured protection (8 to 10 mm); capable of being used for different types of gun. Two prototypes were developed and quantity production was ordered to start about the middle of 1945 with a monthly turn out of 300 to 350 vehicles. After careful evaluation of different designs it was decided to adopt the chassis parts of Pz Kw 38(d), though it was necessary to make alterations in the layout. The engine was moved to the front next to the driver and, by a re-arrangement of the transmission, the rear part of the hull could now be used for a platform on which the gun could be fixed and on which some of the ammunition supply could be stowed. The hulls were so low that it was necessary to protect the driver's head with a special tank helmet. Two models were planned for production and the smaller vehicle with four bogies on each side was intended to carry either the 8·8 cm PaK L/71 or the 10·5 cm light field howitzer. This was designated "leichter Waffenträger" (light weapons carrier). The vehicle's total weight was about 14 tons. The larger vehicle, with six road wheels on each side, was intended to carry the 12·8 cm K 81 gun and the heavy field howitzer Type 18 L/29·5. It was finally decided to produce an "Einheitswaffenträger" (standard weapons carrier), which, with a ground contact of 4·4 metres and a width (between wheel centres) of 2·7 metres, could carry the 10·5 cm light field howitzer Type 18/40 (L/28), the 15 cm heavy field howitzer Type 18 (L/29.5), the 8·8 cm PaK 43 (L/71), or the 12·8 cm K 81 (L/55) gun. With an axis height of about 190 cm and a combat weight of about 18 tons, this multi-purpose vehicle could be used, once it had off-loaded the main armament, as a munitions carrier or as a tractor.

Development of this vehicle was entrusted to Ardelt of Eberswald while Krupp were made responsible for the production. Prototypes were ordered from Krupp and Steyr-Daimler-Puch, who produced a prototype with the 8·8 cm PaK 43, by using spare Pz Kw 38(t) parts. A similar vehicle was also built by Rheinmetall-Borsig in collaboration with Ardelt. This interesting machine, the Waffenträger, was intended to replace all existing anti-tank and artillery self-propelled carriages from 1945 onwards. However the prevailing war situation curtailed future development of the vehicle.

At the end of 1944, it was proposed to use the chassis of the Pz Kw 38(t) as a fully-tracked personnel carrier in order to increase the cross-country mobility of Panzergrenadier units. To carry a Panzergrenadier squad as well as the crew of four it would have been necessary to lengthen the chassis by adding a further bogie wheel on either side. Planned armament was a 2 cm KwK 38 fitted into a revolving turret and capable of action against ground or air targets. A wooden model of this machine is said to have been produced towards the end of 1944, but no prototype appears to have been built.

Interestingly enough, advertisements in trade journals published by Ceskomoravska Kolben Danek after 1945, illustrated "caterpillar-tracked vehicles of all types, for civil and military purposes". These were all based on the original design of the Pz Kw 38(t). In view of its life and reliability, the suspension and transmission was truly one of the most advanced and most reliable of its day.

Panzer T 15 and T 25

During the war Skoda of Pilsen produced, at the request of the Army Weapons Department, two extremely advanced vehicles. These were the 10·5-ton reconnaissance vehicle type "T 15" and the 22-ton "T 25", which was designed as a battle tank. Both vehicles had a maximum speed of 60 kph.

The T 15 was a fast fully-tracked reconnaissance machine with a power-to-weight ratio of 21 hp/t. The drive was at the rear through a mechanical transmission. Initially fitted with a 3·7 cm gun in a revolving turret, the armament was later increased to a 5 cm gun. The armoured thicknesses were initially 15 mm, 20 mm and 50 mm though later improvements to the hull included the addition of thicker sloped armour plates.

The T 25 was designed to specifications formulated by the Weapons Department. The vehicle existed only in blueprint form and no prototype was ever built. Main features of this design were:

1. Main armament consisted of a 75 mm tank gun with a muzzle velocity of 900 metres per second.
2. The turret could be traversed both electrically and hydraulically.
3. The armoured plates of the hull were well sloped to achieve a satisfactory shape for optimum shot deflection.
4. An air-cooled V-12 450 hp petrol engine was initially planned but this was later changed to diesel.
5. It was planned to use an auxiliary engine of about 45 hp to drive the starter motor and the dynamo and to operate the fans.
6. Six large road wheels were to be fitted on each side making conventional return rollers unnecessary. The armour was 30 mm thick at the front, 20 mm at the sides and 10 mm at the rear. A crew of five would have been carried.

Pictures of a wooden model of a vehicle of the "Heuschrecke 10" series show this to be based on the T 25 chassis. The 10·5 cm light field gun Type 43 was fitted in a traversing turret. The estimated total weight was 24·2 tons. Sixty rounds of 10·5 cm ammunition could be carried. This vehicle also existed only as a project.

In conclusion it can be said that the tanks of the former Czech Army made an important contribution to the armoured vehicle strength of the German Army at a critical period when the German tank industry was not itself able to produce sufficient vehicles of the Pz Kw III and IV types.

Panzerkampfwagen III (Pz Kw III) and its Variants

Development

From 1935 onwards the collective knowledge gained during the development and production of the Pz Kw III at last enabled the German tank building industry to finalise its own design ideas. No longer had it to rely on foreign inspiration, though Germany's ideas did sometimes prove complicated and did not always lend themselves to mass production.

According to General Guderian two types of armoured fighting vehicle were envisaged for Germany's new armoured divisions. The first would be fitted with an armour-piercing gun as well as bow and turret machine guns, and the second type would be a support vehicle, mounting a larger-calibre cannon. It was planned to equip the three light companies of tank battalions with the first of these two types. This was the vehicle later to become well known as the Pz Kw III.

There were certain fundamental differences of opinion on the question of arming the vehicle. The Weapons Department and the Artillery Inspectorate considered the 3·7 cm gun to be sufficient, while the Inspectorate for Mechanised Troops demanded a 5 cm gun. The infantry was already equipped with a 3·7 cm anti-tank gun and, for simplicity's sake, it was thought desirable to standardise on this single armour-piercing weapon. The installation of the more powerful weapon was therefore rejected at this time. But one important concession gained was that the Pz Kw III's turret ring would be of a diameter large enough to accommodate a much larger calibre weapon at a future date. The safe loading of German road bridges limited the combat weight of both new types to 24 tons, while a maximum speed of 40 kph was specified. The crew was to consist of five men—commander, gun layer and loader in the turret, with the driver and radio operator in the front of the hull. The commander had a central raised seat between the layer's and the loader's positions, and his own cupola allowing an all-round view. Throat microphones were used both for inter-com and also for tank-to-tank communications in the field.

In 1935 the Weapons Department issued development contracts for the Pz Kw III to MAN, Daimler-Benz, Rheinmetall-Borsig and Krupp.

A 15-ton vehicle was specified with the characteristics already mentioned. The Weapons Department's "concealed-purpose" name was Zugführerwagen/ZW (Platoon Commander's Vehicle). From 1936 onwards the prototypes were thoroughly tested and, as a result of these trials, Daimler-Benz were made responsible for the development and production. In contrast to that of the Pz Kw IV, this machine's suspension system showed the influence of the automobile industry, reflecting the Daimler-Benz tradition, in that torsion-rod springing was standardised in the Pz Kw III, from the fourth development model of the "ZW" vehicles onwards. Krupp's experience of locomotive building led to a coupled bogie suspension with longitudinal leaf springs in the Krupp prototype "MKA", which combined the design features of the "ZW" and the "BW" (Pz Kw IV) tank.

It is noteworthy that the selection of tank building contractors seems to have been made with little regard to experience in mass production on the part of the firms concerned. The conclusion which can be drawn from this is that no mass production of these tanks had been planned at that particular time. The two largest car manufacturers in Germany at that time—Ford and Opel—were deliberately excluded from the tank programme because of their foreign connections.

Production

In 1936 the first model of the Pz Kw III was produced by Daimler-Benz and ten vehicles designated "1/ZW" underwent troop trials. Eight of these were fitted with the 37 mm gun and chassis numbers started at 60,001. Although the hull, superstructure and turret already took the form familiar in the later Pz Kw III models, the suspension consisted of five large double bogies, which were suspended on coil springs, plus a front driving sprocket and a rear idler together with two return rollers. Armour was between 5 and 14·5 mm thick and the overall weight was 15 tons. The power unit was a development of the Maybach DSO 12-cylinder high-performance 108 TR petrol engine of about 11 litres which produced a maximum of 250 hp. Maximum sustained output was however only 230 hp and top speed was 32 kph. Transmission was by a ZF SFG 75 five-speed gearbox. One hundred and fifty rounds were carried for the main armament and 4500 rounds for the three machine guns, two of which were coaxial with the main armament in the turret. This vehicle was known unofficially as the Pz Kw III (3·7 cm) Ausf A.

The marks B and C appeared in 1937. A new suspension was tried, consisting of eight small bogie wheels suspended on longitudinal leaf springs and the number of return rollers was increased to three. Armament remained a 3·7 cm tank gun L/45 in an internal mantlet and two MG 34s, while a third machine gun, mounted beside the driver, was worked by the wireless operator. Fifteen of each of the B (type 2/ZW) and the C (type 3a/ZW) models were constructed. Armour was retained at 14·5 mm all round. The Model D (type 3b/ZW) which finally went into quantity production, appeared at the end of 1938. With the introduction of Model D all previous trial models were redesignated Model D. The various original suspensions were retained, but these vehicles were uparmoured to 30 mm all round, increasing the total weight to about 19 tons. The ZF Aphon SSG 76 transmission was used.

From the Model E onwards the more powerful Maybach 12-cylinder HL 120 TR was fitted, which increased the maximum output to 320 hp by enlarging the bore from 100 to 105 mm and increasing the cylinder capacity to 11·9 litres (torque 80 m/kg). The gearbox in this vehicle was the Maybach Variorex pre-selector with 10 forward and one reverse speed. This complicated transmission was intended to make gear changing easier as the change was carried out by a vacuum after the gear had been selected and the release valve activated by depressing the clutch pedal. The 9th and 10th gear positions were overdrives. The speed of 40 kph at 2800 rpm was not to be exceeded. Fifty-five vehicles of this version were produced.

On 27th September 1939 the Army Regulations circular announced "Panzerkampfwagen III (3·7 cm) (Sd Kfz 141), has been adopted as a result of its successful troop trials".

In the mass production which now followed the participating manufacturers were: Altmärkische Kettenfabrik GmbH (Alkett)—Spandau (assembly) and Falkensee (chassis construction); Daimler-Benz AG—Berlin-Marienfelde; Fahrzeug- und Motorenbau GmbH (Famo)—Breslau; Henschel & Sohn AG —Werk III, Mittelfeld-Kassel; Maschinenfabrik Augsburg-Nürnberg AG (MAN)—Nuremberg; Mühlenbau und Industrie AG (MIAG)—Amme Werk, Brunswick; Waggonfabrik Wegmann AG— Kassel; and Maschinenfabrik Niedersachsen-Hannover—Hannover-Linden.

The Pz Kw III Ausf E (type 4/ZW) (reference order 652/17 of 23rd April 1940), which appeared in 1939, featured the finalised chassis design of this series. There were now six bogies on each side (bogie size 520×95–398, track roller size, 310× 70–302), mounted on transversely-fitted torsion bars. The vehicle weighed 19·5 tons when fitted with all-round armour 30 mm thick and was still equipped with the Maybach HL 120 TR engine. The chassis weighed 13·8 tons. Two coupled machine guns (MG 34s) in the turret had, until now, been coaxial with the main armament, but from this version onward a single coaxial machine gun was fitted. Some Pz Kw III Ausf E versions had the old model D type turrets with an internal mantlet and two turret machine guns however. Transmission was via a main clutch to the Maybach Variorex pre-selector gearbox already described. This gearbox was of the constant-mesh type where sliding gear switch sleeves transferred the drive to the two cog wheels required for the correct gear. The main clutch was hydraulically operated and the bevel gear and the steering gear were flanged to the variable gears. Clutch steering was affected by means of mechanical servo-internal, expanding brakes with hydraulic assistance. Steering and standard brakes were located in the same housing and from these the drive went to the driving sprocket. The rear idler wheel, in this version, consisted of a boss upon which two wheel discs were welded. The 3·7 cm gun now had an external mantlet. By 1940 100 of these vehicles had been built, intended as the main equipment of tank regiments. The German tank industry could only produce in limited numbers, and this low production capacity became more and more apparent. The Pz Kw III received its baptism of fire in Poland and there proved itself. For the attack on France on 10th May 1940 a total of 349 Pz Kw IIIs was available.

Uparmoured versions

On 4th January 1939 the Weapons Department received a contract to develop further the Pz Kw III and to arm it with a 5 cm tank gun. Once again Daimler-Benz was made responsible for the chassis and superstructure, and Krupp for the design of the turret. It was proposed to install the 5 cm tank gun L/42 which had a muzzle velocity of 450 to 685 metres per second. The first vehicles equipped with the 5 cm armament were not ready by the 10th May 1940 for the offensive in France and Flanders but were issued during the course of this campaign. The designation of this version was "Pz Kw III (5 cm) Ausf F (type 5/ZW)".

In this model the Maybach HL 120 TRM was installed, which had an output of 300 hp at 3000 rpm and a sustained output of 265 hp at 2600 rpm. This power unit was constructed under licence by Norddeutsche Motorenbau (Nordbau). The weight of the vehicle was not appreciably altered, but the somewhat lower cupola was a distinctive feature. An equipment box was now fitted at the rear of the turret. From this version on the drive and idler wheel patterns were altered, the new idler being spoked. Four hundred and fifty machines of this type were produced.

On 1st November 1940 the production schedule for the Pz Kw III was laid down as 108 vehicles per month, but only 96 vehicles were built in the first month of the new schedule due to tooling up. This seventh version Pz Kw III (5 cm) Ausf G (type 6/ZW), first produced in October 1940, now formed numerically the backbone of German tank regiments. For African service special tropical equipment consisting of a larger radiator and air filter was fitted. The latter was generally a felt bellows filter which, partly protected by armour, was carried over the exterior of the engine compartment. Despite these precautions the average life of a piston was only 2000 to 3000 km in desert conditions. Vehicles with this sort of equipment received the designation "Tp" (Tropical). The Pz Kw III was the main type of German tank used during the fighting in Jugoslavia and Greece in 1941. Four hundred and fifty G version machines were built and altogether a total of 2143 chassis of the ZW type were produced during 1940–41.

During September and October 1940 volunteers of the 2nd Tank Regiment in Putlos were formed into Tank Battalion A and trained for Operation Sea Lion, the invasion of Great Britain. Two other special formations, Tank Battalions B and C, were being raised at the same time and the same place.

These units later formed the 18th Tank Regiment of the 18th Panzer Division and adapted the Pz Kw III and IV for submerged wading. The following measures were taken. All openings, vision slits, flaps, etc, were made watertight with sealing compounds and cable tar, the turret entry ports were bolted from the inside and air intake openings for the engine completely closed. A rubber cover sheet was fixed over the mantlet, the commander's cupola and the bow machine gun. An ignition wire blew off the covering sheet upon surfacing and left the vehicle ready for action. Between the hull and the turret there was a rubber sealing ring which, when inflated, prevented the water from entering. The fresh air supply was maintained by a wire-bound rubber trunk with a diameter at about 20 cm, 18 metres long. To one end of this tube was fitted a buoy with attached antennae. The exhaust pipes were fitted with high-pressure non-return relief valves. When travelling submerged sea water was used to cool the engine and seepage was removed by a bilge pump. The maximum diving depth was 15 metres. Three metres of the air tube's 18 metre length was available as a safety measure. These submersible tanks were to be launched from barges or lighters. They slid into the water down an elongated ramp made of channel plates. Directing was achieved by radio orders from a command vessel to the submerged vehicle. Underwater navigation was carried out by means of a gyro compass and the crew was equipped with escape apparatus. The submerged machines were relatively easy to steer as buoyancy lightened them. After Operation Sea Lion was abandoned these vehicles were eventually used operationally during the Russian campaign in 1941 for the crossing of the River Bug.

An instruction from Field Marshal Keitel to the Army High Command dated 7th July 1941 says "The Führer considers it desirable that all new production tanks be radically uparmoured by fitting spaced armour plates, in addition to the main armour, and to neutralise thereby the increased penetrating power of the British anti-tank weapons. The increase in weight and the loss of speed must, in the Führer's opinion, be accepted." Effective thickness of the additional armour was in fact 30 mm.

The H version of the Pz Kw III (7/ZW reference D 652/62 of 1st November 1942), which appeared in 1940, had meanwhile featured a stronger torsion bar suspension. It also became necessary to increase the track width from 360 to 400 mm (track type Kgs 61/400/120). The track gauge was therefore increased from 249 to 251 cm. The chassis weight of this model was 15·8 tons and the combat weight had risen to 21·6 tons. The complicated Maybach Variorex drive was replaced by a normal six-speed Aphon transmission with ZF SSG 77 type synchromesh. The main clutch was of the dry-plate multi-disc type. Although Hitler had demanded from the start that Pz Kw III be rearmed with the 5 cm long-barrel tank gun in fact only the 5 cm L/42 gun had been fitted on models F, G and H. The total number of "ZW" (i.e. Pz Kw III) vehicles equipped with the 5 cm L/42 was 1924.

The inadequacy of this armament was only fully realised in 1941 after the appearance of the T-34 on the Russian front. This very advanced Russian tank had a shock effect on the leaders of the German Army. While it was still calculated on 17th July 1941 that the raising of a proposed 36 tank divisions would require 7992 Pz Kw IIIs a note dated 29th November 1941 after the introduction of the Russian T-34 shows a complete reversal. At this period doubts were already being expressed as to the efficacy of armoured forces and Hitler had personally described the Pz Kw III as an unsuccessful design. It must however be made clear that for its time this vehicle was extremely advanced and that if Guderian's original demand for a 5 cm long-barrel gun had been met at the outbreak of war the Pz Kw III could have been, in 1940 and 1941, the best fighting tank of all the belligerent powers.

A memorandum dated 21st July 1941 and issued by the Inspector General for Transport stated that additional capacity and manufacturing areas would be made available to extend tank production and that these would include, among others, a Daimler-Benz factory, the Krupp vehicle works, Fross-Büssing in Vienna, Tatra in Kolin, Framo in Hainichen as well as parts of MAN, Henschel, Hanomag, Auto-Union and NSU.

It was thus not until 1941 that the order was given for the introduction of the 5 cm gun (KwK 39) L/60 calibre (barrel length 300 cm) for Pz Kw III. Using the "Panzergranate 40" this weapon produced a muzzle velocity of 1180 mps. Production Pz Kw IIIs so equipped were designated J (Sd Kfz 141/1), type description 8/ZW. In addition all Pz Kw IIIs returned to Germany for general overhaul after April 1941 were refitted with this weapon. In contrast to the 99 rounds which could be carried for the 5 cm gun L/42 only 78 rounds could be stowed for the L/60. Small technical differences distinguished the J version from its predecessors. The reverse gear change, which was secured by a spring-loaded pedal, had been worked by a button with a wire pull, but

from the Model J onwards a hand lever was used. The internal expanding brakes too for this and for subsequent models were activated concentrically, whereas formerly an eccentric disc, which fitted under the upper brake shoes, had been used. Levers were introduced to replace the steering pedals which had operated the brakes in earlier models. The total weight of Model J was 21·5 tons and the overall length was increased to 556 cm. On 1st July 1941 a total of 327 Pz Kw IIIs with the 3·7 cm tank gun and 1174 with the 5 cm tank gun were available to the German Army. By 1st April 1942 the number of the 3·7 cm vehicles had fallen to 131, but a total of 1893 machines with the 5 cm gun was now available. The estimated monthly production for January 1942 was scheduled to be 190 machines, but because of delivery problems with the guns and the armoured housings only 159 were in fact built.

This model L (type 9/ZW) was introduced at the end of 1941 and had increased frontal armour on the turret and 20 mm "spaced armour" plates on the mantlet and superstructure front. By increasing the front and the turret front armour to 70 mm, the combat weight was raised to 22·3 tons. The MG ammunition stowage was increased from 2000 to 4950 rounds.

As an experiment the 0725 gun with a conical barrel was fitted into the Pz Kw III, but because of high barrel wear the promising trials of this weapon could not be continued. The model M (type 10/ZW) which appeared in 1942 had a total weight of 23 tons and the price of this vehicle (without weapons) was RM 96,183. The following totals of Pz Kw IIIs with the 5 cm L/60 gun were produced: 1941—40; 1942—1907; 1943—22. After 1943 Pz Kw III variants were equipped with 5 mm thick side plates, known as aprons or skirt armour to increase protection against hits from anti-tank rifles and hollow-charge ammunition. The aprons, which fitted on to longitudinal rails on both sides of the vehicle, were removable and could be fitted around the turret (Army Technical Pamphlet 1943, No 433). The width of the vehicle, which was first shown on 19th March 1943 in Rügenwalde, was 341 cm. For tank units on the Eastern Front a wider track was issued in 1944 (Army Technical Pamphlet 1944, No 256), the so-called "Ostkette" (literally Eastern track). This was intended to increase the cross-country capabilities of the Pz Kw III and its variants in snow and on soft going. This was simply a makeshift, for the track with its extension on one side could only be used with safety in flat country. The width with the Ostkette fitted was 326 cm.

From 1943 onwards vehicles were coated with a paste known as "Zimmerit" to prevent the attaching of magnetic anti-tank charges. This substance was applied by means of a spatula and then hardened with a blow lamp. Its use was discontinued towards the end of 1944 (Army Technical Pamphlet 1944, No 733).

In 1943 the improved Fliegerbeschussberät (anti-aircraft mounting) 42 replaced the Fliegerbeschussberät 41. This could be fitted to the commander's cupola with clamps, which were also suitable for the MG 34 and 42. From 1943 onwards all newly-completed tanks and all AFVs which had been repaired in Germany were fitted with smoke candle projectors.

From the end of 1942 10/ZW variants (i.e. Pz Kw III Ausf M) were re-equipped with the 7·5 cm gun L/24 (formerly the main armament of the Pz Kw IV). This gun was first installed as standard however in the final version of the Pz Kw III, Model N (Sd Kfz 141/2) (type 11/ZW). A total of 64 rounds of 7·5 cm ammunition could be carried and 3450 rounds for the two MG 34s. The total weight was 21,300 kg. Six hundred and sixty of these vehicles were produced. In August 1943, production of the Pz Kw III was officially terminated and the capacity now available was turned over to the building of assault guns.

In 1942 MIAG delivered 100 Pz Kw III Ausf M versions (type 10/ZW), without main armament, to the Wegmann factory, where these vehicles were converted into "Flammenwerfer-Panzer" (flame-throwing tanks). DKW two-stroke engines were used to drive the pumping system for the flame projectors. With an oil load of 1000 litres between 70 and 80 flame shots, each of 2 to 3 seconds duration were possible and flame length was between 55 to 60 metres. The steel flame projector, with a 14 mm nozzle was fitted into the mantlet in place of the usual 5 cm main armament. Both the coaxial and the hull MG were retained. The combat weight was about 23 tons and the crew consisted of three men. Wireless equipment carried was the Fu 2 and an Fu 5. Described as designated Pz Kw III (Fl) (Sd Kfz 141/3), these vehicles saw service in special units.

Engine Developments

As with nearly all other German AFVs, it was planned to replace the Pz Kw III eventually with improved designs. The result of a works conference held on 25th May 1938 at Daimler-Benz was that they were to develop a new AFV of the 20-ton class for which a 400-hp engine would be required. The Army Weapons Department again proposed the use of Maybach petrol engine. How exclusively the German Armed forces were supplied with Maybach engines is shown by the fact that the company (plus licensees) produced during war years, nearly 140,000 engines of varying sizes, having a combined output of 40 million horsepower. Daimler-Benz suggested to the Weapons Department as an alternative the use of diesel engines of its own manufacture and decided to develop the MB 809 diesel engine for the VK 2001 (DB)—the proposed Pz Kw III replacement. This power unit was to be constructed with the same capacity as the Maybach HL 190 (a 12-cylinder petrol engine with a 19-litre capacity weighing 1000 kg) which was proposed by the Army Weapons Department. Daimler-Benz, starting in June 1938 developed a V-12 diesel engine of almost 25·5 litres capacity and producing 400 hp at 2100 rpm. Continual alterations during the assembly of the vehicle demanded corresponding adjustments and alterations in the diesel engine design.

The four projects which had been worked on until mid-December 1938 produced the following results:

	date	DB engine MB 809	Maybach HL 190	alterations
1st Project	1/6/38	25·5 litres; 400 hp at 2100 rpm	19 litres; 400 hp at 2400 rpm	ZW 40
2nd Project	24/6/38	21·5 litres; 360 hp	16 litres; 300 hp	VK 2001 with completely altered area and fittings
	8/9/38			Test of transverse engine installation with angled drive
3rd Project	31/10/38	19·7 litres; 400 hp at 2400 rpm (steel cylinder)	12 litres; 400 hp at 3300 rpm	
4th Project	14/12/38	14·8 litres; 300 hp at 2400 rpm	HL 116 11·6 litres; 6-cylinder; 300 hp at 3300 rpm	

Daimler-Benz also experimented with the transverse installation of engines in order to save on overall length and weight of the vehicle. The tests showed no worthwhile advantage however. An attempt was also made to achieve a higher power-to-weight ratio by using welded steel cylinders, even though these were considerably more expensive to produce. The reduction in weight would have allowed heavier armour and smaller water and oil radiators could have been used.

Following the completion of the engineering developments at the beginning of June 1940 the first dynamometer run took place in February 1941, and the acceptance run of the first engine on 12th March 1941. This engine arrived at Marienfelde for installation into the test vehicle on 21st March 1941 after which cross-country tests took place on the proving grounds and in Kummersdorf.

Efforts to improve the performance of both vehicles and engines were made when, shortly after the start of the Russian campaign, it was discovered that the enemy was using considerably heavier vehicles and more powerful engines. The VK 2001 project and the diesel MB 809 engine were consequently cancelled.

Klöckner-Humboldt-Deutz AG of Cologne were busy at this time designing a diesel engine for the VK 2001. The contract for this power unit, issued by the Army Weapons Department, specified delivery by the end of 1941. The engine was to be an 8-cylinder radial engine which was to produce 350 hp at 2500 rpm. A test vehicle was constructed but it did not go into production.

Sturmgeschütze (Assault Guns)

After specification had been completed for German tank designs the infantry demanded an armoured close-support vehicle. Inspectorate 4 in their memorandum 449/36 g.Kdos of 15th June 1936 therefore asked the Army Weapons Department to produce an "armoured artillery close-support weapon for infantry and anti-tank purposes". The firm chosen to develop the chassis and carry out production was once again Daimler-Benz, while Krupp were made responsible for installing the guns.

The armoured vehicle duly evolved was armed with the 7·5 cm L/24 gun. The low silhouette demanded meant that the main armament was not mounted in a revolving turret but directly in the hull. The "assault guns" proved themselves to be extremely valuable in close support of the infantry and later, with heavier armament, in an anti-tank role. The chassis of the Pz Kw III tank was used as a basis for the vehicle

because it was able to take the probable total weight of 20·2 tons. The specified armour thickness was 10 to 50 mm. Four men formed the crew.

An initial series of 30 vehicles was scheduled to go into production during February 1940. Troop trials continued throughout 1940 and five "assault guns" on Pz Kw III Ausf F chassis (5/ZW type) took part in the campaign in France. The production contract was signed in July 1940 and output was scheduled to reach 50 machines per month by September 1940. The official designation was "Gepanzerte Selbstfahrlafette für Sturmgeschütz 7·5 cm Kanone (Sd Kfz 142), (ref D 652/41 of 1st April 1943)". The model "A" version of the assault gun had the Maybach HL 120 TR engine and was fitted with the Maybach Variorex pre-selector gearbox · with 10 forward speeds and one reverse.

When production began these vehicles were assembled exclusively by Alkett. MIAG also participated in StuG III production from February 1943 to March 1945. Daimler-Benz also started building them in 1943.

Firms which supplied armour plate for these vehicles were: Brandenburgische Eisenwerke of Brandenburg, Harkort-Eicken of Hagen, Deutsche Edelstahlwerke AG of Hannover, and Bismarckhütte of Upper Silesia.

In 1940 184 StuG IIIs were produced. The monthly production average was 30 by 1st November 1940. During 1940 and 1941 StuG III models B to E came into service. These were fitted with the Maybach HL 120 TRM engine of 265 hp. A variable six-speed Aphon synchromesh gearbox type ZF SSG 77 was installed in these models. A few detail alterations were made in successive models.

For the short 7·5 cm Assault Gun 37 44 rounds of ammunition were carried but no machine gun was fitted for local defence. During 1941 548 vehicles were built. The monthly production figure of 40 machines, which had been decreed in 1941, was in fact reduced because of the increased numbers of Pz Kw III tanks which diverted chassis from assault gun production.

On 28th September 1941 Hitler demanded that assault guns be uparmoured regardless of the increase in weight and the reduction in speed. The machine was also to carry a gun with a longer barrel and of increased muzzle velocity. An instruction to this effect was issued by the Ordnance Department (No OKW/002205/41 g.Kdos), naming Daimler-Benz, once again, as the firm responsible for the chassis and selecting Rheinmetall-Borsig for fitting the new gun and for the superstructures. The vehicles were first shown to Hitler on 31st March 1941 with the hint that mass production could not begin before February 1942.

On 1st July 1941 there were 416 StuG IIIs on hand and by 1st April 1942 a total of 623. The new StuG III, designated Model F, which appeared in the spring of 1942, was now fitted with the 7·5 cm StuK 40 L/43 as the main armament. The total weight was 21·6 tons and 44 rounds were carried. Some of these weapons were issued without a muzzle brake. In June 1942 the bow armour was increased to 80 mm by fitting additional plates.

From the 120th model F onwards the longer 7·5 cm StuK 40 L/48 was fitted and this was retained until StuG III production ceased in the spring of 1945. Vehicles thus armed were officially designated "7·5 cm Sturmgeschütz 40, Ausf G (Sd Kfz 142/1)". The combat weight of the StuG III had now been raised to 23·9 tons and the price per vehicle was RM 82,500. From 1943 onwards, in common with the basic Pz Kw III series, armoured side aprons were fitted and the MG 34 or 42 was installed for local defence. Total StuG production was: 3041 in 1943; 4850 in 1944 and 123 in 1945.

The final variants of the StuG 40 had partially cast superstructures and cast "Saukopf" (pig's head) mantlets. From the end of 1943 and the beginning of 1944 the armour was improved, without increasing the thickness, by interlocking the bow plates, and by this means a greater degree of resistance was achieved. It was planned to turn out 220 assault guns per month by June 1943. Of these 24 were to have been equipped with a light howitzer. These vehicles which had already been produced during 1942 with the description "10·5 cm Feldhaubitze 42" (Sd Kfz 142/2), were similar in construction to the StuG 40 and had the 10·5 cm Sturmhaubitze (assault howitzer) 42 L/28 as their main armament. Thirty-six rounds of 10·5 cm ammunition were carried. This weapon had originally been fitted with a muzzle brake (as a field piece) so that the gun could fire supercharge. Army Instruction Leaflet 1944 No 635 however ordered the removal of the muzzle brake on future production. Where the brake was fitted to the 10·5 cm StuH 42 this was retained until it became unserviceable. If no other StuH 42 brake was available for replacement, then a brake from the leFH 18 M or the leFH 18/40 was sometimes fitted as a substitute. The gun could then no longer fire supercharge. Some vehicles of the assault gun series were not fitted with guns but were used as ammunition carriers, designated "Munitionspanzer III".

In 1941 in an attempt to improve the mobility of the heavy infantry gun sIG 33 it was mounted on a Pz Kw III chassis. According to a file entry of 16th July 1941 the Weapons Department stated that 12 heavy infantry gun sIG 33 B (Sfl) vehicles were to be produced by the 15th September 1941. Following discussions with Bochumer Verein and Alkett the completed hulls and other components were delivered by the end of July and the beginning of August 1941. The prototype was shown to Hitler on 31st March 1941 and a contract given to Alkett for an experimental series of 12 vehicles. Designated "Sturm-Infanteriegeschütz", they had a fighting weight of 21 tons. Thirty rounds were carried. The normal Pz Kw III tank hull was used and the armoured superstructure had thicknesses of: front 80 mm; side 50 mm and rear 15 mm. A crew of five was envisaged. The production series, which was anticipated for the spring of 1942, was never started. The Sd Kfz 166 on a Pz Kw IV chassis replaced it.

Panzerbefehlswagen (Armoured Command Vehicles)

Command vehicles were required to lead the large armoured formations and much thought was given to their construction from the very beginning of tank development. By 1938, the first "Grossen Panzerbefehlswagen" (large armoured command vehicles) had been produced and the following versions were issued to the troops:

Sd Kfz 266 with FuG 6 and FuG 2 (Wireless set 6 and 2)
Sd Kfz 267 with FuG 6 and FuG 8 (Wireless set 6 and 8)
Sd Kfz 268 with FuG 6 and FuG 7 (Wireless set 6 and 7)

Externally these vehicles were identical. The first two types of armoured command vehicles designated 3c/ZW were converted from Pz Kw III tank Model D. The official designation was "Panzerbefehlswagen III Ausf D¹". Like the armoured car command variants these vehicles carried a distinctive loop aerial above the engine compartment, though this was replaced by the whip aerial in 1943. Armament was an MG 34. A dummy gun replaced the main armament. The third command type on the Pz Kw III chassis Model E (4/ZW) appeared during 1940 as the Panzerbefehlswagen III Ausf E, though later models based on the Ausf H chassis were fitted with additional armour in front of the driver's position and at the bow. At the start of the campaign in France in 1940 there were 39 large armoured command vehicles with the tank divisions. According to a report dated

1st November 1940 an Army Weapons Department contract for 145 of these vehicles was placed with Daimler-Benz. Production schedule was 10 machines per month; the final 14 of the contract were delivered during January 1942.

The absence of main armament restricted this vehicle's use in action and special components had to be made. There was meanwhile an urgent need for command vehicles which could be quickly adapted from existing AFVs in the field. In January 1941 a development contract covering this particular item was issued to Daimler-Benz. It was specified that these vehicles were to have the 5 cm KwK L/42 or L/60 in a revolving turret. Described as "Panzer-befehlswagen 4c/ZW", these vehicles were troop tested from August 1941. The 7/ZW Model K was the chassis selected in this case. The designation was "Panzerbefehlswagen III Ausf K". With a five-man crew (the loader was also the wireless operator) the vehicle had a combat weight of about 23 tons. The cost of the vehicle (without armament) was about RM 110,000. Production ran from August 1942 to August 1943. The total of large and small command vehicles available on 1st July 1941 was 331 and on 1st April 1942 the total was 273.

To enable forward observation officers of the armoured artillery to accompany tank attacks, armoured artillery observation vehicles were also introduced in 1940. For this role a variant of the light half-track personnel carrier (Sd Kfz 253) was used from 1940 to 1942. A true OP tank entered service during 1943, based on the Pz Kw III. The official designation of this vehicle was "Panzerbeobachtungs-wagen III (Sd Kfz 143)". There was no main arma-ment, only an MG 34 ball mounted in the centre of a mantlet. This vehicle remained in service until 1944 and incorporated the progressive improvements of the Pz Kw III as they were produced. There was a four-man crew.

Variants

Relatively few variants of the Pz Kw III were built. One was "Bergepanzerwagen III" and 32 of these were completed in 1939, 34 in 1940, 132 in 1941, 50 in 1942 and 14 in 1943. They were converted from existing standard Pz Kw III chassis. For supply purposes, particularly in the difficult country of the Eastern Front, the "Schlepper III" was brought into service. In this conversion a wooden platform was fixed to the chassis of an old Pz Kw III. These vehicles were generally fitted with "Ostketten".

Guderian recalls in his memoirs that among others the rail-mounted model of the Pz Kw III tank was shown at the troop training ground at Arys on 20th October 1943. This railway track vehicle was in-tended to afford protection for the railways in partisan-infiltrated areas.

The "Minenräumpanzer III" (mine-clearing tank) was also produced. A converted Pz Kw III hull was fitted with a track and suspension system and, by incorporating extra chassis components and extend-ing the suspension arms, an increase in ground clearance was achieved. More detailed information is not available.

From 1935 to 1945 15,350 "ZW" chassis were produced and this speaks for the reliability of this vehicle. The Pz Kw III tank was a very advanced fighting vehicle for its period, and proved adequate on all fronts, in relation to the tactical demands made upon it.

A few neutral countries took delivery of small numbers of Pz Kw IIIs partly for political reasons. For example in 1942 a number of Pz Kw III Ausf Js were sent to Turkey. Captured vehicles of these types were used on a limited scale particularly by the Red Army, which put into service a re-armed assault gun designated "Sturmgeschütz SU-761". The Free Polish Forces used some captured Pz Kw III and IV tanks for instructional purposes in Africa. Hungarian troops, like those of other Balkan countries, were to a limited degree equipped with German tanks.

Further Developments

There was little difference in the technical and tactical design of the Pz Kw III and IV and, due to continued improvements in armament, became more and more alike in their gunpower. This similarity precipitated the decision to produce only one fighting tank in place of the two vehicles. According to a note from a report dated 6th September 1941, the follow-ing advantages could be anticipated from the merger of the Pz Kw III and IV, the resulting design to be called Pz Kw III/IV:

1. Easing of demands upon the drawing offices.
2. Ease of testing.
3. An easing of the position regarding the pro-duction of experimental vehicles.
4. Complete standardisation of all parts (except for the armament), this leading to increased output and simplification of the supply position as well as simpler and standardised training.
5. The ability to switch production so that, if required, the Pz Kw III could be produced in a relatively short space of time in place of the Pz

Kw IV, and vice-versa, giving greater organisational flexibility.

6. Increased ammunition stowage for the Pz Kw III (about 40 per cent more than formerly, although the projected round would be larger than that used until then).

7. The possibility of developing the turret so that it could take an even more powerful armour-piercing weapon than the 5 cm L/60 at that time being developed, e.g. the 0725 gun with the conical barrel.

8. Hydraulic turret traverse, even for the Pz Kw III, thus easing the crew's work and allowing faster target acquisition.

The external distinguishing feature of the Pz Kw III nA and IV nA was the large interleaved bogie arrangement like that of the "Halbketten-Zugmaschine" (half-tracked tractor) (Zg Kw).

The armour thicknesses (in mm) of each type were:

	front	*rear*	*side*
Pz Kw III nA	50	50	50
Pz Kw IV nA	50	40	40

To keep the maximum weight of both tanks down to 23·5 tons the Pz Kw III nA had a hull width of only 1·65 metres, as opposed to the 1·8 metres of the Pz Kw IV nA. The overall aim was complete standardisation on the one type and the only difference lay in the necessary differences in armament. This ambitious standardisation could only be achieved if when the 1·8 metre-wide hull of the Pz Kw IV nA was used a compromise could be reached by using Pz Kw III nA side armour to keep the weight down to 23·5 tons. This, it was thought, would be achieved if the chassis, sides and rear, originally planned to have armour of 50 mm thickness, had this reduced to 40 mm thick.

A letter from the Head of the Army Equipment Branch and BdE, Staff Equipment 11a, No 2944/41 g, dated 14th September 1941 confirmed this and said

(a) Standardisation of a single type Pz Kw III/IV is advantageous and should be proceeded with (the only difference will be in the armament).

(b) The reduction of the armour thickness on the chassis sides should not be implemented since it is not reasonable to keep to the specified weight of 23·5 tons at the expense of defensive armour. Following the Führer's order to fit appliqué armour for added frontal protection the specified maximum weight has had to be exceeded in the past. The specified weight limit of 23·5 tons for the Pz Kw III/IV cannot be adhered to.

Prototypes of the Pz Kw III/IV, with the interleaved suspension and body and turret of the 5 cm L/42 Pz Kw III were in fact built. The continuing rise of anti-tank gun sizes and power necessitated an increase of armour for all tanks from 1942 onwards. The Pz Kw III/IV could not, as it was designed, be generally uparmoured however, and in the autumn of 1944 plans for its production were finally abandoned.

Panzerkampfwagen IV (Pz Kw IV) and its Variants

Development

At a conference of Departmental Heads at the Army Weapons Department on 11th January 1934 the outstanding decisions regarding Panzer equipment for the Army, expected to total 63 armoured divisions, were to a large extent clarified. The agenda contained, among other things, the question of arming the "Grosstraktors" (large tractors) and the determining of the weight limits of the "medium tractors". The first development contracts for the "Mittleren Traktors" (medium tractors), with which it was proposed to equip the medium companies of the future tank battalions, had already been issued in 1934. It was intended to fit these vehicles with a large calibre gun as well as turret and hull machine guns. It would therefore be able to fulfil a support role for the lighter tanks during combat and engage targets which the smaller armour-piercing weapon of the "ZW" machine was not able to affect or penetrate. The gun calibre chosen for the medium tank was 7·5 cm. Total weight of this vehicle, like that of the Pz Kw III, was to be 24 tons. Both these vehicles were alike in layout and, superficially, in appearance. The crew consisted of five men. Rheinmetall-Borsig undertook the main development work and had produced a wooden model of the VK 2001 (Rh) by the end of 1934. The first prototypes were built by this company during 1934 and 1935 and were given a complete testing in Kummersdorf. The suspension on these vehicles consisted of eight paired bogies and three track return rollers. The bogies, suspended from a long beam-type arm, were standard at the time for Rheinmetall-Borsig's commercial tractor design. The idler wheel fitting was altered many times, while the driving sprocket was at the front. The "camouflage" designation was "Bataillonsführerwagen/BW" (battalion commander's vehicle). All "camouflage" names for tanks and artillery were discarded in 1935 however. The new VK 2001 (Rh) weighed 18 tons and the designed engine power of

320 hp gave a maximum speed of 30 kph. Overall dimensions were 5600×2900×2650 mm, and the armour was 5–14·5 mm thick. It could climb gradients of 30° and cross trenches 2·2 metres wide. One hundred and forty rounds of main armament ammunition were carried together with 3000 rounds of SAA for the two machine guns.

The design study for the BW vehicle made during 1935 by MAN (VK 2002/MAN) provided for an interleaved suspension. The overall height of this design was somewhat more than that of yet a third BW design which was submitted at the same time by Krupp. This Krupp design (VK 2001/K) included interleaved bogie suspension asked for originally by the Army Weapons Department but despite this the design did not go into production. The turret, hull and superstructure already showed a certain similarity to what later became the production model, however Krupp's Heerlein division, by accepting the task of designing this turret, subsequently took over the responsibility for practically all further development work and retained this responsibility, with few exceptions (e.g. Panther), until the end of the war. Krupp used the experience of their design work on the Pz Kw II, and prototypes were produced and thoroughly tested during 1935–36. As a result of these trials Krupp were appointed as the main developer and manufacturer for the complete production of the BW design.

Production

The first production version of the Pz Kw IV (7·5 cm), produced in 1936 with the designation "I/BW", went into production in the Krupp-Gruson works at Magdeburg as "Ausf A" (Vskfz 622) (chassis numbers of the A to D types were 80,000 to 80,750). The suspension, which had now been finalised and which remained unaltered until the end of the war, consisted of paired bogies, size 470×75–660, mounted on longitudinal twin quarter elliptic springs, and there were four return rollers.

Sprocket wheels were mounted at the front and idlers at the rear.

Engine was the same as the Pz Kw IIIs, the 250 hp 12-cylinder Maybach HL 108 TR. The basic shape of the engine compartment was altered and this necessitated a different cooling arrangement. On the Pz Kw III there was an exhaust behind each of the radiators on both sides of the engine, but in the Pz Kw IV both exhausts were fitted in the engine compartment on the right-hand side of the vehicle. In the Pz Kw III air was drawn through grilles on the rear decking and exhausted through openings at the rear of the vehicle. In the Pz Kw IV however the air was taken in at the right side of the rear superstructure and was expelled on the left side after passing through the radiator. On both vehicles the radiator system was so regulated that satisfactory cooling could be achieved at temperatures up to 30°C. The cooling fan drive was from the engine crankshaft via belts and double V-belts. A five-speed ZF SFG 75 gearbox gave a maximum speed of 30 kph. Transmission was similar to the Pz Kw III and went via a dry-plate three-disc clutch and a five- or six-speed Aphon gear to the sprocket. Steering was achieved by Wilson-Krupp type clutch and brake. A 7·5 cm L/23·5 tank gun with a coaxial MG 34 was mounted in the turret and a second MG in a ball mount was fitted in the superstructure front. The vehicle had a five-man crew. Turret traverse was electric by means of a second generator powered by a shunt motor. Drive for this came from an auxiliary DKW 2-cylinder two-stroke engine, type "P/6", which produced 15 hp at 2800 rpm and had a capacity of 585 cc. Ammunition stowage was 122 rounds of 7·5 cm and 3000 rounds of SAA for the machine guns. Hull armour basis was 14·5 mm all round and that of the turret 20 mm all round. The combat weight was 17·3 tons. Externally the vehicle could be distinguished from later models by the projecting driver's compartment. Thirty-five were constructed during 1936 and 1937 and were used mainly for instructional purposes. Years later they were still in service as training vehicles in tank driving schools.

The second production series of the Pz Kw IV, which appeared in 1937, was in production until 1938 as the "B" version, under the "camouflage" designation "2/BW". The frontal armour was however increased to 30 mm, which raised the combat weight to 17·7 tons. The more powerful Maybach HL 120 TR motor was used for the first time, as was the ZF 6-speed SSG 76 gearbox. Forty-two of these vehicles were produced. Together with the Pz Kw IV Ausf C (type 3/BW), which also appeared in 1938, these vehicles comprised the equipment of the medium companies of tank battalions during the Polish campaign. Several years later they could still be seen on all fronts, by then reinforced with extra armour plates. It should be noted that tanks brought back to Germany for a complete overhaul were usually improved by the incorporation of the latest technical developments, which included additional armour plates, improved engines and upgunned turrets, etc. Exact type identification from photographs taken in the later war years becomes more difficult since appearances could change considerably with the addition of such improvements.

The "C" model, briefly mentioned above, in common with the "B" model, had a straight, plain superstructure front plate. The hull MG was replaced in this version by a vision slit. The total weight, with 30 mm thick frontal armour and 14·5 mm side armour, was raised to about 20 tons. Main armament, as in the case of previous models, was fitted in an internal mantlet. One hundred and forty "C" models were produced.

After 1938, when re-equipment of tank regiments with the Pz Kw IV had been completed, production was considerably run down. Thus in 1939 only 45 Pz Kw IVs were built. The "D" model, built during 1938–39, designated "4/BW", was once again fitted with a bow MG, but had an external mantlet. After thorough trials of the vehicle in Poland an Army Regulation was published on 27th September 1939 (1939: No 685), which directed that "the Pz Kw IV (7·5 cm) (Sd Kfz 161) is hereby declared fit for service following its successful troop trials".

Because of the German tank building industry's low production capability however, and also because most new tanks were held as reserve stocks, only limited progress was made in re-equipping the tank regiments with the Pz Kw III and IV. Thus between 1st September 1939 and 31st March 1940 only 46 Pz Kw IIIs and 12 Pz Kw IVs were supplied new to the tank divisions. Eisen and Hüttenwerke in Bochum as well as Krupp produced the armour and turrets for the Pz Kw IV.

Uparmouring

As a result of front-line experience during the campaign in Poland an improved Ausf E version (type 5/BW) (Ref D 653/1 of 1st November 1942) appeared during 1939. The armour thickness which had proved insufficient was increased by fixing additional plates on the bow and sides of the hull. This increased the frontal armour to 60 mm and the side armour to 40 mm. Rear and turret armour remained unchanged. The total weight was increased to 22 tons. At the start of the campaign in France in May 1940 278 Pz Kw IVs were available for the assault divisions. Total production of Pz Kw IVs during 1940 was only 280. A memorandum of 1st November 1940 states that the planned monthly target for the Pz Kw IV was laid down as 30 vehicles.

The Pz Kw IV tanks, models A, B, C and D, distributed to the tank battalions assembled for Operation Sea Lion, were converted as already described for Pz Kw III, into "submersible tanks". In this way 210 Pz Kw IIIs and IVs were prepared for this undertaking and, together with 52 amphibious Pz Kw IIs, formed the equipment for a complete tank division. These tanks, later supplied to the 18th Armoured Division made a submerged crossing of the River Bug at the start of the Russian campaign (Operation Barbarossa) on 22nd June 1941 at 04.45 hours.

It was estimated that for the 36 armoured divisions proposed on 18th July 1941, 2160 Pz Kw IV tanks, among others, would be needed. However, during 1941 a total of only 480 Pz Kw IVs were actually produced. The total stock of Pz Kw IVs on 1st July 1941 was 531 vehicles and, due to losses on active service, the total on 1st April 1942 had risen to only 552. In this connection a file note referring to a discussion with Hitler at the Berghof on 26th May 1941, is of interest. At that time the Pz Kw IV was being upgunned by replacing the short 7·5 cm KwK L/24 by the 5 cm PaK 38. The original document (dated 31.5.1941) says

... It must be exactly the same for the tank. *En masse* we can first use the vehicles with the 5 cm tank gun with success. But we must immediately produce a spearhead, which can be estimated to be about 20 machines per armoured division. What is needed is to produce vehicles which

(a) have a greater penetrating power against enemy tanks,

(b) are more heavily armoured than they are now,

(c) which have a speed of not less than 40 kph.

It is necessary therefore in the present programme to take advantage of each possible increase in penetrating power—for example by installing the PaK 38 in the Pz Kw IV (Director Hacker says that as a result of the decision on the Krupp solution up to August 1941 a total of about 80 Pz Kw IVs with an anti-tank gun could be produced by spring 1942 by Nibelungen). Nibelungen are making preparations for this installation.

In addition Krupp have a contract to introduce a Pz Kw IV with the PaK 38 (in place of the 7·5 cm tank gun) by 15th November 1941. The Weapons Department will contact Krupp with a view to giving this job priority. The first 5 cm tank gun L/42 new type, goes for proof testing on 1st August 1941.

The proposed use of the "Bottle Cartridge" for the 5 cm tank gun should, if anything comes of it and the expected difficulties in crimping the cartridge are surmounted, not be restricted to this weapon but also tested for the PaK 38 . . .

Front-line experience in Russia however showed that this plan was unworkable as the 5 cm anti-tank gun proved useless against the more heavily armoured Russian vehicles.

At the start of the Russian campaign the Pz Kw II, III and IV tanks were equipped with two-wheeled trailers containing two 200-litre petrol tanks. In some cases a further supply of 20-litre petrol cans was carried on the turret roof. In addition twice the normal ammunition supply was stowed inside the tank. By these means the tank formations were reasonably independent of their supply columns during the early days of the fighting in Russia. The Pz Kw IV Ausf F (6/BW), which appeared during 1941, had its bow armour increased to a thickness of 50 mm. The instruction, issued on 7th July 1941, to uparmour all new production tanks meant that in the case of the Pz Kw IV additional armour plates 30 mm thick were fitted to the bow and in front of the driver.

The increased total weight of 22·3 tons meant an increase in track width from 380 to 400 mm. A new sprocket wheel was fitted, constructed of welded tubing. The idler wheels, too, were altered in pattern during production. The turret was re-designed by Krupp and adapted to take the long 7·5 cm tank gun. The armour was thickened, the turret access hatches were given double flaps and the commander's cupola was brought forward so that it no longer cut into the turret rear plate. These alterations were carried out simultaneously on the turret of the Pz Kw III. Generally speaking only small numbers of a series were completed. A communication signed by Field Marshal Keitel, dated 14th November 1941 and sent to the Army High Command, showed the influence of reports coming from the Russian front and says

... the Führer sees it necessary, having regard to our over-stretched and limited production capacity, to restrict the tank programme regarding the various models and to determine the future types. Therefore, to ease the pressure upon the industrial and military drawing offices and to release engineers for other production, those current developments whose production during this war would in any case have been terminated will be discarded. The Führer demands a simplification and a limiting of the programme so that mass production can be more easily introduced (the standardisation of engines, gears, suspension, tracks, etc).

The Führer proposes the following four basic types: Fast (reconnaissance) tank; Medium tank (on the lines of the existing Pz Kw IV); Heavy tank (Porsche and Henschel); and Super Heavy tanks.

The Führer wishes to take the decisions personally and intends to speak to Colonel Fichtner and Professor Porsche at his Headquarters after the next trip to the Front . . .

In order to produce a weapon which would to some extent restore the balance the Weapons Department issued a contract to Krupp on 18th November 1941 with the number 917/41 g.Kdos Wa Prüf 4, ordering them to collaborate with Rheinmetall-Borsig in producing a successor to the short 7·5 cm cannon of the Pz Kw IV. The order specified a development of the existing KwK 44 (later KwK 40) with a barrel length of 3218 mm (=L/43). The muzzle velocity, using the Panzergranate (armour-piercing shell) 40 had, by comparison with the old short 75 mm tank gun, been raised from 450 to 990 mps. The range was 8100 compared to 6500 metres. Mass production was expected to begin from March 1942.

The initial production version of this new gun had a single-baffle, spherical muzzle brake, first fitted in the Pz Kw IV Ausf F. The combat weight was once again raised, this time to 23·6 tons. The ammunition carried totalled 87 rounds and the price per vehicle (without weapon) was RM 103,462. In order to distinguish the version with the longer gun vehicles so fitted were known as Ausf F2 (7/BW), while the vehicle with the original shorter main armament was known as the Pz Kw IV Ausf F1. The "F" series ran until 1942. Pz Kw IV production during 1941 was estimated, in a note dated 24th January 1942, to be 40 units per month. In January 1942 the production target of 57 machines was exceeded for the first time when 59 Pz Kw IVs were actually produced, and from this date on the Pz Kw IV went into mass production. A regulation dated 15th December 1942 describes the Schiess searchlight for the Pz Kw III and IV which was mainly used for night fighting.

Pz Kw I, II, III, IV and VI vehicles which were sent for service in Africa between 1941 and 1943 had

modifications to the exhaust carried out in Germany. In addition felt bag filters were fitted externally on the engine compartment or on the body as a pre-filter. Vehicles so converted received the description "Pz Kw IV (Tp)". Tests of this version were also carried out in Russia. According to Guderian there was a proposal to invade Malta in March 1942. For this undertaking 12 Pz Kw IVs with 80 mm frontal armour were ordered.

The Pz Kw Ausf G (Type 8/BW) (Sd Kfz 161/1), with chassis numbers starting at 83,072, which was delivered in 1942, still had front armour 50 mm thick. In contrast the "F" model had its side armour of 20+20 mm reduced to 30 mm, though the roof armour was increased from 10 to 15 mm thick. The 7·5 cm KwK 40 L/43 now had a double-baffle muzzle brake. The vehicle's bow was partly reinforced with 30 mm plates. From this version on the "traverse cut off", which had been fitted to all previous Pz Kw IIIs and IVs and which had given a warning light signal to the driver that the gun was overhanging the vehicle's track width, was no longer fitted. Experience of the Russian winter led to the installation of a "Kühlwasser-Austauscher" (radiator water exchanger), which made it possible to pump hot radiator water from one machine to another and thus avoid the difficulties of cold weather starting.

Of the total of 964 Pz Kw IVs which were completed during 1942 Krupp produced 400, the Nibelungen works of the Steyr-Daimler-Puch AG in St. Valentin (Lower Austria) 165, and the remainder were supplied from Prague and Vomag. Production of the hulls, superstructure and turrets was subcontracted by Krupp to Böhler of Kapfenberg and Eisenwerke Oberdonau of Linz. Krupp's Essen factory was by this time achieving an output of 25 Pz Kw IV hulls, superstructures and turrets per week.

A comparison of the raw material requirements of the Pz Kw III and IV gives the following figures (raw material in kg—without weapons, optics or wireless):

Pz Kw III		Pz Kw IV
39,000·00	Iron (Fe)	39,000·00
1·40	Tin (Sn)	1·20
60·10	Copper (Cu)	195·10
90·40	Aluminium (Al)	238·00
71·70	Lead (Pb)	63·30
49·10	Zinc (Zn)	66·40
—	Magnesium (Mg)	0·15
125·00	Rubber	116·30

In June 1942 an order went out to increase the front armour of the Pz Kw IV to 80 mm. The final version of the 7·5 cm KwK 40, with a barrel length of L/48, was now available for installation. All current Pz Kw IV versions which had been serviced and maintained in Germany were now equipped with this weapon. In January 1943 a sloping bow armour 100 mm thick was ordered but it was not possible to carry out this order as the vehicle would have had its cross-country mobility impaired through being nose heavy.

On 19th March 1943 a Pz Kw IV with additional apron armouring was introduced. This was the Model H (Type 9/BW) (Sd Kfz 161/2), which was in production at that time, fitted retrospectively with this 5 mm apron armour. It had 85 mm front armour and the long tank gun. The chassis was practically unaltered and the transmission system of the Pz Kw III, the ZF SSG 77, was installed. This hardly differed from the earlier ZF SSG 76 transmission and had a six-speed gearbox with hand levers. It had synchromesh on all gears, with the exception of first and reverse. The forward gears were in constant mesh and, because of their helical gearing, were noiseless. Some of these modified vehicles had an anti-aircraft MG fixed to the commander's cupola and were given "Zimmerit" protective coating.

Vehicles of the "H" series, fitted with additional communications equipment, were designated (and used as) "Panzerbefehlswagen IV". These vehicles retained the fighting capabilities of the standard combat tank, but the gun loader also served as a second wireless operator. Fittings for additional antennae were built in during production and alteration to command role could even be made in the field in certain circumstances.

Vehicles of the "H" series had no vision slits for the loader and aimer; such slits would have been pointless because of the additional 8 mm apron armour which was fitted round the turret. The commander's cupola hatch was no longer double flapped, and was closed by a one-piece round cover.

An interesting experiment was carried out on an "H" series vehicle during 1944. Zahnradfabrik of Augsburg built a Pz Kw IV with hydrostatic drive. This did not have mechanical transmission; in fact it had no gears at all. The drive—known as the "Thoma"—was so constructed that the main motor (a Maybach HL 120 TRM) was linked directly to a pair of high-performance hydraulic pumps. These oil pumps supplied two hydraulic motors. A swash plate drive drove the rear-lying sprocket wheels through reduction gearing. The sprockets had a diameter of about 550 mm, while that of the front idlers was about 750 mm. With the hydrostatic drive the turret traverse and the elevation of the main armament was also hydraulic. Road test results are no longer available; the vehicle was taken to America after the war and given a thorough testing by Vickers of Detroit. This company was busy at that time with a similar design for American AFVs. The test report of the Company, dated 12th April 1946, describes the Thoma-drive as follows:

The motor drive mechanism consists of two swash plate oil pumps which are fitted as a single unit and driven by a 12-cylinder Maybach HL 120 engine. Oil is forced through from the pumps to two separate oil motors which turn the track driving sprockets. The oil engines are flanged onto the reduction gear housing. The engine and the drive mechanism are in the rear of the vehicle and the machine is propelled by the sprockets at the back. The volume of the pumps is controlled by the driver, who adjusts the torque to the varying load condition, brought about by steering and stopping the machine. In the same manner by re-routing the oil flow, a forward and reverse movement of the vehicle is achieved. Oil for the pumps and motors is fed by a gear type pump which is connected with the vehicle's engine by means of a direct drive.

The tests were discontinued because the supply of replacement parts was not available. The vehicle itself stands today in the US Army's Tank Museum in Aberdeen, Maryland.

On 9th March 1943 General Guderian gave a lecture at Hitler's HQ in which he outlined his ideas on the development of the German tank arm. It was shown that the Pz Kw IV was the backbone of the force. The construction of this vehicle was to be continued at maximum rate throughout 1944–45. This proposal was passed on to the tank building industry during April 1943 as an order. Personal struggles for power inside the leadership led to attempts to bypass this order however and to phase out the production of the Pz Kw IV in favour of assault guns. This was done to change the offensive character of the tank arm to the defensive strategy which had become the trend of the last year of the war.

The Army's Technical Regulations Leaflet 1944 No 256 speaks of the introduction of an "Eastern Front Track" (German: Ostkette) for the Pz Kw IV which increased the overall width to 320·6 cm. In March 1944 the final version of the Pz Kw IV appeared, the Model J. Army Technical Regulations Leaflet 1944 No 184 of 3rd March 1944 states that the electric turret-traversing gear was discarded in this "J" version, and an auxiliary fuel container of 200 litres capacity was built into the engine compartment. The total fuel load was now about 680 litres. At the same time the hand traversing mechanism had to be fitted with a second reduction gear to permit the turret to be turned when the vehicle was travelling on an incline. Some armoured aprons fitted to the sides of this version, consisted of a strong wire netting in place of the usual sheet steel. Rheinmetall-Borsig of Unterlüss were made responsible for the production of the 7·5 cm KwK 40 L/48 which armed the Model H.

The vehicles were produced practically until the end of the war in 1945. During November 1944 Krupp undertook to upgun the Pz Kw IV by attempting to fit a "Panther" turret, with a long 7·5 cm KwK 42 L/70. A wooden model of this long gun was actually installed into a normal Pz Kw IV turret. However it became necessary to enlarge the turret to fit the gun. The experiment was abandoned because the chassis was overloaded.

Suspension

At this point reference should be made to the evolution of German AFV suspension during the period covered by this book. While the first experimental and production tanks were fitted almost exclusively with helical springs or leaf springs, in 1936, shortly after E. Kniepkamp took over the Weapons Department, the first designs with torsion bar suspension appeared. This was preferred to leaf springs as torsion bars were less vulnerable to gunfire and less likely to be jammed by mud, snow and ice. The improvement in the riding characteristics was considered less important at that time. Despite the obvious advantages, particularly the increased vertical movement of the wheels, the engineers at Krupps insisted on the old leaf spring suspension for the Pz Kw IV, in spite of the opposition of the Army Weapons Department.

The desire to produce bogies with larger diameters for fully-tracked vehicles resulted however in a number of developments at Krupps, as for example the interleaved suspension and wider track of the UK 2001. In 1934 the Weapons Department contracted several leading German tyre manufacturers to produce rubber tyres and caterpillar track pads for AFVs and tractors from 100 per cent synthetic rubber. During 1938 these contracts were completed and during the war a number of additional firms in occupied Europe were brought into this programme. The shortage of rubber and the high replacement rate of bogie and return roller wheels,

which were very quickly worn out, resulted from 1944 in a fundamental change in the wheels of several AFV types. Bogies were produced at this period without rubber tyres but with rubber rings inserted and compressed between the steel outer rim and the hub of the wheel. Bogies with these inserts required only half the rubber and in addition the rubber's vulnerability was greatly reduced. This idea, which was copied from the Russians, saved rubber and increased the life of the bogies, though some increase in track wear was observed. No complaints were made of the higher noise level caused by these metal-tyred wheels. Tests at Kummersdorf showed that the drag had increased by about 10 per cent. These rubber-sprung bogies were used on certain versions of vehicles whose chassis were overloaded, but not always on the whole suspension.

Volkswagen were among the firms which made bogies for the Pz Kw III and IV, and they produced, between 1941 and 1944, about 6000 bogie wheels per month. The final versions of the Pz Kw IV received a further suspension simplification, which was introduced during the last months of the war, the four return rollers each side being reduced to three. Total production of Pz Kw IV was 3366 vehicles in 1944 and 343 in 1945. The grand total of Pz Kw IVs produced was about 9000.

During the war and in the post-war years large numbers of Pz Kw IVs went into service in certain other countries. Spain obtained a number and during 1944 Bulgaria received from Germany, among others, 88 Pz Kw IVs and 50 StuG IIIs. After the revolution of 8th September 1944 these passed into the hands of the Bulgarian troops fighting under the Russian flag. They were also used against German troops in Hungary. Vehicles captured by the Russians were used principally by units of the "National Committee for a Free Germany" fighting on the Russian side. The Pz Kw IV was also used by other countries chiefly for training purposes. The Syrian Army was still using models H and J of the Pz Kw IV for training a long time after the war had ended, and some were still in use at the time of the Israeli-Arab War in June 1967. A Pz Kw IV, which had been exhibited in the British Army's tank museum, was returned to the Bundeswehr as a present in 1960.

It was obvious that the tried and tested Pz Kw IV chassis, which was available in such large numbers, would be used for other purposes. In fact, including variants, it was the most widely used armoured chassis in the German Army.

1 A platoon of grey-painted Pz Kw I Ausf A tanks fording a stream during Army manoeuvres in Germany in 1939. The floppy protective beret, not unlike the British pattern, was standard issue for German tank crewmen until 1940–41. The driver of the nearest vehicle is seen climbing out through his access door.

2   Two Pz Kw IV Ausf B tanks move forward along a flooded Belgian road during the German advance into Flanders in May 1940. The familiar black and white cross, painted on the superstructure as a recognition sign, was just coming into use at this time.

3   Infantrymen advancing under cover of a Pz Kw 38(t) tank during the campaign in France. These Czech-built tanks were widely used at this period to supplement the German Pz Kw III and IV types, which were in short supply.

4 Infantrymen being carried forward on Pz Kw III tanks to occupy a village during the victorious days of the advance into Russia. It is interesting to note the large amount of spare equipment carried on these vehicles at this time due to the need to make units as self-reliant as possible in hostile country.

5 Rolling onward to the war in the desert, here newly arrived Pz Kw III tanks of the Afrika Korps are seen parading through the streets of Tripoli past the Mussolini statue, March 1941.

Jagdpanzer IV

At a conference with Hitler at the Berghof on 26th May 1941 it was decided to order, in addition to the 12·8 cm SP mount, a similar vehicle with a 10·5 cm howitzer. Both vehicles were to be used against concrete fortifications and for defence against the heavy tanks which were expected to come into use in Britain and America. Two 10·5 cm K 18 auf Panzer-Selbstfahrlafette IVa, which were based on the Pz Kw IV chassis, had previously been for troop trials at this period. It was borne in mind at this time however, on the occasion of a demonstration for Hitler on 31st March 1941, that mass production could not begin until spring 1942.

This vehicle, which had a five-man crew, entered service at the start of the Russian campaign, though it did not go into mass production. When tank production was terminated at the Krupp-Gruson works the Sturmgeschütz IV (L/48) (7·5 cm StuK 40), which was similar in construction and armament to the "StuG III", went into production. Assembly and chassis construction was carried out in Magdeburg while the hulls were delivered by Böhler, Eisenwerke Oberdonau, Krupp and EHW of Bochum. With frontal armour 80 mm thick and side plates 30 mm thick the combat weight was 23 tons. There was a four-man crew and 63 rounds of main armament ammunition were carried. The 7·5 cm StuK 40 L/48 was built by Wimag of Berlin and Skoda of Pilsen. The StuG IV, together with the StuG III, equipped the Assault Artillery Brigades from October 1943 and, according to Guderian, were also to be used as supplementary equipment by armoured regiments.

The StuG IV was replaced at the beginning of 1944 by "Panzerjäger IV". This vehicle had been demonstrated before Hitler as a wooden model on 14th May 1943 by the Vomag Betriebs of Plauen/Vogtland. The first production vehicle ran on 20th October 1943 and mass production followed soon after at the Vomag works. The armour was supplied by Witkowiter Bergbau- und Eisenhütten. The main armament (the 7·5 cm PaK 39 L/48) was made by Rheinmetall-Borsig and Seitz of Kreuznach. This design, which entered service from January 1944, was designated "Jagdpanzer IV, Ausf F (Sd Kfz 162)". In contrast to the wooden mock-up these vehicles had a hull front of 60 mm interlocking plates. Additional side armour plating was fitted in common with most vehicles of that period. The combat weight was 24 tons, the crew was four men and 79 rounds of ammunition were carried. The chassis was of the 10/BW type. The axis of the gun was 1400 mm high

and the overall height of the vehicle was 186 cm. In all 1530 tank destroyers with either the 7·5 cm L/48 or L/70 gun, all mounted on the Pz Kw IV chassis were built during 1944.

The SP carriages to be described later, which were mounted on the shortened Pz Kw IV (Gun Carriage IVb) chassis, were also intended for anti-tank purposes. With a new body these vehicles were designated "Panzerjäger IVb (E39) für 7·5 cm PaK 39 L/40". Armour thickness was 80 mm in front and 30 and 20 mm at the sides and rear.

Vomag were occupied for some time installing more powerful armament in the Panzerjäger IV and introduced a prototype in May 1944 which carried the long 7·5 cm StuK 42 L/70 gun. This armament had been proposed in September 1942 as a result of experiences in the fighting in and around Stalingrad. At that time it was proposed that the assault gun should be uparmoured so as to have frontal armour 100 mm thick and should be fitted with the long 7·5 cm gun. This weapon, which in performance was the equal of the Panther gun, had no muzzle brake initially. The prototype had a silhouette which was considered rather too high, so was re-worked and went into limited production, succeeding another interim design, which was based on the original Pz Kw IV hull, and known as the Pz Kw IV/70 (Sd Kfz 162/1). This vehicle weighed 25·8 tons and had a four-man crew. It entered service in August 1944 and because of its considerably higher fire-power was a match for all enemy AFVs. Nicknamed "Guderian's chicken" this vehicle was top-heavy and extremely difficult to steer in rough country because of the thick bow armour (80 mm) and the long gun.

The StuK 42 L/70 was manufactured by Gustloff of Weimar and Skoda. Limited numbers of these vehicles remained in service with anti-tank battalions of infantry and tank divisions until the end of the war. It should be noted here that in 1943 Guderian was not convinced of the value of the StuK L/70. He asked that a check be made to determine the necessity for constructing a vehicle armed with this weapon to see whether the project could be abandoned. For him the light assault gun with the 7·5 cm L/48 gun was sufficient for all purposes.

The final development in the anti-tank vehicle field was a proposal by Krupp to mount an 8·8 cm PaK 43/3 (L/71) gun on the Pz Kw IV chassis. This weapon had already been fitted experimentally on the chassis of the Pz Kw III/IV (qv) during 1942, though this had only limited armour protection. The Krupp project dated 17th November 1944 would have greatly exceeded the load capacity of the Pz Kw IV chassis due to the increased weight of armour involved in the mounting. The Panzerjäger IV mit 8·8 cm PaK 43/3 (L/71), as it was called, therefore remained a project only.

A further project in the field on tank destroyer development in 1944 was a wooden mock-up which demonstrated, for the first time, the mounting of a recoilless 7·5 cm projector. Various versions of this vehicle were considered. They all had one or two projectors, together with a Deutgewehr (ranging gun), mounted in a revolving turret, open at the rear.

Selbstfahrlafetten (SP Carriages)

From 1942 onwards the idea of producing self-propelled armoured gun carriers became more and more prominent. The first experiments in this field, carried out by Krupp, involved the carriage of the "leichte Feldhaubitze (light field gun) 18/1", on an armoured SP mount. Pz Kw IV chassis parts were used and the number of double bogies on each side was reduced from four to three, while the bogie diameter was increased. Three return rollers were used. The vehicle was designated "leFH (Sf) auf GW IVb (Sd Kfz 165/1)". Eight machines were said to have been completed, and trials started in November 1942. These experimental vehicles were fitted with the Maybach 6-cylinder in-line engine HL 66 P. During production this 180 hp motor was to be re-placed by the HL 90 6-cylinder petrol engine producing 320 hp. The main armament in the turret had only light armour protection (20 and 14·5 mm), had a traverse of 70° while the elevation was adjustable from −10° to +40°. The armour thickness of the hull was 20 mm in front and 15 mm at the sides. With a crew of five and an ammunition supply of 60 rounds, the combat weight was 17 tons. The range of the 10·5 cm light field gun leFH 18 was 10·5 km and the rate of fire was six rounds per minute. The production of a special chassis for tank artillery could however no longer be justified in 1942 and it was therefore decided to use obsolescent tank chassis exclusively for this purpose. The 10·5 cm field guns were therefore subsequently fitted only on the chassis of the Pz Kw II (Wasp), which has already been described.

The "Heuschrecke" (Locust) development has already been referred to in the chapter on the Pz Kw II. Experiments of this type also took place with chassis of the Pz Kw IV series. The chassis was lengthened at the rear, without increasing the track length in contact with the ground, so that now 107 links per track were needed instead of the usual 99. Once again it was proposed to produce an armoured multi-purpose vehicle which would meet all the requirements of the armoured artillery. On the right and left of the track covers were fitted hinged travel-ling crane rails. By means of block and tackle the turret and gun could be raised and moved to the rear on these rails. They could then be unloaded on to a simple platform fitted at the rear of the vehicle. The weapon (a 10·5 cm light field gun 18/1) was then ready for action with a 360° traverse, while the un-loaded chassis (which had a simple superstructure) could be used as an ammunition carrier or for any other supply purpose, using the folding rails and the block and tackle for loading and unloading. The weapon had, of course, a 360° traverse while on the vehicle. This 17·3 ton vehicle which was designated "GW IVb für 10·5 cm leFH 18/1" (Heuschrecke IVb). A crew of five men was planned. The armour was 20 mm all round on the hull and 14·5 mm on the turret. This project was not developed however.

A memorandum dated 9th June 1941 (No 548/41 g.Kdos) queried the practicability of carrying a 15 cm heavy infantry gun with strong armour protection, against the enemy. Solutions using the heavy infantry gun SP carriages on Pz Kw I, II and III chassis had been tried as early as 1940. The Sturmpanzer IV (assault tank) Brummbär (Sd Kfz 166) was the final ver-sion of this development. A 15 cm Sturmhaubitze (assault howitzer) 43 (L/12) was mounted, with heavy armour protection (hull front 100 mm, superstructure front 50+50 mm) on the Pz Kw IV type 9/BW chassis. The weight was raised to 28·2 tons and the vehicle had a five-man crew and carried 38 rounds of 15 cm ammunition. Development was undertaken by Alkett. The chassis were produced by Nibelungen and were assembled by Deutsche Eisenwerke of Duisburg with superstructures supplied by Bismarck-hütte. Some of these vehicles had driver's compart-ments differently shaped from others. The height of the gun was 182 cm. According to Guderian 40 to 60 of these vehicles were built and were from April 1943 useful support vehicles in Tank and Panzer-grenadier divisions.

Waffenträger (Weapons Carriers)

Subsequently most of the Waffenträger develop-ments from 1942 onwards were based on the Pz Kw IV chassis. Two designs were produced at this time for a medium Waffenträger which could take the 15 cm 18 (L/29·5) heavy field gun or the 12·8 cm 81 (L/55). Documentary evidence shows that these remained only at drawing-board stage.

In October 1942 Hitler considered mounting the 30·5 cm Mortar M16 on a Pz Kw IV chassis to fire HE demolition bombs. It was proposed to mount the mortar in two parts on a Pz Kw IV chassis. Guderian says of this: "Interesting as these designs may have been, in effect they wasted the production of the only serviceable tank of that period, the Pz Kw IV, whose output in this particular month amounted to the modest figure of only 100 vehicles."

Flakpanzer (Armoured anti-aircraft guns and AA tanks)

The increased Allied air superiority on all fronts compelled a re-organisation of the available defence measures. The original, completely unsatisfactory, defence of armoured formations had rested mainly on the tractors of various sizes, which had been fitted with 2 cm and 3·7 cm anti-aircraft guns. The few available 38(t) chassis which could be spared and were fitted with 2 cm AA guns could offer little extra protection. Guderian continually asked for anti-aircraft tanks with increased fire power for tank formations. Finally, in September 1943, Hitler approved the Flakpanzer IV AA with 3·7 cm twin AA guns which had been demonstrated on 14th May 1943. A hastily improved 2 cm quadruple AA mount did not meet with his approval. Nevertheless Böhmisch-Mährisch of Prague received a contract for 150 vehicles so armed. Delivery began during 1943. These machines, described as "Flakpanzer IV (Möbelwagen)", could either be fitted with the 2 cm, quadruple Flakvierling 38, or the 3·7 cm Flak 43. The weapon was mounted on an unaltered Pz Kw IV hull and protected by hinged armour flaps 10 mm thick. As these flaps had to be lowered on all four sides when the vehicle was in action, the crew was left completely unprotected. This, and the relatively high profile of the vehicle (310 cm) made its tactical value questionable. It was, however, the first practical attempt to give troops in the field protection from air attack.

For this, and for all the other AA tanks on Pz Kw IV chassis which will be described later, the engine performance was improved by raising the rpm from 2600 to 2800 and the hp to 272. The engine was the Maybach HL 120 TR 112. The Flakpanzer IV (2 cm Flakvierling) with its five-man crew had a combat weight of 25 tons. The Flakpanzer IV (3·7 cm) (Möbelwagen) had the same weight with a seven-man crew and an ammunition stowage of 416 rounds. Both vehicles had a 360° traverse. They remained in service with AA platoons of tank regiments until 1944. The unsatisfactory armoured protection given to the crew compelled a re-shaping of the superstructure. In December 1943 the first Flakpanzer IV (2 cm) mit Panzerfahrgestell "Wirbelwind" (Whirlwind)

appeared. On the unaltered Pz Kw IV chassis a completely armoured (16 mm all round) revolving barbette was mounted, which gave satisfactory protection to the crew. These vehicles were built by Ostbau of Sagan/Silesia and had a combat weight of 22 tons with a five-man crew. A total of 3200 rounds of ammunition was carried for the quadruple cannon and 1350 rounds of SAA for the radio operator's MG. The overall height was reduced to 276 cm but had only limited value for engaging ground targets chiefly because of the open topped turret.

From March 1944 the "leichte Flakpanzer (light AA tank) mit 3·7 cm Flak 43 auf Pz Kw IV Ausf J", known as "Ostwind" (East Wind), was produced by Deutsche Eisenwerke. As in the Whirlwind the crew was now housed in a strongly armoured (25 mm all round) rotating turret. The combat weight with a seven-man crew and 416 rounds of ammunition was 25 tons. Forty of these vehicles were built. The Ostwind was also capable of engaging ground targets and served with the AA platoons of Panzer divisions until the end of the war. As with the other Flakpanzers this open-topped relatively tall vehicle was only an expedient.

The final stage of the development was the leichte Flakpanzer IV (3 cm) "Kugelblitz" (Fireball), developed by Daimler-Benz. Two 3 cm machine cannon type 103/38 produced by Rheinmetall-Borsig were mounted in a spherical fully armoured totally enclosed revolving turret. With a volume of fire of 15 rounds per second, a traverse of 360° in 25 seconds and a time of 20 seconds to elevate from −7° to +80°, this vehicle had an extraordinarily high rate of fire. It had a five-man crew and an ammunition stowage of 1200 rounds. Although the Army announced the introduction of this vehicle, only five prototypes were in fact built, and these were intended to be used on the Western Front after their completion in 1945. Mass production was planned at Deutsche Eisenwerke in the Ruhr, but did not commence because of the war situation. These vehicles were intended, together with the "Zerstörer (Destroyer) 45", which was still in production at Ostbau, to give AA protection for tank formations against low-flying and ground attack aircraft. The Zerstörer 45 was to be equipped with the 3 cm AA quadruple 103/38 cannon or the AA gun produced by Alkett, mentioned above, the 3·7 cm Flak 43. Ostbau were also developing the Flakpanzer IV Ostwind II, which was to be equipped with the twin 3·7 cm Flak 44 mount. No satisfactory supply of these machines, then so urgently required by tank formations, was ever forthcoming since German industry was by this time seriously disrupted by the Allied bomber offensive.

Variants

Of other special variants on the Pz Kw IV chassis two are particularly worthy of mention: the Pz Kw IV "Brückenleger" (Bridgelayer) and the Pz Kw IV "Infanterie-Sturm-Steg" (Infantry Assault Footbridge), which were intended for the Tank Engineer Battalions. Although Army General Orders of 1941 state that the proposed bridgelaying vehicles would be discontinued in the near future because suitable chassis were not available and could not be produced in the immediate future prototypes of Pz Kw II and Pz Kw IV bridgelayers were built. Individual examples of the Pz Kw IV Infanterie-Sturm-Steg were however used in France and Russia, mainly for the capture of strongly fortified defences.

Pz Kw IV Ausf F vehicles were converted at Krupps into munition carriers following the formation of Super Heavy Artillery Units (Siege Artillery) equipped with the "Gerät 040" (the Karl mortar). They were designated Pz Kw IV Ausf F—Munitionsträger für Karlgerät. This vehicle, which was equipped with special fittings, could carry three of the 600 mm shells fired by Karl, each of which weighed 2200 kg. They could offload them direct on to the Karl SP carriage by means of an electric 3 ton crane fitted on the hull top. In addition to these variants of the Pz Kw IV series the armoured observation and recovery vehicles, which only saw service in small numbers, should be mentioned. The Panzerbefehlswagen (Armoured Command Vehicle) IV Ausf H had already been described.

For the recovery of disabled or abandoned AFVs the AHA/AgK ordered on 11th April 1941 from Georg Kirsten of Sebnitz/Sa a recovery equipment for AFVs. This was to ensure that broken-down or wrecked vehicles could be towed away by heavy tractors or by other AFVs. A contract was also given in May–June 1940 by the Weapons Department to Daimler-Benz and EFG for the production of a suitable trailer to transport Pz Kw III and IV tanks. Both the recovery jib and the trailer were issued in 1941.

Workshop companies in the field had so-called "Grosse Werkstattzelte" (Large Workshop Tents), which could accommodate six to eight vehicles, including tanks, undergoing repair. The contract for these tents had been given to Salzmann of Kassel on 19th May 1938 and they rendered good service in tank repair units, particularly in bad weather.

Geschützwagen (Gun Carriages) III/IV

Finally, mention must be made of the "Geschützwagen III/IV" (Gun Carriage), which was developed by Alkett. Deutsche Eisenwerke were responsible for the construction of the chassis. In this chassis the engine (a Maybach HL 120 TRM) was moved to the front and installed directly behind the transmission gearing. This allowed the fighting compartment, which now lay in the rear of the vehicle, to be laid out more clearly. The unaltered chassis of the Pz Kw IV was used for this variant. The Geschützwagen III/IV fitted with Ostketten (Eastern Front tracks) had a track width of 326 cm. One of the difficult tasks of the troops at that time was to move the long 8·8 cm, PaK 43/1 (L/71). This very important anti-tank weapon was too heavy and immobile as a towed unit and, particularly in the difficult terrain of the Eastern Front, its use was limited. Because of the low load-carrying capacity of the IV chassis only a small amount of defensive armour could be fitted. Nevertheless, this 8·8 cm PaK 43/1 (L/71) mounted on a Pz Kw III/IV chassis was a useful addition to the anti-tank equipment on every front. By November 1942 (the contract was issued in February 1942) it was with the Army's heavy anti-tank battalions. The name suggested was originally "Hornisse" (Hornet), which was changed to "Nashorn" (Rhinoceros) by Hitler's order.

Designated Sd Kfz 164, the Nashorn had an open-topped fighting compartment, a five-man crew and carried 40 rounds of ammunition. The combat weight was 24 tons. The height of 265 cm was relatively tall and the mean height of the gun was 226 cm. Because of a shortage of armour plate the hull was protected with unhardened plate (30 mm in front and 20 mm at the sides). The superstructure armour supplied by Witkowitzer Bergbau- und Eisenhütten had a basis of 10 mm. Chassis were supplied by Werk Duisburg and assembly was carried out at Teplitz-Schönau by Deutsche Eisenwerke. A grand total of 473 vehicles of this sort were built during 1944; some of them had drivers' plates of different shapes. Although they were suitable for anti-tank work they were only a transitional solution because of their insufficient armour. They were replaced during 1944 by the "Jagdpanther".

Equipping the armoured artillery was a slow process. Various temporary solutions to the problem of mounting the 10·5 cm light field gun led finally to the whole Pz Kw II production being changed over to SP carriages to carry this gun. Nevertheless there were, during 1942, attempts to fit the same weapon onto the Geschützwagen III/IV. Prototypes designated "le Pz Haub 18/40/2 auf Fahrgestell Pz Kw III/IV (Sf)" were in fact built. With a five-man crew and 80 rounds of ammunition it had a combat weight of 25 tons. Hull armour was 20 mm, while the armour round the superstructure, which had been supplied by Deutsche Röhrenwerke of Mülheim/Ruhr, was 10 mm thick. The chassis construction and the final assembly was done in Duisburg. However, these chassis could not even be supplied in sufficient numbers to mount the 15 cm heavy field gun, and this version was not pursued any farther.

Final development of a heavy tank howitzer was the 15 cm Panzer-Haubitzer 18/1 auf Fahrgestell Pz Kw III/IV (Sf) (Sd Kfz 165), designed by Alkett. The original name suggested was "Hummel" (Bumble-bee), but this was discontinued on the special order of Hitler on 27th February 1944. Prototypes of this vehicle had a muzzle brake, but this was dropped during production in 1944. The Hummel, which had been in service with the tank artillery battalions of Panzer divisions since 1943, had a six-man crew and an ammunition stowage of 18 rounds. Its fighting weight was about 23·5 tons. The mean height of the gun was 230 cm. Deutsche Eisenwerke assembled 666 Hummels and the armour was supplied by Stahlindustrie (Deutsche Röhrenwerke) of Mülheim/Ruhr and Deutsche Edelstahl in Hannover. DEW produced 12 vehicles during December 1942 and from January to March 1943, 100 superstructures for this vehicle. Once again the all-round armour for the hull was 20 mm and for the superstructure 10 mm. In this type, too, there were variations in the shape of the bow.

Similar vehicles, but with armament omitted, were distributed to tank artillery units as Munitionsträger Hummel. They were similar in construction to the heavy tank howitzers. The forward access plate could be unscrewed however, so that if necessary the vehicle could be armed. Mainly they were used as ammunition carriers, though they were also used as supply vehicles, and 150 of them were built. The same ammunition carriers with different interior fitting were planned as ammunition carriers for the light tank howitzer and were planned to go into production from October 1944 at the rate of six vehicles per month.

Einheitsfahrgestell (Standard Vehicle Chassis) III/IV

The Vorläufige Richtwertprogramm (provisional optimum value programme) IV of 14th July 1944 postulated the multiple use of the Pz Kw III/IV

chassis. It was intended, after certain alterations, to adopt this chassis as a standard vehicle chassis. DEW produced a superstructure during September 1944 for the leichte Panzerjäger (light anti-tank vehicle) III/IV and delivered it to MIAG in Brunswick. It was never assembled however as the project had already been abandoned by the Army Weapons Department. In the above programme this vehicle appears as the 7·5 cm Sturmgeschütz III/IV L/70. Alkett and MIAG planned to start mass production during November 1944, Krupp-Gruson in January, Nibelungen in February and Vomag in March 1945. The output per month was expected to be 800 vehicles as from May 1945. Alkett proposed using the same chassis for the 10·5 cm Sturmhaubitze III/IV when production of the 10·5 cm Sturmhaubitze 42 was stopped after April 1945. The anticipated monthly output was 125 vehicles. Stahlindustrie contracted to supply Artillery SP carriages on this chassis to the Army authorities. A "schwere Panzerhaubitze" (heavy tank howitzer) with an accompanying carrier was planned. The monthly output was to be 25 and four vehicles respectively. In addition a "leichte Panzerhaubitze" (light tank howitzer) and munition carrier for this vehicle were planned. Total production figures for this were 45 and six vehicles respectively per month. As well as these the programme provided for a Sturmpanzer III/IV to be produced from January 1945 onwards. Twenty of these vehicles per month were to be constructed. The final version was the Flakpanzer "Kugelblitz" (Fireball) III/IV, of which 30 machines were expected to be completed each month.

To sum up it can be said that the Pz Kw IV formed the backbone of the German Tank Arm until the end of the war. At the beginning of 1943 there was a General Staff proposal to halt the production of all Pz Kw IVs. The proposal was not however carried out as the Panther was not yet ready and the output would have been reduced to 25 Tigers a month.

Despite the obvious weaknesses in shape and armour thickness and despite the technical defects resulting from shortages of raw materials, the Pz Kw IV was the most reliable of the German AFVs and was, particularly after 1943, when better armament was available, the equal of nearly all enemy tanks.

Panzerkampfwagen V and VI, old model

The Pz Kw IV was the last production vehicle to have been developed in peace time. It was then the heaviest German tank in service. When German tank development began in 1934–35 other heavy types were considered, for example Rheinmetall's prototype "Neubaufahrzeug" (new construction vehicle), known also as Pz Kw V. Following contemporary ideas these vehicles strongly resembled English, French and Russian designs of multi-turreted AFVs. The suspension, taken straight from the "BW" prototype VK 2001 (Rh), was simply extended by a single pair of bogies. The driving sprockets were at the rear however. Only six of these machines are thought to have been built. Some sources state that these vehicles were constructed for propaganda purposes and were armoured only with 14·5 mm steel. The overall weight was between 24 and 26 tons. It is known that they were used at the start of the Norwegian campaign in 1940. The main revolving turret was fitted with the 7·5 cm KwK L/24 gun with a co-axial 3·7 cm tank gun, while on the bow of the vehicle alongside the driver's position there was an auxiliary turret, like that on the Pz Kw I tank, which housed two MG 13s. Immediately behind the main turret, on the left hand side of the vehicle, was another such turret. The crew consisted of seven men (commander, driver, gunner for the main turret, loader, wireless operator and two other men who were needed to serve the auxiliary turrets). The drive was taken from a Maybach 360 hp, 12-cylinder, rear-mounted petrol engine. This vehicle did not correspond to the Army Weapons Department's tactical and technical conceptions and can only be regarded as an experimental exercise.

Panzerkampfwagen V (Pz Kw V) "Panther" and its Variants

Development

Although a number of companies had completed drawings of heavier vehicle projects and had in some cases constructed prototypes, the Army authorities were in no way convinced of the need to develop heavy tanks. Only after the appearance of the Russian T-34, and then with great urgency, was any attempt made to start production of heavier vehicles.

After 1935 there had been attempts made to produce a 600 hp Grosstraktor. On 28th October 1935, at an Army Weapons Department technical conference, Daimler-Benz suggested using, among others, the M 71 (later the DB 600) aircraft engine in armoured fighting vehicles. With a sustained output of 550 hp and a peak performance of 600 hp at 2200 rpm, this power unit was to be rebuilt. During the course of the development petrol injection and a change over to diesel power were both provided for. As this power plant was intended for AFVs, it was called MB 503 in its petrol version and MB 507 for the diesel. On 3rd June 1937 the Army Weapons Department, in a communication numbered 6/1c 63104/37, gave the following contract to Daimler-Benz.

(a) Two 700/800 hp, 12-cylinder MB 503 engines (standard price RM 40,000) RM 80,000
(b) Part cost of patterns and moulds RM 50,000
(c) Part cost for technical testing in the factory RM 20,000
(d) Completion of an assembly mock up RM 3600

It was anticipated that delivery of the engines could take place during the spring of 1938 immediately after their acceptance trials. Work on these experimental engines fell behind schedule however, due to changing priorities. Finally two diesel engines of the MB 507 type were converted and provided for use in the VK 3001 (DB) prototype.

Contracts for the development of 30-ton vehicles (as replacements for the Pz Kw IV) had been issued at the beginning of 1937 and had gone to Daimler-Benz, Henschel, MAN and to Porsche. To comply with High Command directives it was originally planned to install the 7·5 cm KwK L/24 tank gun in this vehicle and then at a later date the 10·5 cm KwK L/28.

The breakthrough tank Dw 1 which was accepted for development by Henschel at the start of 1937 weighed 30 tons and was of similar appearance to the Pz Kw IV. Several basic chassis alterations were tried. Whereas formerly all German tank designs had small-diameter bogies, this version had an interleaved arrangement of large-diameter bogies for the first time. These larger wheels resulted in lower bogie drag and increased the running life of the tyres. The satisfactory results obtained with this type of track and suspension during the development of the chassis led to the expectation that equally satisfactory results would be achieved with heavier AFVs.

The Dw 2, which succeeded the Dw 1, was ordered as a result of a conference with the Army Weapons Department on 2nd April 1937. The vehicle was envisaged as a further development of the Pz Kw VI (see previous chapter). The relevant contract was issued on 9th September 1938. With 50 mm of armour, the total weight had now been increased to 32 tons. The Maybach HL 116 6-cylinder engine, producing 300 hp, gave a maximum speed of 25 kph. There was a crew of five and armament was, once again, the short 7·5 cm gun and 2 MG 34s. The initial series of eight vehicles was delivered at the beginning of 1940. The turret design was by Krupp, who produced the first turret in the same year.

VK 3001

The VK 3001 (H) project was a logical development of this vehicle. Four prototypes were constructed, of which two were completed during March and the others during October 1941. This machine had medium-size interleaved bogies set on torsion bars. There were three return rollers. The Henschel three-speed steering mechanism, type L 320, which was used in this vehicle, was later fitted, in a simplified form, in the Tiger tank. The steering was operated hydraulically. A Maybach Olvar 40 12 16 gearbox was installed. This gearbox had originally been developed for a 400 hp engine and for that reason bore the numbered designation 40 12 16 (40=400 hp; 12=torque 120 metres kg; 16=impulse 16). There were eight forward speeds and one reverse.

The two VK 3001 (H) completed during March 1941 were converted into SP carriages. The demand for 12·8 cm SP guns to attack fortifications and to repulse the heavily armoured fighting vehicles which were expected to be used by the British and the Americans led to the utilisation of this experimental chassis. In order that this could take heavier armament it was necessary to lengthen the rear. The open-topped fighting compartment was only lightly armoured, and 15 rounds of ammunition could be carried. Conversions were carried out by the Rheinmetall-Borsig and only two vehicles of this type were produced. The first was delivered during August 1941. They were used in Russia during 1942.

Daimler-Benz and MAN VK 3001 designs followed well-defined specifications and the Daimler-Benz vehicle was actually fitted with the MB 507 diesel engine mentioned above, a V-12 producing 650 hp.

Towards the end of 1939 Porsche were instructed to develop a heavy tank of between 25 and 30 tons which would be able to carry at least the 7·5 cm KwK L/24 gun, and possibly the 10·5 cm KwK. This is how Porsche described their resulting design:

"The Porsche type '100' (known within the firm as the Leopard) has twin engines of the '101' type (V-10 petrol driven, air cooled, 320 hp) each coupled to an electric dynamo. Independent rear-sprocket drive is provided for each track via an electric motor connected to it by an epicyclic gear. Speed control and steering are carried out completely electrically using a 'Nita' special gear Voith transformer. The bogies are suspended by toggle joints with torsion bar springs."

Two prototypes were built in 1940 by the Nibelungenwerke in St. Valentin and thoroughly tested.

The Russian T-34 had a profound effect on all succeeding German tank design. When it first appeared few tanks, tank guns or anti-tank guns could match it. The design of the "Panther" was thus greatly influenced by this vehicle. The T-34 was the most advanced AFV of its time and confirmed the optimum virtues of fire power, armour and mobility. Among its disadvantages however were the sometimes faulty transmission and the inadequate crew of four men.

The surprise created by the T-34's first combat appearances need not have been so great had the responsible German authorities used a little foresight. In particular front line units would have been spared unnecessary losses. The suspicion that in 1941 the Russians already possessed a considerably better vehicle is underlined by the following extract from Guderian's *Panzer Leader*. He says:

"A singular instance regarding tank equipment surprised me. Hitler had given permission in the spring of 1941 for a Soviet officers delegation to visit our tank schools and view our tank factories, and had given orders that they were to be shown everything. On seeing our Pz Kw IV the Russians did not believe that this represented our heaviest type. They continually declared that we were keeping back our newest designs which Hitler had promised to show them. This insistence on the part of the Russian mission was so great that our manufacturers and Weapons Department officials finally said 'The Russians appear to already have heavier and better types than we'." The appearance of the T-34 towards the end of July 1941 eventually confirmed this.

Several new German developments were consequently terminated. Henschel and Porsche, two of those firms which were taking part in the planning of the VK 3001 turned immediately to the development of a 45-ton vehicle able to carry the 8·8 cm gun. With this it would be possible to out-gun the T-34.

VK 3002

Daimler-Benz and MAN received contracts from the Army Weapons Department on 25th November 1941 to develop a tank (the VK 3002) with 60 mm frontal and 40 mm side armour and sloping sides. The maximum speed was to be 55 kph and sustained speed was to reach 40 kph. The weight was limited to 35 tons. MAN produced its design project for the VK 3002 (MAN) by April 1942 and presented it to the Army Weapons Department. The first mild steel prototype was ready for tests in September 1942 and ran trials in Nuremberg. The second prototype, which was finished shortly after, went to Kummersdorf. As a result of this design and the trials MAN were chosen to develop production vehicles.

In contrast to the MAN designs Daimler-Benz produced their VK 3002 (DB) prototype with a diesel engine, rear drive and leaf springs instead of torsion bars. One advantage of this design however was the fact that the installation of the MB 507 diesel engine considerably reduced the danger of fire and, because of its higher torque and a more satisfactory torque curve in the lower speed range, a higher tractive power was available. By fitting the transmission at the rear of the vehicle and in the smallest possible space, there was a larger area available for the installation of the gun, which allowed for a choice of calibres. The external leaf springs were easily accessible and permitted a larger internal height or a lower overall height. Before building began and in order to study the problem of rear-sprocket drive, the VK 3001 (DB), which was of course already running, had superimposed steering gears fitted and steering controls modified to test the ideas evolved for the VK 3002 (DB). With hydraulic steering action remote control was possible and the driver could even be accommodated in the turret cage.

Total weight of the VK 3002 (DB) was 34 tons and it had a maximum speed of 54 kph. A constant-mesh Maybach Olvar eight-speed gearbox was fitted, controlled by multi-clutch plates worked by oil pressure. The clutch was of the hydraulically-operated multi-disc type. The same system was adopted for the clutch steering. For spot turns the inner track was fully locked and the machine turned on its track. The bogies (bogies and return rollers were planned) were similar to those of the Russian T-34 and, because of the shortage of materials at that time, the wheels were without rubber tyres. Each pair of bogies was secured by a leaf spring. Prototypes of these vehicles were actually built and tested with the Daimler-Benz MB 507 diesel engine installed, but the contract which had been given to Daimler-Benz for 200 VK 3002 (DB) type vehicles was actually withdrawn.

On 18th July 1941 Rheinmetall-Borsig received a contract to develop a tank gun which could penetrate 140 mm of armour at a range of 1000 metres. This firm was authorised at the same time to design an armoured turret for the VK 3002 which was able to take this main armament. At the beginning of 1942 a test barrel L/60 was fired, whose performance nearly came up to the specification. Then a barrel length of L/70 was chosen and a delivery date in June 1942

was promised. This armament was intended for use in the VK 3002 as well as in the VK 4501 (Henschel) and VK 3602 designs. The first version of the weapon had a spherical, single baffle muzzle brake which was later replaced by a double baffle brake.

Pz Kw V

The VK 3002 (MAN), which was known unofficially as the Panther during the course of its development, was well shaped but was too heavy and too high to be a medium tank replacement for the Pz Kw IV. As usual the constant modifications called for during development increased the original weight from 35 tons until it finally reached 43 tons. After 20 vehicles had been built with the specified frontal armour 60 mm thick, an increase of the nose armour to 80 mm was ordered. The engine originally planned, the Maybach HL 210, was no longer considered powerful enough and was replaced by the more powerful HL 230 P 30. This was basically the same engine but its capacity had been raised from 21 to 23 litres by enlarging the cylinder bore. This engine was put into all production vehicles and was used until the end of the war. The HL 230 P 30 was a short V-12 petrol-driven engine producing 700 hp at 3000 rpm. In service however it was limited to 2500 rpm. Maybach used an eight-bearing crankshaft which just fitted the limited area of the Panther engine compartment. Together with several other licensees (including Daimler-Benz and Auto-Union) Maybach produced nearly 1000 of these 700 hp engines each month.

As the Pz Kw V differed radically from the Pz Kw III and IV, newly developed mechanical units had to be fitted because of the increased weight and the alterations to the hull shape. The hand-operated AK 7-200 type gearbox had seven speeds, all with synchromesh. It was intended for an engine producing 800 hp at 3000 rpm and a torque of up to 175 mkg. The weight of the gear with clutch and crown wheel was 750 kg. An LAG 3/70 H dry clutch was fitted. New steering gear and steering brakes were developed by MAN. Steering was effected by Argus disc brakes, operated hydraulically. Each track could be halted separately when the steering brake was used to steer the tank, after the epicyclic brake had been released and the steering clutch disconnected. In addition to this, when the epicyclic brake was released the direct gear of the epicyclic could be driven, via a steering clutch and a pair of pinions, against the direction of the main drive. In this way the relevant track was retarded and the vehicle travelled in each gear through a curve of fixed radius. Hence the description "single radius steering gear".

The bogies were carried on double torsion bars which lay transversely, each radius arm having two hair-pin-shaped torsion bars. This arrangement gave the Panther the best designed suspension of all German tanks. One disadvantage was the amount of space taken up by this type of springing. The bogie wheels were of the interleaved disc type with rubber tyres. Front sprockets and rear idlers, which also acted as tensioning wheels, together with two hydraulic shock absorbers and a return roller each side, completed the suspension. The unlubricated, 86-link track, designed for the original 35-ton prototype, was 660 mm wide and the width was not increased in the heavier production model. To increase the adhesion on icy surfaces the track was fitted with non-skid ribs, which were placed between the links. Chassis, hull and superstructure were integral and corners of the armour-plated hull were interlocked.

In addition to the 7·5 cm 42 L/70 gun there were two MG 34s. Seventy-nine rounds of tank gun ammunition were carried and the fuel supply of 720 litres was in five tanks. Power take-off to traverse the 8-ton turret was taken from a main shaft which lay between the two half shafts. This main shaft was mounted in a housing and worked the turret drive and the two oil pressure pumps for the steering mechanism.

Initially the specifications called for a fording depth of 1900 mm and a submersible depth of up to 4 metres. Full waterproofing was never fully developed however, and in consequence it was not 100 per cent effective on production vehicles.

In the Marks III, IV and VI the crews' kit was carried in stowage boxes on the rear turret walls, but in the Panther these were fitted left and right of the lower hull plate.

Production of the Panther began in November 1942 at the MAN factory, and its official designation was "Pz Kw V Panther Ausf D (Sd Kfz 171)". In the first production model the wireless operator's bow MG aperture was of the shutter type. Some of these early machines had the commander's cupola fitted on the left hand side of the turret. The combat weight was 43 tons.

The Panther's importance in the re-equipping of armoured units is evident from the fact that the production programme, which went into operation immediately, called for an output of 250 vehicles per month. A revised production programme dated September 1942 increased the monthly output to 600 Panthers up to and including the spring of 1944.

It was clear from this ambitious scheme that additional manufacturers would have to be brought into the production programme. The first production vehicles very quickly showed the teething troubles resulting from over-hasty development. Representatives of the industry and of the troops continually warned against putting these new vehicles into service prematurely. There were not only the usual teething troubles of a new design, but deep-rooted problems which could only be eradicated after thorough tests and fundamental alterations, and the armoured units had little confidence in the vehicle. The increased weight, which was greater than the original specification laid down, led to excessive wear of gears and shafts and the more powerful engine stretched the transmission to its limits. In this and the suspension were the main weaknesses of this otherwise very successful vehicle. In a speech at Hitler's HQ in March 1943 Guderian emphasised that under no circumstances could the Panther be expected to enter service earlier than July 1943. The results of troop trials at Erlangen and Grafenwöhr only confirmed this.

Despite these deficiencies tank battalions equipped with Panthers were ordered to take part in the Kursk Offensive or Operation Citadel. All the gloomy mechanical predictions were fully realised. Most of the vehicles unloaded in Orel and driven to Byelograd broke down en route. Engine fires caused by insufficient cooling and damage to gears and tracks ruined the outstanding potential of the armament as the vehicles were continually being taken out of service because of mechanical troubles and in some cases did not reach the battlefield at all.

These mechanical troubles made the first production batch of Panthers, almost without exception, unfit for front line service. In 1944 an official High Command memorandum acknowledging these weaknesses said: "... the mechanical weakness of the cross shaft on the Pz Kw IV and V led to such high unserviceability that the demand for replacement parts could not be met, despite the great efforts of the factories, without interfering with production...."

In February 1943 the Maschinenfabrik Niedersachsen-Hannover were brought into the Panther production programme. Henschel produced 200 Panthers between March and November 1943. From mid-1943 onwards Daimler-Benz went over to mass production of the Panther. The following firms took part in the production of armour and turrets: Dortmund-Hörder Hüttenverein of Dortmund, Eisenwerke Oberdonau of Linz, Ruhrstahl of Hattingen, Böhler of Kapfenberg, Bismarckhütte of Upper Silesia and Harkort-Eicken of Hagen. Numerous other component suppliers took part in the Panther building programme and production was given the "SS" priority rating.

The second production model of the Panther appeared in 1943 and was built until 1944. It was designated Pz Kw V Panther Ausf A (Sd Kfz 171) and these vehicles could be identified externally, by the ball-mount for the bow MG manned by the wireless operator. The Panther was by now also given the 5 mm thick apron armour and the usual "Zimmerit" protective coating, while some were fitted with an AA machine gun mount, which was fixed to the commander's cupola. This cupola had been improved in shape, even on the earlier version, and indeed the whole turret had been simplified for production purposes. During 1943 a total of 1768 Panther A models were produced. A directive from Hitler dated 27th February 1944 ordered that the vehicle was to be known simply as the Panther, and the designation Pz Kw V was discarded.

The "G" version of the Panther (Sd Kfz 171), which appeared during 1944, was given a different hull shape. Whereas in the D and A models the hull side plates had been horizontal, on the Panther G they were sloped. This resulted in a considerable reduction in production costs. The driver's visor flap in the glacis was also discarded in this model and rotating periscopes were substituted. Some vehicles of the G type also had the new steel bogies produced by Deutsche Eisenwerke and the same wheel arrangement as the Tiger II (King Tiger). In addition new idlers were fitted. The ammunition supply was 82 rounds. The vehicle cost (without weapons and communications equipment) was RM 117,100. Panther Ausf G stayed in production until the end of the war, and in 1944 3740 were manufactured. The gun cleaning gear, which had previously been carried in a cylindrical container on the side, was fitted, in the late production vehicles, at the rear across the engine compartment. Chassis numbers of the G series started at 120,301.

An unusual variant of the Panther used in action during the Ardennes Offensive of 1944 was the standard vehicle disguised, by using metal sheets, as the American M 36 tank destroyer, and such altered vehicles were issued, together with some captured US tanks, to German special units. With German crews and American markings they were intended to create chaos among Allied units at the start of the offensive, and they were sometimes very successful.

As with earlier German tanks, it was suggested that the Panther should be upgunned. In November 1944 Krupp proposed the installation of the 8·8 cm KwK 43 L/71 gun, without its muzzle brake, in the original Panther turret. This idea never left the drawing board however.

The highest production figures were reached in August 1944 with a total of 155 Panthers. This figure later dropped because of shortages of raw materials and due to enemy action. Only 25 vehicles per month were produced in the closing stages of the war. In 1945 Maschinenfabrik Niedersachsen-Hannover built 161 vehicles.

After overcoming initial difficulties the Panther remained to the last an excellent design which was never quite perfected.

Panther II

In February 1943 the Army Weapons Department commissioned MAN and Henschel to collaborate in an attempt to achieve as much standardisation as possible between the Panther and the Tiger. Unit construction was to be used to facilitate the replacement of defective parts in both vehicles. The improved designs were to be designated Tiger II and Panther II. While the Tiger II actually went into production at the end of 1943, only a few prototypes of the Panther II were ever built. These vehicles, known as Ausf F variants, had a number of alterations. Although the main differences were in the turret design and main armament, the following improvements were also incorporated in the Panther II.

(a) Zahnradfabrik Friedrichshafen's improved transmission, type AK 7-400, which had already been fitted into the Jagdpanther, was also fitted in the Panther tank.

(b) The bogies were to be replaced by Deutsche Eisenwerk's rubber-sprung steel wheels (already carried out on some Ausf G vehicles).

(c) Although it was decided to incorporate the L 801 steering gear and transmission of the Tiger II, MAN were busy with several other steering gear designs. Thus in place of the normal friction clutch, an electro-magnetic clutch and brake parts were used. Hydraulic drive mechanisms were considered, but these projects were still uncompleted at the end of the war.

(d) The question of raising the power-to-weight ratio by installing a more powerful engine came up in 1944. Priority was to be given mainly to diesel engines.

(e) The turret design by Rheinmetall-Borsig and Daimler-Benz, mentioned above, closely resembled the Tiger II turret. The Army

Weapons Department laid down several new requirements for this turret development. It had to (1) eliminate the shot trap beneath the mantlet found in the original Panther turret; (2) have an increase in armour strength without an increase in weight; (3) offer a reduction of the frontal area without reducing the internal measurements; (4) incorporate a horizontal stereoscopic rangefinder; (5) incorporate a co-axial MG 42; (6) be cheaper to produce.

To fulfil these requirements the following alterations were necessary:

(a) The development of a new gun, the 44/1, which had the barrel recuperator under the gun barrel. It was then possible to replace the semi-circular mantlet by a pigs-head (Saukopf) mantlet and, in addition, the complicated, welded gun cradle would be unnecessary. The compressed air required was produced by an additional cylinder built into the barrel recuperator, which absorbed the barrel recoil of about 420 mm. The pneumatic air compressor for the barrel recoil mechanism was increased from 12 to 18 tons pressure. The new mantlet shape also eliminated the shot trap.

(b) The new mantlet made a smaller turret front possible and thus reduced the surface area. Originally the mantlet had consisted of an armoured steel casting which required costly machining. The new turret front plate could be produced from rolled steel without much machining. As a result of the reduction of the frontal area and the incorporation of the new mantlet the weight of the turret was also lowered so that the armour thickness could be increased without exceeding the total weight of the original turret. The following increases became possible:

turret	original version	new version
front	80 mm	120 mm
side	45 mm	60 mm
rear	45 mm	60 mm
roof	12 mm	30 mm

Lighter armour was envisaged because the German steel industry could not produce sufficient rolled steel because of disrupted industrial conditions.

The following turret fittings were considered:

(a) close defence weapon (Nahverteidigungswaffe)—on the right rear of the roof;

(b) commander's cupola—left hand side of the turret;

(c) rangefinder—in front, below the roof top.

The periscope for the gun loader was dispensed with.

Due to the new turret design it was possible to reduce production time (less the fittings) by about 30 to 40 per cent. In spite of an increase of 30 per cent in the weight of armour, the original turret weight (about 8000 kg) was not exceeded. The internal diameter of the turret remained unaltered at 1650 mm. When the turret was in the planning stage the installation of an 8·8 cm tank gun was provided for in combination with a stabilised gun platform.

Official documents dating from 1944 talk of a Pz Kw V 7·5 cm KwK L/100. Apparently it was intended to lengthen the 7·5 cm tank gun L/70 to L/100, whose performance figures must then have reached their absolute maximum. From the metallurgical and constructional points of view all possibilities had by now been exhausted with this weapon.

Further changes on the Panther II tank included an increase of the hull decking thickness from 12 to 25 mm, while the ball mantlet of the bow machine gun was altered to take the MG 42. The F version of the Panther did not however, ever go into production again because of the war situation.

The Armaments Ministry also proposed building the Panther as a reconnaissance vehicle like the Leopard, which was then being planned. A turret had originally been developed by Daimler-Benz for the ARK 8-wheeled scout car and this was to be adapted with somewhat stronger armour, for the Leopard and the Panther recce tanks. The contract for developing the main armament went to Krupp and Rheinmetall-Borsig in January 1942. The 5 cm KwK 39 L/60 on a narrower mount was to be adapted for the smaller turret. Delivery was scheduled for October/November 1942. The scheme for mounting this turret on a Panther chassis was however very sensibly allowed to drop.

From 1943 to the end of the war experiments were carried out at Fallingbostel tank training school with infra-red searchlights for tanks. This apparatus consisted basically of a searchlight mounted on the tank turret. The light had a diameter of about 30 cm and incorporated a scanner with cathode ray tubes about 20 cm in diameter. These tubes were fitted in front of the commander's cupola. The commander had to aim the searchlight and the scanner on to the selected target. Then he saw the target illuminated in the darkness in front of him ready to be engaged.

The equipment, officially known as "Uhu" or "Biwa", was fitted principally to the Panther tank and, after a number of improvements had been carried out, was used experimentally with great success at Stuhl-weissenburg in 1945. Widespread introduction of the infra-red searchlight was forestalled by the end of hostilities however.

Heating fighting compartments was a problem given much consideration from the very beginning of tank development. About the middle of April 1944 the Army Weapons Department ordered anti-gas equipment (of the Dräger type) for all AFVs. Fighting compartments were to be kept under light high pressure while attached to the engine itself there was to be a radiator heating apparatus, which would make starting from cold easier. The low winter temperatures, especially on the Russian front, required special starting equipment, particularly for large engines. These starters were usually constructed as plug-in devices and were linked to the crank shaft through an opening in the rear hull armour. Bosch took a major part in the development and construction of this equipment. Porsche developed a starting gear during 1944–45 designated "198", which could be used in conjunction with the Volkswagen type 82 light personnel carrier. The tank to be started and the Volkswagen stood tail to tail and were connected by a starting shaft with a friction clutch. There were two speeds available. The starting shafts were intended for the Panther and the Tiger.

During 1944 experiments were carried out to protect the tank against close attack by infantry by the use of high-power cables. It was intended to fit the Panther with two complete coils of cable. This was another project which remained in the experimental stage however.

Nearly 6000 Panthers were built by the end of the war and a few captured vehicles were used by the French Army for some years afterwards.

The Jagdpanther

The various chassis which had been available for mounting the long 8·8 cm PaK did not always satisfy military requirements. For instance, the chassis of the Pz Kw III/IV tank was too weak to act as a carrier and could only permit the installation of an open-topped fighting compartment with light armour protection, while the tank destroyer variant of the Porsche Tiger (Jagdtiger) chassis was too complicated and too heavy. This state of affairs led ultimately to the production of the tank destroyer version of the Panther—the Jagdpanther. This vehicle, which had been developed by MIAG, was first shown on 20th

October 1943 at a demonstration for Hitler in Arys. On the basic chassis of the Panther tank an enclosed turretless well-shaped superstructure was fitted to hold the 8·8 cm PaK 43/3 L/71. There was an 11° traverse and the elevation limits were from −8° to +14°. The superstructure armour was 80 mm thick in front, 50 mm at the sides and 40 mm at the rear. The combat weight with a five-man crew and 60 rounds of ammunition was 46 tons. The designation was "8·8 cm PaK 43/3 auf Panzerjäger Panther (Sd Kfz 173)". Hitler, in an order dated 27th February 1944, suggested that it be redesignated "Jagd-panther".

In this chassis MIAG fitted the improved ZF AK 7-400 gearing which was also scheduled to be fitted in the standard Panther tank. MIAG started quantity production of Jagdpanthers in February 1944 and continued until April 1945. From December 1944 the Maschinenfabrik Niedersachsen-Hannover also started building these vehicles.

A total of 382 Jagdpanther were constructed. The armour was supplied by the Brandenburgische Eisen-werk Kirchmöser of Brandenburg/Havel and the main armament was produced by Dortmund/Hyrder Hüttenverein of Lippstadt. These very useful vehicles were in service before the end of the war with some Army anti-tank battalions.

As usual Krupp were actively investigating the installation of even more powerful main armament. There is a drawing of a design for a Jagdpanther variant with the 12·8 cm PaK 80 L/55. The design number is Hln—E 143, dated 17th November 1944.

SP Carriages and Weapons Carriers

It was inevitable that attempts would be made to use the Panther chassis as a basis for SP guns and weapons carriers. A number of vehicles were planned in 1942 based on the Panther chassis. A contract was sent from the Army Weapons Department to Rhein-metall-Borsig to produce a 12·6 cm gun on an armoured SP carriage. The designation was "Gerät 5-1213 12·8 cm K 43 (Sfl) Rh B". The travelling weight of the vehicle was 38 tons and the unloaded weapon weighed 6·2 tons. One prototype vehicle was ordered with the summer of 1943 as the proposed delivery date. The 12·8 cm L/47 gun had no muzzle brake.

Krupp also received a contract for a similar vehicle designated "Gerät 5-1211 12·8 cm K 43 (Sfl) Kp 1". A further contract placed with Krupp specified the development of the 15 cm L/30 field gun as a heavy tank gun. The contract for the "Gerät 5-1528 sFH 43 (Sfl) Kp 1" was placed in spring 1942 as an experimental vehicle for delivery in summer 1943. The travelling weight was to be about 38 tons and the empty weight 10 tons. A similar contract was also sent to Rheinmetall-Borsig, who were ordered to produce a prototype of the "Gerät 5-1530 sFH 43 (Sfl) Rh B" by the summer of 1943. This vehicle was to have a travelling weight of 40 tons and an empty weight of 8·2 tons. A 15 cm L/32·5 gun without muzzle brake was projected as main armament. The Krupp versions were given the collective name "Grille", and those Rheinmetall-Borsig "Skorpion". Classified according to size, Type 10 was able to carry either the 10·5 cm light field gun or the 10 cm cannon. The Type 15 carried the 15 cm heavy field gun or the 12·8 cm K 43 gun. For the type 17/21, the chassis of the Tiger was suggested. Wooden models of the vehicles were produced by both firms.

Daimler-Benz, in conjunction with Rheinmetall-Borsig, produced a wooden model and later a mild steel prototype of a Weapons Carrier in 1943–44, which was based on a Panther chassis. This chassis had been shortened by a pair of bogies. The Army Weapons Department had suggested this development in order to produce a vehicle which could be used both as a tractor and as an SP carriage. The gun could be lowered from the chassis by means of a crane, which the vehicle also carried, and could subsequently be brought into action on the ground. The vehicle could then be used to carry ammunition or as a tractor. The armoured plate thicknesses were 20 and 30 mm. As the field units could not even be supplied with adequate numbers of standard Panthers, however, the project was never developed further.

Later developments of anti-aircraft tanks were also based on the Panther chassis. A wooden model of a Panther Flakpanzer was built which featured an 8·8 cm Flak 41 mounted in a heavily armoured open-topped revolving turret. In addition to this Rheinmetall-Borsig were busy with the Coelian Flakpanzer, which was also based on the Panther chassis. It was intended to fit this vehicle with the twin 3·7 cm Flakzwilling 341. Each barrel had a rate of 500 rounds per minute and a muzzle velocity of 1000 metres per second, the guns being mounted in an armoured barbette with a 360° traverse. This very necessary and advanced project was interrupted by the end of the war.

Variants

Several versions of the Panther series were delivered as Armoured Command Vehicles, which differed mainly in turret design. The loader also served as the second wireless operator and had a receiver and transmitter fitted next to him on the right-hand turret wall. The second antenna was fitted on the rear of the turret roof, and the ammunition stowage was reduced to 64 rounds. Two versions of the Panzerbefehlswagen Panther were issued to units—the Sd Kfz 267 with Fu 5 and Fu 8 radios and the Sd Kfz 268 fitted with Fu 5 and Fu 7 sets. The main armament was retained in each case. A few vehicles of the "D" series were converted into Panzerbeobachtungswagen (OP tanks). In this variant only dummy main armament was fitted. These vehicles were used as OP tanks for senior officers and observer officers of armoured artillery units.

Another important variant was the Panther Recovery Vehicle, known as the Bergepanther. After formation of the first Tiger and Panther equipped units the need for specialised vehicles to tow these heavy tanks was fully appreciated. The vehicle which had been used for recovery work until then, the 18-ton half-track tractor, could only tow these heavy tanks when used in pairs or in threes. Because of this many damaged Tigers and Panthers had had to be abandoned. In 1944 at the request of the Army Weapons Department Demag of Berlin-Falkensee developed a special recovery version of the Panther.

The basic Panther hull and chassis were used and a powerful winch, which could be moved backwards and forwards, was fitted into the turretless fighting compartment. A heavy hinged spade for providing additional purchase when winching was fitted at the rear of the vehicles. This spade was worked by the vehicle winch, which was driven from the main engine. The fighting compartment was protected by screens and covered by a canvas awning. A 2 cm demountable gun was provided for local defence, and there was a five-man crew. This vehicle's designation was "Bergepanzerwagen Panther (Bergepanther) Ausf A (Sd Kfz 179)". Ruhrstahl of Hattingen supplied the armour. These vehicles were fitted with the improved ZF gearing and had their fuel capacity increased to 1075 litres. A total of 297 machines of this type were built. A few turretless vehicles without the tail spade and winch were used as Panther ammunition carriers (Munitionspanzer Panther), but conversions were mainly carried out in the field.

Mention should also be made of the experiments to produce a mine-clearing Panther (Minenräumpanzer Panther) and a bulldozer Panther (Räumschaufelpanzer Panther). These did not progress beyond the project stage however.

The "Optimum Value Programme IV", which was begun on 14th July 1944, laid down the High Command proposals regarding the equipping of the Army with armoured vehicles up to the end of 1945. The most remarkable fact is that only two vehicles in the programme—the Panther and Tiger II—had 360° traverse. In both these vehicles it was proposed to fit stabilised main armament. Firing experiments carried out by Panthers fitted in this way showed a 2:1 improvement in hits scored. Together with the experiments using infra-red night aiming devices (qv) it was expected that a decisive advantage in tank combat tactics would result from these developments.

Since two Panthers could be completed in the same number of man-hours as one Tiger the emphasis was soon placed on Panther production. A monthly output of 400 machines was expected by the beginning of 1945. The programme also anticipated 150 Jagdpanthers per month. Despite these efforts the loss of equipment on all fronts was so great in the last year of the war that the German tank industry could not produce enough replacements. In professional circles it is unanimously agreed that the Panther was the most successful of all German tank designs. Suitable for both the offensive and defensive roles, and with all the planned improvements, it would have been superior to all opposing tanks. How much it and the Russian T-34 influenced modern tank design is shown by the fact that almost all new tanks developed since 1945 show unmistakable design features of both these vehicles. The Panther, with reservations, was the best of all German tanks.

Panzerkampfwagen VI (Pz Kw VI) Tiger I(E) and II(B)

Tiger I(E)

The Tiger series had its origins in a number of tank developments initiated in 1937. In that year Henschel were instructed to design and construct a 30 to 33 ton tank intended to replace the early Pz Kw IV tanks, the vehicle being designated Dw 1 (Durchbruchswagen, or "breakthrough vehicle"). However, after one chassis with interleaved road wheel suspension had been built and testing had commenced, the trials were suspended in 1938 to allow work to be carried out on a further design for a 65-ton tank, the VK 6501 (Vollkettenkraftfahrzeug—"fully tracked experimental vehicle, 65 tons, first design"). It was also known as the Sw (Sturmwagen) or Pz Kw VII. The VK 6501 was itself a further development of the Pz Kw VI (Nb Fz Pz Kw VI; Nb Fz for Neubaufahrzeug—"new construction vehicle" of 1934, a multi-turret design of which only a few were produced). Two prototypes of the VK 6501 were built and were undergoing trials when this project was cancelled and development resumed on the Dw 1. By 1940 Henschel had so improved the original design that it was renamed Dw 2; in this form it weighed 32 tons and accommodated a crew of five. The planned armament was the short 7·5 cm gun with two Model 34 machine guns. Trials were carried out with a prototype chassis until 1941, by which time Henschel had received an order for a new design in the same class and weight as the Dw 2, the development code for the new vehicle being VK 3001. This order was also given to Henschel's competitors Porsche, MAN and Daimler-Benz. The Henschel version, VK 3001 (H), was a development of the Dw 2; four prototypes were built, differing only in detail from one another, two in March 1941 and two the following October. The superstructure of the VK 3001 (H) resembled that of the Pz Kw IV, and the suspension consisted of seven interleaved road wheels and three return rollers per side. It was planned to mount the 7·5 cm L/48 gun in this vehicle, but due to the appearance of the Russian T-34 with its 76 mm gun the vehicle became obsolete and development was discontinued. Two of the VK 3001 (H) chassis were, however, converted to self-propelled guns by lengthening and fitting a lightly armoured superstructure, and mounting a 12·8 cm K 40 gun. These two vehicles were used in Russia in 1942. The Porsche version, VK 3001 (P), was also known to its designers as the Leopard. This turretless prototype incorporated several new design features such as petrol-electric drive and longitudinal torsion bar suspension. MAN and Daimler-Benz also constructed prototypes to this design but like the Henschel project they had become obsolete.

Concurrently with the order for the VK 3001 an additional order had also been placed in 1941 for a 36-ton tank designated VK 3601. The specification for this design had been proposed by Hitler and included a powerful high velocity gun, heavy armour, and a maximum speed of at least 40 kph. A prototype of this project was built by Henschel in March 1942, but experimental work on both the VK 3001 and VK 3601 was stopped when a further order for a 45-ton tank was received in May 1941. Designated VK 4501, the vehicle was designed to mount a tank version of the 8·8 cm gun. With the order came a stipulation that the prototype was to be ready in time for Hitler's birthday on 20th April 1942, when a full demonstration of its capabilities was to be staged. As design time was limited, Henschel decided to incorporate the best features of their VK 3001 (H) and VK 3601 (H) projects into a vehicle of the weight and class required. Henschel planned to build two models, the type H1 mounting an 8·8 cm 36 L/56 and the type H2 a 7·5 cm KwK L/70, although the H2 existed only as a wooden mock-up at that time. Porsche had also received the order for the VK 4501 and like Henschel they decided to use the experience and features from

6   The Pz Kw VI Tiger II tank was an example of the very heavily armoured heavy tanks coming into service towards the end of the War when the German Army was on the defensive. Here a newly equipped Tiger II company is shown on parade in late 1944.

7 The Ardennes Offensive of 1944 was the last big attack by German armoured forces. Here German paratroops, fighting as infantry, are carried forward to the attack on a Tiger II—known to the Allies as the King Tiger.

their previous model, the VK 3001 (P), which had performed well on trials.

The demonstration of the two competing prototypes, the VK 4501 (H) and VK 4501 (P) type 101, duly took place before Hitler at Rastenburg on 20th April. The Henschel design was judged to be superior. An order for production to commence in August 1942 was given and the vehicle was designated Pz Kw VI Tiger Ausf H (Sd Kfz 181).

The Tiger was in production for two years, from August 1942 until August 1944, and in this period a total of 1350 vehicles were delivered out of 1376 ordered. Chassis numbers ran in a continuous series from 250,001 to 251,350. Maximum monthly production was achieved in April 1944, when 104 Tigers were built. It is interesting to note that the specified weight of 45 tons was exceeded in production by as much as 11 tons.

The Henschel Tiger

At the time of its arrival in service in late 1942, the Pz Kw VI Tiger I Ausf E was an outstanding design among its contemporaries by virtue of its powerful gun and armour protection up to 100 mm thick. These factors made the 56-ton Tiger the most formidable fighting vehicle then in service. It was, however, relatively costly to produce in terms of man-hours and difficult to adapt for mass production. In January 1944 the heavier and generally superior Tiger II Ausf B went into production with the result that successively fewer E models were produced until they were finally phased out of production completely in August 1944.

The Porsche Model

Production of the Porsche VK 4501 design had been ordered before the trials as a safeguard against the failure of the Henschel design. As 90 vehicles were already in hand when the result of the trials was announced, it was decided to utilise the chassis as the basis of a self-propelled carriage for the 8·8 cm L/71 gun. This equipment was designated Panzerjäger Tiger (P) Ferdinand Sd Kfz 184; it was subsequently redesignated 8·8 cm 43/2 L/71 Ausf Pz Jäg Tiger (P) Elefant früher Ferdinand. The original name "Ferdinand" had been adopted in honour of the designer, Dr. Ferdinand Porsche. Only two of the VK 4501 Porsche vehicles had actually been completed as tanks and in this form they had been designated Pz Kw VI VK 4501 (P) Tiger (P). Two other variants of the Porsche Tiger were projected but never materialised. These were a Ramm-Tiger, or "dozer-tank", ordered for production by Hitler and

visualised for street-fighting and ramming enemy tanks; and a converted Porsche chassis designed to mount a 21 cm mortar.

Tiger I was the first German combat tank to be fitted with overlapping road wheel suspension, arranged with triple overlapping and interleaved wheels of a steel disc type with solid rubber tyres (although after chassis number 250,822 these discs were steel-tyred and internally sprung). The overlapping wheel system was adopted for optimum weight distribution. There were eight independently sprung torsion bar axles on each side. In order to carry all the axles inside the hull envelope it was necessary to stagger them on the floor so that the right-hand axles trailed aft and the left-hand axles led forward. It was thus possible to incorporate the maximum number within the vehicle's length, and this resulted in an extremely soft and stable ride for a tank of this weight and size. Two types of track were used: a wide type measuring 71·5 cm was fitted for combat and narrow, 51·5 cm wide, for travel and transportation. When the narrow tracks were fitted the outer wheels were removed from each suspension unit. Though this type of suspension gave a superior ride, it also had its drawbacks; one being that the interleaved road wheels were liable to become packed with mud and snow during winter fighting, and if ignored until frozen this could jam the wheels. The Russians discovered this and took advantage of the situation by timing their attacks for dawn when the vehicles were likely to have become immobilised.

The Tiger was originally fitted with a Maybach V-12 petrol engine, the HL 210 P 45 of 21 litres capacity, but it was soon realised that the vehicle was under-powered and, from December 1943, the HL 230 P 45 of 24 litres was substituted. The Tigers used in North Africa were fitted with an air cleaner system called Feifel. This was attached to the rear of the hull and linked to the engine by means of the engine cover plate. These tropical Tigers were known as the Tiger (Tp). The Feifel air system was discontinued on vehicles built after the cessation of fighting in Tunisia in early 1943.

While all earlier designs of German tanks had the simple clutch-and-brake type of steering, the Tiger's greatly increased weight necessitated a more refined system. Henschel therefore developed and adopted a special steering unit, similar to the British Merritt-Brown type which was fully regenerative and continuous. It had the added feature of a twin radius of turn in each gear. The gearbox, which was based on earlier Maybach types, gave no less than eight forward gear ratios and, with its preselector, made the

Tiger very light and easy to handle for a vehicle of its size. The Tiger's mechanical layout followed that of previous operational German designs in that the transmission shaft led forward beneath the turret cage to the gearbox set alongside the driver. The steering unit was mounted transversely in the nose of the tank, a bevel drive leading to a final reduction gear in each front sprocket. Power take-off for the hydraulic turret traverse unit, mounted in the turret floor, was taken from the rear of the gearbox, and it is typical of the Tiger's well thought-out design that the hydraulic unit could be disconnected from the power drive shaft by releasing a dog-clutch, thus allowing the turret to be lifted from the vehicle without the complications of disconnecting any other joints or pipes.

The first 495 production Tigers were elaborately equipped for totally submerged wading to a depth of 3·9 metres with Snorkel breathing but this proved an expensive luxury and with the need to simplify production this was discarded. Subsequent Tigers had a wading capability to a maximum depth of four feet.

Production

In order to simplify assembly as much as possible and allow the use of heavy armour plate, flat sections were used throughout the hull. Machinable quality armour plate was employed. Hull and superstructure were welded throughout, in contrast to previous German tanks where a bolted joint was used between hull and superstructure. The Tiger front and rear superstructure was in one unit and interlocking stepped joints, secured by welding, were used in the construction of both the lower hull and the superstructure. A pannier was, in effect, formed over each track by extending the superstructure sideways to full width and the complete length of the vehicle was so shaped from front vertical plate to tail plate. The top front plate of the hull covered the full width of the vehicle and it was this extreme width which permitted a turret ring of 183 cm internal diameter to be fitted which was of ample size to accommodate the breech and mounting of the 8·8 cm gun. The belly was also in one piece, being a plate 26 mm thick.

Internally the hull was divided into four compartments; a forward pair housing the driver and the bow gunner/wireless operator, a centre fighting compartment and rear engine compartment. The driver sat on the left and steered by means of a steering wheel which acted hydraulically on the Tiger's controlled differential steering unit. Emergency steering was provided for by two steering levers on either side of the driver operating disc brakes. A visor was provided for the driver and this was opened and closed by a sliding shutter worked from a handwheel on the front vertical plate. Fixed episcopes were provided in both the driver's and the wireless operator's escape hatches. The gearbox separated the two forward crew members' compartments. The machine gunner/wireless operator seated on the right manned a standard 7·92 mm MG 34 in a ball mounting in the front vertical plate; this was fired by a hand trigger and sighted by a KZF cranked telescope. The wireless sets were mounted on a shelf to the operator's left.

The 8·8 cm KwK 36 gun which formed the Tiger's main armament had ballistic characteristics similar to those of the famous Flak 18 and Flak 36 8·8 cm guns from which it was derived. The principal modifications were the addition of a muzzle brake and electric firing by a trigger-operated primer on the elevating handwheel. A 7·92 mm MG 34 was co-axially mounted in the left side of the mantlet and was fired by mechanical linkage from a foot pedal operated by the gunner. The 8·8 cm had a breech of the semi-automatic falling wedge type scaled up from the conventional type used on smaller German tank guns. The great weight of the barrel was balanced by a large coil spring housed in a cylinder on the left-hand front of the turret. Elevation and hand traverse were controlled by handwheels to the right and left of the gunner respectively and an additional traverse handwheel was provided for the commander's use in an emergency. The hydraulic power traverse was controlled by a rocking footplate operated by the gunner's right foot. Because of the turret's great weight, traverse was necessarily low-geared both in hand and power.

Variants

Three Tiger variants entered service:

1. Tiger Command Tank (Panzerbefehlswagen), designated Pz Bef Wg Tiger Ausf E (Sd Kfz 267 or 268). The difference between these two sub-variants was solely in the wireless equipment fitted, the Sd Kfz 267 carrying combinations of the Fu 5 and Fu 8 radio and the Sd Kfz 268 being fitted with combinations of the Fu 5 and Fu 7.

2. Tiger Armoured Recovery Vehicle, designated Berge Pz Tiger I Ausf E (Sd Kfz 185) (the actual number is unconfirmed). This was no more than a towing vehicle for assisting crippled or otherwise malfunctioning Tigers back to an area where repairs could be effected. The adaptation involved the removal of the main armament, sealing of the mantlet, fixing the turret in the traversed position and fitting

a winch to the turret rear with a wire rope guide on the front. No lifting gear was provided.

3. Sturmtiger, designated 38 cm RW 61 Ausf Stu Mrs Tiger. This 65 ton vehicle consisted of a 38 cm Type 61 rocket projector or mortar mounted as an assault howitzer on a modified Tiger E chassis. The Raketenwerfer 61 L/54 was originally developed as an anti-submarine weapon for the German Navy. A model of the Sturm Mörser (Assault Mortar) Tiger was first shown to Hitler and the General Staff on 20th October 1943 and limited production was started in August 1944. Only 10 vehicles were built, all being standard chassis converted by Alkett. These vehicles were heavily armoured and were intended for mobile assault against troop concentrations and fortifications. A small crane was fitted to the rear of the vehicle to load the projectiles of which 13 were carried, including one on the loading tray of the projector. An MG 34 was ball-mounted in the offside of the superstructure front plate. Being slow, cumbersome, and of limited tactical value they played no significant part in the closing months of the war; they were to have been used in ones and twos only, and were swiftly immobilised and captured when they put in an appearance.

Tiger II (B)

The Tiger II resulted from the need to produce an even larger version of the Tiger, superior in armour and hitting power to anything the Soviets were likely to produce. Porsche and Henschel were asked to tender designs to the VK 4500 requirements, and Porsche's first effort was simply a heavier version of his previously rejected VK 4501 design which had competed with Henschel's VK 4501 for the Tiger I requirement. (The limited production run of VK 4501 (P) chassis has been developed into the Panzerjäger Tiger (P) Ferdinand as described in a previous section.) As redesigned, this chassis would have carried a 15 cm L/37 or a 10·5 cm L/70 gun. This design was discarded in favour of a much modified design, the VK 4502 (P) with re-shaped hull, and larger turret to mount the 8·8 cm L/71 which was not stipulated. Engines, electric transmission and suspension were similar to those of the VK 450 L (P). Subsequently, however, this project was cancelled, due mainly to the shortage of copper which was needed for parts of the electric transmission. At the time of cancellation turrets for the first 50 production vehicles were already in hand and these were subsequently fitted to early production Henschel vehicles.

The Henschel design VK 4503 (H) was formally ordered in January 1943, and work on this was finished in October 1943. As has been mentioned in the chapter on the Panther, the German Ministry of Production insisted that the Tiger II should incorporate as many common features and components of the projected Panther II as possible. This work, involving close co-operation between MAN and Henschel engineers, delayed completion of the Tiger II design by three months.

Production of the Tiger II started in December 1943 at Kassell on a parallel production line to the Tiger I. The first 50 vehicles had the Porsche turret already mentioned, but all subsequent vehicles had the Henschel-designed turret intended for them. The Pz Kw IV Tiger II (Sd Kfz 182) had the same HL 230 P 30 engine as the later production Panthers, and it weighed 68·4 tons, and had a crew of five. The road speed was about 42 kph and the cross-country speed 15–19 kph. Cruising range was up to 171 km. The Tiger II was massively armoured with 100 mm thickness on the turret front and lower hull front, 150 mm on the glacis plate, 80 mm at the sides, and 40 mm on upper surfaces. Hull layout was similar to that of the Panther, with in fact the same radiators and engine deck fittings. Stowage for the 8·8 cm KwK 43 gun totalled 78 rounds of mixed HE, AP and Hollow Charge ammunition.

The Tiger II first went into action on the Russian Front in May 1944, and was first encountered on the Western Front by the Allies in August 1944. To the Allied troops it was known as the "Royal" or "King Tiger", and the German nickname was the "Koenig Tiger". The Tiger II was underpowered and mechanically unreliable, while its great bulk—it was the heaviest tank to enter service with any nation in World War II—restricted its operational use. At the period of its introduction and service, however, it reflected the contemporary German tendency towards big heavily armed defensive vehicles, which was taken to its ultimate conclusion by the E 100 and Maus projects described in the next chapter.

The Jagdtiger B

The chassis differed from that of the Tiger II(B) battle tank only in the increased length (about 260 mm), and certain unimportant track suspension changes connected with this. The structural parts were the same except for the armoured hull, whose side walls were extended so as to form the fighting compartment and provide the housing for the 12·8 cm L/55 gun. The superstructure front carried the mantlet and was made of cast steel 250 mm thick. The rear wall of the superstructure was 80 mm thick. It had a double flap door which served as an entrance and an exit and allowed access for gun maintenance. The superstructure was completed by a roof which was secured by bolts. Included in the roof were a hatch, roof ventilators, a revolving close-defence weapon and smoke equipment. The sighting equipment and vision devices were also fitted in the roof.

The fighting compartment was maintained under pressure by means of Dräger apparatus.

The ammunition was of the "separate" type, projectile and charge, and 38 rounds was carried.

The gun carriage, armoured cradle, and elevating and traversing gear were all made by Krupp.

These vehicles were built at Nibelungen-Werk (Steyr-Daimler-Puch) of St. Valentin.

The Later Programmes

The E Series

In mid-1943 a programme for the development of a completely new series of AFVs was initiated by the Weapons Department. The principal intention was to draw upon the potential of those firms in the automobile industry who were not yet engaged in AFV production. The vehicles were to be standardised within the shortest possible time and were to be capable of being used in a variety of roles.

Development contracts were to be sent to Klöckner-Humboldt-Deutz and Magirus.

The following types were planned:

E 5   A light vehicle in the 5-ton class, intended to serve as a light armoured personnel carrier, small tank, radio-controlled tank or recce tank.

E 10   In the 10-ton class, intended as a personnel carrier, light tank destroyer or weapons carrier.

E 25   In the 25-ton class intended as a reconnaissance tank, medium tank destroyer or heavy weapons carrier. Development contracts went to Argus, though there was a Porsche design for a vehicle of this class.

E 50   In the 50 to 65-ton class as a light battle tank intended eventually to replace the Panther. Development contracts went to Adler, Argus and Auto-Union.

E 75   In the 75- to 80-ton class this was a medium battle tank intended as a Tiger replacement. The development contract went to Adler. The E 50 and E 75 were to be equipped with the Maybach H 234 engine producing 1200 hp at 3000 rpm, and the Makrüdo mechanical/hydraulic two-speed clutch steering gear. In appearance and size they were similar but the E 75 was to be more heavily armoured.

E 100   In the 140-ton class this was to be the heaviest ever tank. Development was undertaken by Adler.

The E 100, developed principally by Adler, was the project on which the most progress had been made. A prototype without a turret was discovered by the Allies on the Henschel testing ground at Haustenbeck. The vehicle was similar to the Tiger II, with a designed weight between 140 and 150 tons and it was to be armed exactly like the Maus.

The vehicle was to have been powered by the Maybach HL 230 P 30 V-12 engine producing 700 hp at 3000 rpm. This would have given the low power-to-weight ratio of 5 hp per ton.

A further engine development, the HL 234 with 900 hp and the Bosch fuel injection system, was completed. With supercharging this engine was expected to attain 1100 to 1200 hp. This would have raised the power-to-weight ratio to only 8·5 hp per ton. The high ground pressure of 1·4 kg per sq cm could not be reduced even with tracks 100 cm wide. When the hull was ready it was found that the vehicle could not carry the planned 50 ton turret although the hull was 450 cm wide. Plans were therefore made to install the weapon without using a revolving turret. Frontal armour was 200 mm at 30° and the side armour 120 mm. This was less than on the Porsche Maus.

The chassis was fitted with interleaved steel wheels and was sprung with MAN conical springs, as were all the E projects. Little more is known about this vehicle. The project was discontinued in mid-1944.

The Maus

The contract for this design was given orally to Professor Porsche by Hitler on 8th June 1942. It may be that this project was thought of as compensation for the Army High Command's rejection of the Porsche Tiger, which later formed basis of the Elephant tank destroyer. In any case no proof has been found that the Army Weapons Department ever issued a proper contract.

Development began shortly afterwards. A few of the Porsche special design features were incorporated, and these included the torsion bar suspension assembly and an electric drive. A model was shown to Hitler on 4th January 1943, but further development was however delayed because of certain alterations to the armament and the difficulty of procuring suitable engines.

Work on the first actual prototype was begun at the Alkett factory on 1st August 1943 and the first test run—with a weight in place of the turret—took place on 23rd December 1943. Further trials were carried out until May 1944 in Böblingen. On 9th June 1944 construction was completed following receipt of the turret and armament from Krupp. A second prototype had been finished during this time. After this however further development was halted. Both prototypes were sent to Kummersdorf where they were blown up shortly before it was occupied by the advancing Russian troops. A few hulls and turrets were still at the Krupp testing grounds in Meppen at the end of the war, but it appears that originally ten prototypes had been planned. The entire direction of the project and of the design was undertaken by Porsche. Electrical equipment came from Siemens-Schuckert and the engine was designed by Daimler-Benz. Hull and turret armour and armament came from Krupp. The tracks were supplied by the Altmärkische Kettenfabrik and assembly was carried out by Alkett.

The German Minister for Armaments, Speer, asked for the following characteristics and this seems to be the nearest to Hitler's specifications for the Maus.

Armament: 12·8 cm cannon with a 96 cm recoil and 150 cm fixed ammunition. For this a turret ring of 300 cm diameter was necessary.
Armour: Driver's plate 350 mm vertical. Heavy frontal, floor armour against mines.
Speed: 20 kph.

Fulfilling these requirements led to the great weight of 188 tons. An engine of 1200 hp had to be found. A suitable traverse gearing and a new chassis had to be built. Finally special railway transporters would have had to be constructed and, as the machine would be too heavy to cross bridges, it would have had to be submersible for crossing rivers.

The hull of the Maus was like that of the Elephant. an armoured box overhanging the broad chassis. The chassis was completely filled by the engine and transmission, except at the front where there was a compartment for the driver and co-driver. The fuel tanks were in the front of the superstructure, ammunition was carried amidships on the left, and on the right there was an auxiliary engine and more ammunition stowage. The electric drive motors were at the rear, and the V-12 engine was fitted in the front part of the hull. Behind it were the generators and then the drive shaft for the rear sprockets. The chassis featured six spring bogie assemblies in place of the torsion bar bogies which were first planned.

The turret, which weighed 50 tons, had a cast front with the side and rear built of rolled steel plates. Its centre of gravity was 20 cm from the pivoting point. For underwater travel the turret could be lowered on to a rubber sealing sheet by means of a rotating eccentric arrangement of six turret traversing rack rollers. Shock absorbers were fitted to prevent jolting against the turret in horizontal planes and consisted of three compressible, replaceable horizontal limiting rollers.

Originally the 12·8 cm KwK 82 L/55 gun was planned as the main armament. Later, however, the 15 cm KwK 44 L/38 gun was chosen. In addition a semi-automatic 7·5 cm KwK 44 L/36 gun was mounted co-axially. A co-axial MG and an anti-aircraft MG were also planned. The grenade projector was fitted into the turret roof. The electric auxiliary motor could rotate the turret a full 360° in 16 seconds, but the fixed ammunition could not be carried in the vehicle because of its great weight. The weight of a shell for the 12·8 cm gun was 56 kg, and that of one for the 15 cm gun 70 kg. Cranes were provided in the turret to assist with loading and a range finder with 220 cm ground line was to be fitted.

The MB 509 petrol and the MB 507 water-cooled diesel engines were developed from the Daimler-Benz Type 603 V-12. Each was respectively installed in the Maus prototypes (Maus I and II). Approximately 150 hp was required to drive the cooling fans alone. An 8 hp two cylinder two-stroke engine served as a starter motor and maintained the high pressure in the fighting compartment. It also drove the heaters and charged the batteries. On roads the electric drive motors gave a speed of 20 kph at 3100 rpm. They weighed 3770 kg and worked on simple cross shafts which could be operated for road or for cross country. Generators, electric motors, cross shafts and brakes were cooled by an airstream from the engine.

The tracks consisted of 24 identical, double rollers which were combined in 12 bogies, six per side. The average weight per roller was 3565 kg with a total sprung weight of 171,144 kg. The bogie suspension was hung from a cross bar fixed to the hull and to the apron. Each pair of rollers sat on a double rotary arm and was sprung with a helical spring. The rollers were, like those used on the Tiger II, of the steel tyre type with rubber insets. The track was 110 cm wide and was unlubricated.

It was planned that the vehicle should be submersible up to a depth of eight metres. Originally two air trunkings were to be fitted, one as an intake and one as an exhaust. There were difficulties with this arrangement however, and the venting equipment finally consisted of a single trunking which acted as an air intake, as an escape hatch for the driver and wireless operator, and to cool the electric motor. The electric motors were powered under water by means of a cable and generator from a vehicle standing on land, which laid out the cable as the Maus moved forward.

Professor Porsche described the vehicle as a mobile pill box which was useless as a tank. The tactical value of such a monstrosity did not justify the considerable expenditure involved in its development and production, and the armour was already at that time vulnerable to hollow charge projectiles. A mobility of 6·5 hp per ton was the lowest acceptable power-to-weight ratio, while ground pressure was excessive. The gun turret and armament would have done credit to a medium cruiser, but in a service role the use of such a ponderous vehicle would have been limited to very few tactical situations. Technically the machine answered certain problems. The electromechanical drive was certainly, at that time, the fastest possible solution to the problem of transmission in such heavy vehicles, and the track was equally satisfactory. This weighed, relatively speaking, only about half as much as most other tracks, but the proportion of the weight of the turret to that of the whole vehicle was twice as much as normal. Because of the vehicle's limited mobility, however, the weight of the engine remained within normal limits. Finally, the problem of recovering such a vehicle would never have been solved.

In conclusion it must be stressed that the Maus, like the E 100, was a sorry example of misdirection of the German war effort at the highest level, which resulted in a waste of valuable personnel and material on projects whose tactical value was questionable. Despite this the Maus and E 100 prototypes represented remarkable achievements in design.

VK 7001 "Löwe" or "Tiger Maus"

As a rival undertaking to Hitler's Maus the Weapons Department gave a development contract for the VK 7001 (K) to Krupp. Numerous studies for 110, 130, 150 and 170-ton vehicles had originated there. They were all known as the Krupp Maus.

Another study was concerned with a vehicle of this weight class carrying the 30·5 cm mortar. There were even plans for a 1500-ton vehicle with an 80 cm gun and two turrets with 15 cm guns. This vehicle was intended to have 250 mm front armour at 45° slope and was to have been powered by four U-boat diesel engines.

The VK 7001, however, was based on the Tiger II design. A model shows the usual track suspension, a sharply sloping front and a relatively small turret set well back.

None of these projects got past the drawing board stage. They were all, sensibly, allowed to drop.

Half-track Types

Development vehicles and prototypes for the main German half-track types are illustrated in plates 141–169.

Further notes on the Sd Kfz 250 series with gun mounts are given in the armoured car section.

Armoured Cars

Experimental and Development Types

The armoured cars produced by Daimler-Benz and Ehrhardt, which Germany was allowed to have under the conditions of the Versailles Treaty, did not meet the requirements of the Army authorities and in view of this the Weapons Department issued contracts for 8- and 10-wheeled chassis for gepanzerte Mannschaftstransportwagen (armoured personnel transport vehicles) in 1926–27. The specifications were very advanced, as is shown by the following extract from the 1927 specifications.

1. The vehicle must be wheeled.
2. On good flat roads a maximum speed of 65 kph is required and the lowest speed is to be 5 kph at normal revolutions. A daily run of 200 km, at an average speed of 32 kph for three successive days, must be possible.
3. The vehicle must have the greatest possible cross-country mobility. The specific ground pressure must not exceed 0·7 kg/per square cm at a maximum stoped angle of 80°.
4. The vehicle must be able to climb rock gradients of 1:3.
5. The vehicle must be able to cross trenches 1·5 metres wide without using special equipment and without stopping.
6. The vehicle must be able to wade to a depth of one metre.
7. The vehicle must be able to travel backwards or forwards at the same speed. A separate steering device is to be fitted for each direction. The driver must be able to carry out changes of direction within ten seconds.
8. The turning radius may not exceed four times the wheel base.
9. When the vehicle is moving it must produce a minimum of sound.
10. The weight of the chassis is not to exceed four tons and the total weight of the vehicle, ready for service, with superstructure, is not to exceed 7·5 tons.
11. Ground clearance is to be 0·3 metres.
12. At normal cruising speed the vehicle must be able to run on normal standard gauge railway. No special measures are to be taken to achieve this, but the track width is to be such that the inner wheel rims can run on the railway lines.
13. (This referred to buoyancy specifications subsequently withdrawn.)
14. The crew is to consist of five men, namely:

    (a) commander
    (b) driver
    (c) first gunner
    (d) second gunner
    (e) wireless operator.

All the other points in this specification dealt with details such as the engine, gears, steering, brakes, suspension and tyres.

The Army Weapons Department issued contracts for vehicles of this type to C. D. Magirus of Ulm, Büssing-NAG of Brunswick and Daimler-Benz of Stuttgart-Untertürkheim. These firms all produced prototypes by 1929 which were thoroughly tested at Kummersdorf and in Wünsdorf.

It is interesting to note that Magirus and Daimler-Benz were busy with 8-wheeled cars while Büssing were developing those with 10. The planning at Daimler-Benz was under the direction of Professor Porsche. Component parts for the two prototypes were produced in Stuttgart and the assembly of the vehicles was carried out in the Daimler-Benz factory in Berlin-Marienfelde. Martini und Hüneke of Salzkotten were responsible for the production of the superstructure, while the installation of the turret, the turret ring and the fitting of the weapon were carried out by Rheinmetall of Düsseldorf. For camouflage purposes a cork jacketing was proposed which would also increase the vehicle's inherent buoyancy. The rear steering was so laid out that the steering column and all the hand and foot pedals in the rear driving position were detachable. This was done principally to deceive the Interallied Control Commission officials. The first vehicles were taken into service in the Reichswehr at the end of 1930 and the beginning of 1931 after they had undergone thorough road trials. Some vehicles were sent for further trials at the Tank Testing Establishment in Kazan in Russia. However as a result of the unfavourable economic conditions in 1929 and 1930 it was neither possible to start production of these all-wheel-drive designs, nor could the technical advances be incorporated in commercial vehicles.

Heavy Six-wheeled Types

In June 1929 the Army Weapons Department of the Reichswehr Ministry issued specifications for the delivery of 6-wheeled motor lorries with a rear 4-wheel drive. Magirus, Büssing and Daimler-Benz were the main firms which sent in tenders. Magirus produced the type "M 206", and Büssing the type "G 31". Daimler-Benz developed the type "G 3" in 1928 which was modified as the "G 3a" in 1929.

Preliminary tests with the long-frame Daimler-Benz chassis, "G 3" type, supplied by the Army Weapons Department, showed that this chassis could also possibly be used to take on armoured superstructure. The chassis weighed 2200 kg, the superstructure 2300 kg and the total weight was 4·5 tons. The front axle load was about 1200 kg. A strengthening of the front axle and an increase in the radiator surface area of about 20 per cent with an increased cooling water capacity were considered to be necessary.

All the chassis which were scheduled to be fitted with superstructures were also given double steering, and the alterations named above were carried out on the chassis on the production line. The question of using larger tyres was also examined. Thirty-seven Daimler-Benz chassis of the "G 3a" type were ordered in 1932 by the Weapons Department and Büssing received a contract for 12 chassis for armoured cars.

The armoured superstructures for these vehicles were built mainly by Deutsche Werke of Kiel. The total weight with superstructure was about 5000 kg.

Guderian's book *Panzer Leader* refers to these armoured cars' initial service.

"During the 1932 manoeuvres German armoured reconnaissance cars appeared for the first time. These were improvised armoured vehicles based on the chassis of a 6-wheeled lorry."

Structurally all these vehicles were normal 6-wheeled lorries, with three rigid axles on longitudinal leaf springs. Both double-tyred rear axles were driven. Daimler-Benz installed the 68 hp 6-cylinder "M 09" petrol engine. Büssing used the 65 hp 4-cylinder type "G" petrol engine and Magirus fitted the 6-cylinder "S 88" petrol engine which produced 70 hp. With improved superstructures these vehicles came into service in large numbers and from 1933 formed the backbone of the reconnaissance units. They were designated "Schwerer Panzerspähwagen (6 Rad) (Sd Kfz 231)" (heavy scout car—6-wheels); "Schwerer Panzerspähwagen (6 Rad) (Fu) (Sd Kfz 232)" (heavy scout car—6 wheels—radio) and "Panzerfunkwagen (Sd Kfz 263)" (armoured wireless car).

The Sd Kfz 231 and 232 were fitted with a 2 cm gun and an MG 13 in a revolving turret, while the Sd Kfz 263 had only an MG 13 in a fixed turret. The large-frame radio antennae fitted to the Sd Kfz 232 and 263 were characteristic of the wireless cars of the period. The armour had a basis of 14·5 mm and was proof against steel-cored small arms ammunition. Deutsche Werke and Deutsche Edelstahl were the main suppliers of the superstructures.

These vehicles were considered to be only provisional equipment and were replaced by the later 8-wheel type with the standard chassis. They saw service at the beginning of the war in Poland and in France and were later used for training.

From 1932 to 1934 commercial motor car chassis were fitted with the lightly armoured superstructures so that reconnaissance units would have light and more mobile vehicles in addition to the heavy scout car. Daimler-Benz developed these vehicles and the armoured superstructures came mainly from Deutsche Edelstahl. They were constructed exclusively on Adler chassis and were open topped. They were designated "Maschinengewehrkraftwagen (Kfz 13)" (machine gun lorry) and "Funkkraftwagen (Kfz 14)" (wireless truck).

The thin 8 mm armour gave these vehicles a very poor combat value and the cross-country performance of the motor-car chassis of the period left a lot to be desired. The Kfz 13 was armed with an MG 13 and had a crew of two, while the Kfz 14 had a three-man crew and had no armament.

Until the light scout car on the standard chassis was introduced in 1937 these vehicles rendered valuable service for training, mainly equipping cavalry regiments. These vehicles also saw action in Poland during 1939, but were subsequently used for training.

Light Reconnaissance Cars

From the Type 1 standard chassis built for the heavy personnel carrier of 1935 vintage, a chassis with a rear engine was developed for the light scout car, which was planned as a replacement for the Kfz 13 and 14. This vehicle was developed by Eisenwerk Weserhütte of Bad Oeynhausen. The chassis was built by Auto-Union in Zwickau and assembly was carried out by F. Schichau of Elbing and Maschinenfabrik Niedersachsen in Hannover-Linden.

Like all the standard car and light lorry chassis developed by the Weapons Department the suspension consisted of spiral springs suspended on triangular wishbone arms. This independent suspension together with the all-wheel drive and steering at each end gave a satisfactory cross-country performance. The Horch V-8 petrol engine of about 3·8 litres produced nearly 80 hp and gave this 4·8-ton vehicle a maximum speed of 80 kph. The following vehicles were officially taken into service from 1937.

(a) Leichter Panzerspähwagen (MG) (Sd Kfz 221)
(b) Leichter Panzerspähwagen (Sd Kfz 221) mit 2·8 cm s Pz B 41
(c) Leichter Panzerspähwagen (2 cm) (Sd Kfz 222)
(d) Leichter Panzerspähwagen (Fu) (Sd Kfz 223)
(e) Kleiner Panzerfunkwagen (Sd Kfz 260)
(f) Kleiner Panzerfunkwagen (Sd Kfz 261)
  (Leichter Panzerspähwagen: light armoured scout car; Kleiner Panzerfunkwagen: small armoured wireless car.)

The total weight of the vehicles was between 4 and 4·8 tons, the chassis weight being 1965 kg. The vehicle price (without weapon) was nearly RM 19,600.

On 20th April 1940 the Weapons Department issued a contract to Appel of Berlin-Spandau and Schichau of Elbing for the fitting of a 2 cm Hängelafette (pivoted gun mount) 38 to the Sd Kfz 222, so that the vehicle could be used by the Army in an anti-aircraft role. The total weight was thereby increased to 5000 kg.

The superstructure had a thickness of between 8 and 14·5 mm and the front was armoured to a thickness of 30 mm. The crew consisted of two men in the Sd Kfz 221, three men in the Sd Kfz 222/223 and four men in the Sd Kfz 260/261.

Although production of these vehicles was terminated during 1942 many of these armoured scout cars remained in service until the end of the war.

Bad road conditions, particularly in Russia, made the use of wheeled vehicles almost impossible and, therefore, from 1942 onwards more and more half-track vehicles of the Sd Kfz 250 series (light personnel carriers) were used for reconnaissance purposes. At the beginning of March 1942 the Weapons Department received a contract from the Armoured Vehicle Inspectorate for a light personnel reconnaissance vehicle, the Sd Kfz 250/Sp. Gustav Appel of Spandau delivered three development models to the Army by the middle of 1942 and series production began in July 1942 with an output of 30 vehicles per month. The designation was "Leichter Schützenpanzerwagen (2 cm) (Sd Kfz 250/9)". This vehicle was fitted with the turret of the Sd Kfz 222.

In 1941 another attempt was made to improve the 4-wheel light scout car, and a contract was sent to the Weapons Department on 21st July 1941 to develop a chassis from the 8-wheeled Sd Kfz 231 armoured car. By using, where possible, existing parts of this vehicle, the new 4-wheeled scout car was standardised with the 8-wheeler except for motor, gears, suspension and the shortened rear end. The air-cooled 6-cylinder Tatra diesel engine producing 125 hp was intended to give the 7-ton vehicle a speed of 85 kph. Frontal armour was 30 mm face hardened, while the remainder of the armour was to be proof against steel-cored small arms ammunition. Büssing were responsible for developing the chassis and licensed construction of the chassis was expected to be undertaken by Horch. There was a four-man crew. The armament consisted of a 5 cm KwK 39/1 gun and an MG 42 in a revolving turret. A thousand machines were contracted for and mass production was expected to start in October 1943. Series production never took place.

Heavy Eight-wheeled Types

The knowledge gained between 1927 and 1930 with the 8- and 10-wheeled vehicles, resulted in the GS type chassis, whose development was begun during 1934–35 by Büssing as part of the Weapons Department's programme for standard German Army vehicles. This chassis had single wheel suspension on longitudinal leaf springs and was fitted with all-wheel drive and 4-wheel steering. The Büssing V-8 engine of the "L 8 V" type was mounted in the rear of the strongly constructed frame chassis, and two steering mechanisms, for forward and reverse travel, completed this special chassis, which weighed 4120 kg. Originally the rating was 150 hp, but an increase in bore raised this to 180 hp and gave a top speed of nearly 100 kph. Deutsche Werke of Kiel were responsible for the development, and assembly was carried out by Schichau. With varying superstructures this vehicle constituted the standard, heavy vehicle of the reconnaissance units until the end of the war. The following variants were taken into troop service.

(a) Schwerer Panzerspähwagen (8 Rad) (Sd Kfz 231)
(b) Schwerer Panzerspähwagen (8 Rad) (Fu) (Sd Kfz 232)
(c) Schwerer Panzerspähwagen (7·5 cm) (Sd Kfz 233) (Developed by Büssing)
(d) Panzerfunkwagen (8 Rad) (Sd Kfz 263) (Schwerer Panzerspähwagen: heavy armoured car; Fu: wireless; 8 Rad: eight wheels).

The armour basis of all these vehicles was 10 to 14·5 mm but the front armour was increased in most types to 30 mm. The cost per machine (without weapon) was about RM 52,980 and the average development time was twelve months. There was a crew of four men for the Sd Kfz 231 and 232. Armament consisted of a 2 cm KwK 30 or 38 gun and an MG 34 in a revolving turret. The wireless cars Sd Kfz 232 and 263 had their unwieldly frame antennae replaced in 1942 by a dipole antenna. The Sd Kfz 233 and 263 had no turrets. The 233 was fitted out as a support vehicle with a 7·5 cm StuK L/24 gun but the Sd Kfz 263 had only a single MG 34 and fixed superstructure carrying wireless gear and a five-man crew. These later vehicles were built only by Deutsche Werke in Kiel.

These armoured cars on the 8-wheel, standard chassis replaced the heavy, 6-wheel type during 1938. The building of the wireless car Sd Kfz 263 was terminated during January 1942 in favour of the medium scout car 251 and the construction of the remaining 8-wheel, standard chassis was halted during the course of 1942. The production of the "L 8 V" engine continued until 1944.

While the production of the 8-wheel standard armoured car was in full swing, the Weapons Department received, on 5th August 1940, a contract for an 8-wheeled armoured car which, although similar in layout to the existing design, would have a monocoque hull instead of a chassis. As this vehicle was mainly intended for service in hot climates (e.g. the desert) Tatra were asked to develop a 12-cylinder air-cooled diesel engine producing about 220 hp. The prototype of this power unit was to be ready towards the end of 1941.

Büssing were made responsible for developing the hull and superstructure while Daimler-Benz and Schichau were asked to develop the turret. The total weight was to be between 10·5 and 11·5 tons. Frontal armour was 30 mm thick but the other armour was intended to be proof against steel-cored small arms ammunition only. A maximum speed of 85 kph was envisaged. The turret was to mount a 5 cm KwK 39/1 gun and an MG 42, and there was to be a four-man crew. The first test vehicle was delivered in July 1942. Alterations and improvements were carried out on the prototype diesel engine and measures were taken to reduce engine noise. The third tropically proofed engine was scheduled for delivery in June 1942, but development of this was discontinued. The vehicle went into series production from July 1943, however, appearing in the following versions.

(a) Schwerer Panzerspähwagen (Sd Kfz 234/1)
(b) Schwerer Panzerspähwagen 5 cm (Sd Kfz 234/2)
(c) Schwerer Panzerspähwagen 7·5 cm (Sd Kfz 234/3)
(d) Schwerer Panzerspähwagen 7·5 cm (Sd Kfz 234/4)

In the Sd Kfz 234/4 the complete carriage with the barrel and shield of the 7·5 cm wheeled, PaK 40, was mounted without modification, on a pivot in the centre of the fighting compartment, this variant being produced on Hitler's personal order.

The hulls and mountings for the 234 series were produced and assembled by Büssing and the armoured superstructures were made by Deutsche Edelstahlwerke. The armour thickness of the hull and turret was 30 mm in front and that of the hull sides was 8 mm. The turret armour at the sides and rear was 14·5 cm thick. At the rear it was 10 mm. As a result, fitted with a diesel engine and enlarged tyres (270-20), the vehicle's radius of action was about 600 km with a full fuel load, and this greatly increased the vehicle's usefulness compared with the earlier 8-wheelers. From 1944 the armoured cars of the 234 series replaced the earlier 8-wheel vehicles and, because of their modern design, were among the most advanced wheeled armoured vehicles to appear during the Second World War.

Wheeled Personnel Carriers

To complete the coverage of the armoured wheeled vehicles used by the German Army, special mention must be made of the Sd Kfz 247 series. Until 1936 the Krupp-built light cross-country lorry Type L 2 H 43 and 143, basically a commercial type, had been used, but from 1937 the Einheitsfahrgestell (standard chassis) II was also used for personnel carriers. Development of these vehicles had been done by Daimler-Benz, the superstructures were obtained mainly from Deutsche Edelstahl. Vehicles of this type were intended mainly for higher command staffs and were used on active service in relatively small numbers.

Experimental Amphibious Type

Based on Trippel's amphibious vehicle "SG 7", three prototypes of a light amphibious armoured scout car were constructed between 1941 and October 1942. The Schildkröte I was equipped with a single MG and the Schildkröte II with a 20 mm MG 151 or 2 MGs. The installation of the 20 mm MG 151 was intended only for the third prototype Schildkröte III. Originally the armour was 7 to 7·5 mm thick, but this was later increased to 10 mm. The vehicles which were fitted with the air-cooled Tatra V-8 petrol engine were not successful. Trials were therefore discontinued towards the end of 1942, and the project was abandoned.

Captured Types in German Service

The German Army used very few of the numerous armoured cars which had been acquired through the annexation of other states. One of these was the Austrian Saurer Company's "RR 7", which was adopted by the Germans and was designated "mittlerer gepanzerter Beobachtungskraftwagen (Sd Kfz 254)" (medium armoured observation car). Experiments with this vehicle go back to 1930, when the Austrian automobile industry collaborated with the Military Department in producing cross-country vehicles. Saurer at that time manufactured the RR, which was both wheeled for use on roads and tracked for cross-country purposes. The change over from wheels to tracks could even be carried out while the car was travelling at slow speeds. The vehicle, powered by a Saurer 6-cylinder diesel engine was intended to serve as a light artillery tractor and as a chassis for light, fighting vehicles. The "RR" chassis which was originally fitted with solid rubber tyres, was equipped with pneumatic tyres in the "RR 7" version and, as a result of official trials in January 1937, a contract for 15 vehicles was issued.

The events of 1938 (the German occupation of Austria) did not affect development and a contract was sent to the Weapons Department on 21st May 1938 ordering the production of an armoured scout car, running on wheels and tracks, proof against small arms fire and carrying medium wave and radio telephone equipment, thus taking advantage of the Saurer design. Development was undertaken by Saurer in Vienna for chassis and superstructure, and by Daimler-Benz for the turret. Delivery of the first vehicle was scheduled for 31st May 1942. This machine, designated "Panzerspähwagen RK (Ausf A)", had a total weight of 6·5 tons. The armour was from 5·5 to 14·5 mm thick and the engine was the Saurer diesel producing 100 hp. Armament was a single MG 34 in a revolving turret and there was a crew of three.

This vehicle never entered first-line service, but the Sd Kfz 254, mentioned above, was issued to the troops in small numbers. A variant of this machine was the "Instandsetzungskraftwagen" (maintenance and repair vehicle), with a 1500 kg payload, which was based on the same chassis. An improved prototype, known as the "RK 9", underwent tests during 1940–41. Although the Waffen-SS expressed an interest in this machine it did not go into series production.

Another vehicle which, after being taken over by the German Armed Forces attained a certain significance as a wheeled armoured reconnaissance vehicle, was the "Panhard 38" captured from the French Army in 1940. About 190 of these machines were acquired and about 150 of them were issued to German reconnaissance units. The designation of this vehicle was "Panzerspähwagen P 204 (f)". The 4-cylinder Panhard "SS" two-stroke petrol engine with an 105 hp output gave the 8·2 ton vehicle a top speed of 80 kph. A crew of four was carried and the main armament consisted of a 25 mm tank gun and an MG in a revolving turret. Armour thickness varied from 7 to 20 mm.

About 40 of these cars, converted into auxiliary armoured railway trolleys, were intended for use as security vehicles for armoured trains and in carrying out reconnaissance along railway lines. They could also be used in a road or cross-country capacity, but it was not possible to carry road wheels while running on the railway lines. A Weapons Department contract, dated November 1941, sent to Gothaer Waggonfabrik and Bergische Stahlindustrie in Remscheid, called for the necessary railway fittings for these vehicles.

GERMAN TANKS OF WORLD WAR II
Illustrations

Introduction to the Illustrated Section

In this section all principal AFVs used by the German Army until 1945 are presented, within their different type classifications, in chronological order. Exceptions to this are minor variants such as recovery vehicles and a few captured types, which are included in the section describing the basic vehicle. As the illustrations are classified by type there are a few instances where a basic chassis is repeated. An example is the StuG III, which appears in both the assault gun and tank destroyer classifications; howitzer-armed variants are covered in the former section while the others, which can fill anti-tank roles, are classed as tank destroyers.

Drawings are to a constant 1:73 scale and illustrate each basic vehicle or major variant thereof. A side elevation is given for each, while certain very important types are shown by full four-view drawings. In addition there are some supplementary drawings showing cross-sections, development vehicles, prototypes and exploded views, which are not reproduced to a constant scale. Among the rare photographs in this section are a number whose reproduction from old or damaged material is not of the highest order.

Basic data—which includes length, width, height, horse-power, weight, armour basis, crew and speed in kilometres per hour—is given with each principal drawing, using the following abbreviations respectively: L, W, H, HP, Wt, A, Cr and Sp. Dimensions are generally given in centimetres, armour basis in millimetres, but units are omitted for simplicity's sake.

Prototype and development vehicles are shown chronologically, although a fuller description is given in the development histories in the main text. Variants of the basic vehicle (not necessarily all illustrated) are listed under the basic data and main drawings.

In the appendices at the end of the book there are tables for converting metric weights and measures into their British and American equivalents.

8 Under the terms of the Versailles Treaty Germany was forbidden tanks in her re-constituted Army after World War I. Dummy wooden tanks built on light car chassis were used to give troops familiarity with tank tactics prior to the availability of the real thing. This picture was taken during manoeuvres in 1931.

9 The Leichter Traktor (light tractor), which was a "concealed purpose" name for the experimental light tanks built (and secretly tested at the Kazan proving grounds in the USSR) in 1926. Layout of this vehicle was based on the LK II of 1918, with engine mounted in the front and turret towards the rear. Armament was a 3·7 cm gun, the top speed was 12 mph, and the weight approximately 9½ tons. Construction was in mild steel.

10 The Grosstraktor II (heavy tractor), built by Rheinmetall-Borsig to a secret Army Weapons Department order of 1929, was one of several experimental mild steel prototypes of medium tanks produced before Germany overcame the limitations imposed by the Versailles Treaty. This vehicle weighed 21 tons, had a top speed of 12 mph, and was armed with a 7·5 cm gun. Note the similarity to the later Pz Kw V and VI of 1935.

Pz Kw I

Distinguishing features: The Model A identified by four bogies and a low-set idler. Model B had five bogie wheels and a high-set idler. Bogies were suspended in pairs on leaf springs. Small revolving turret offset to the right with twin MGs in a mantlet. Air-cooled horizontally opposed piston engine.

Assessment: Model A had an inferior power/weight ratio. Light and mobile vehicle with slight defensive armour, conforming to the concepts of the early 1930s.

In service: From 1935 to 1940 the Pz Kw I was the main equipment of tank regiments.

11 (*left*) The LKA 1 Krupp-built prototype of the Pz Kw I. The turret has two co-axial machine guns.

12 Panzerkampfwagen I (Sd Kfz 101), Ausf A.
L: 402   B: 206   H: 172   HP: 57   Wt: 5·4
A: 13   Cr: 2   Sp: 37.

14 Panzerkampfwagen I (Sd Kfz 101), Ausf B.
L: 442   B: 206   H: 172   HP: 100   Wt: 5·8   A: 13   Cr: 2   Sp: 40.

Variant:
Kl. Panzerbefehlswagen (small commander's tank).

13 The Pz Kw I Ausf A was the principal equipment of German Panzer regiments from 1935–40. This is a standard production vehicle.

15 The Pz Kw I Ausf B had a more powerful engine necessitating a longer hull and chassis. It had one extra road wheel and one extra return roller to compensate for the extra length.

16 Panzerbefehlswagen I was a commander's variant of the Pz Kw I Ausf B with a fixed full-width superstructure replacing the turret, extra radio equipment, and a single machine gun in a ball mount.

17 The VK 601 was the prototype of the Pz Kw I Ausf C. It was based on the earlier models but was fitted with a 2 cm gun as main armament, overlapping road wheels, and lubricated track for higher speeds on roads.

18 The VK 1801 was the prototype for the Pz Kw I neuer Art (new model), which featured heavier armour as an infantry support vehicle. It was not developed beyond the prototype stage. Note that it retained the twin co-axial machine gun armament of the Pz Kw I.

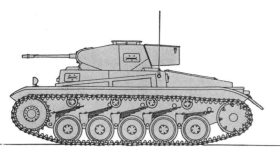

19 Panzerkampfwagen II Ausf C mit 2 cm KwK (Sd Kfz 121).
L: 481 B: 224 H: 198 HP: 140 Wt: 9·5 A: 15 Cr: 3 Sp: 40.

Variants:
Pz Kw II Ausf a1, a2, a3, b, c mit 2 cm KwK
Pz Kw II Ausf A, B, C, F—J mit 2 cm KwK

Derivatives:
Pz Kw II Ausf D, E
Pz Kw II Ausf L

Pz Kw II

Distinguishing features: Pz Kw II Models a and b had six bogies on beam suspension. All others had five bogies on leaf springs. Angular turret offset to the right, with a 2 cm tank gun and co-axial MG in a mantlet. Angular superstructure. The driving sprocket took the form of a single disc.

Assessment: Light robust vehicle which was intended for use against light tanks and carriers. Later used only for reconnaissance.

In service: Models a to c 1935, Model A 1937 strengthening the Pz Kw I in armoured regiments. Model F used as a reconnaissance vehicle with tank regiments from 1941.

20 LKA II was a prototype by Krupp developed from the LKA I by fitting a larger turret with 2 cm main armament. Similar chassis to LKA I.

21 The Pz Kw II Ausf a1, a2, a3 and b were developed from the LaS 100 of 1934. Note the characteristic small bogie wheels. The a1 variant is illustrated. This had no reduction gear. The a2 had a welded rear idler and altered engine compartment to improve cooling. The b had reduction gear added giving a squarer nose. It also had improved tracks and an up-rated engine. Armament on all the Pz Kw II prototype models was the 2 cm gun.

22 The Pz Kw II Ausf c was the final development of the Pz Kw II prototype series and became the basis for the production series. The small bogie wheel suspension of the earlier models was replaced with five independently-sprung bogies (with leaf springs) each side, and this vehicle reverted to the round nose. Further improvements were made with the gears.

23 The Pz Kw II Ausf A, B and C differed from the Pz Kw II Ausf c prototype by reverting to the squared-off nose of the Ausf b. The Ausf A featured minor improvements over the Ausf c including a Zeiss tank periscope for the commander. The Ausf B (illustrated) introduced the squat vision cupola.

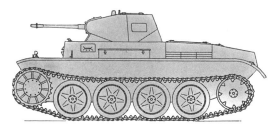

24 Panzerkampfwagen II Ausf D, E mit 2 cm KwK (Sd Kfz 121).
L: 464 B: 224 H: 202 HP: 140 Wt: 10·0 A: 30 Cr: 3 Sp: 55.

Variants:
Pz Kw II (Flamm) Ausf D, E (Sd Kfz 122) (flamethrower tanks).

Pz Kw II Ausf D and E

Distinguishing features: Four large bogies on torsion bars (Christie suspension), otherwise similar to the Pz Kw II Ausf C.

Assessment: The larger wheels offered improved road speed but inferior cross-country performance.

In service: 1938 with tank battalions of the light mechanised cavalry divisions.

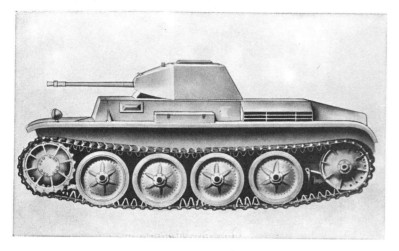

25 The Pz Kw II Ausf D and E had Christie-type suspension replacing the independently-sprung bogies of the Ausf A, B and C. This gave a higher road speed but proved less successful cross-country.

26 The Pz Kw II Ausf F, G and J reverted to the earlier type of suspension. Frontal armour was increased to 35 mm and an improved cupola was fitted which had seven vision blocks. Stowage bin was fitted on Ausf G turret as illustrated.

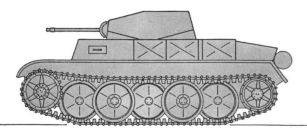

27 Panzerspähwagen "Luchs" mit 2 cm KwK (formerly Pz Kw II Ausf L Sd Kfz 123).
L: 463 B: 249 H: 213 HP: 180 Wt: 11·8 A: 30 Cr: 4 Sp: 60.

Luchs (Lynx)

Distinguishing features: Interleaved suspension with large bogies and no return rollers. High track cover and angular hull. Turret similar to that of the Pz Kw II.

Assessment: Adaptation of the Pz Kw II design for use as a reconnaissance tank. Fast vehicle but lightly armoured.

In service: From 1943, in small numbers, with reconnaissance platoons of tank battalions and recce battalions.

28   A late production Lynx.

29   The VK 1601 (D) also known as the Pz Kw II neuer Art (new model) was developed by Daimler-Benz in 1939 from the Pz Kw II Ausf D. Note that it has two vision ports in the frontplate. Note also the side escape hatch abreast the turret.

30   The VK 901 was a lighter less well-armoured version of the VK 1601, intended as a high-speed 10-ton vehicle.

31 Following cancellation of the initial production order for the VK 1601 (D) (Pz Kw II nA)—shown in 29—some of the few vehicles to be completed were converted into recovery vehicles with a traversing crane fitted in place of the turret. In its new form it became the Bergepanzer auf Fgst Pz Kw II nA (VK 1601) (Bergepanzer: recovery tank). Hull characteristics of the VK 1601, including the side doors, were of course retained.

32 The VK 1301 which was the final development prototype for the Lynx. This was almost identical to the VK 901 but all wheels were fully spoked.

33 The VK 1602 (D) of 1941 was the prototype for the Leopard (Light) with an open-topped turret and 5 cm gun, KwK L/60. Later fitted with a Puma turret. It did not go into production.

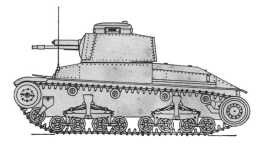

34 Panzerkampfwagen 35(t) mit 3·7 cm KwK.
L: 445 B: 214 H: 220 HP: 120 Wt: 10·5 A: 25 Cr: 4 Sp: 40.

35 The Pz Kw 35(t), one of the Czech types widely used in the German Army in the early days of World War II.

Pz Kw 35(t)

Distinguishing features: Eight small bogies fitted four to each leaf spring. Riveted, angular superstructure and front MG in a ball mount.

Assessment: Well-designed vehicle. Air-assisted gear change steering, which reduced driver fatigue and track wear. A thoroughly serviceable vehicle which was not out-classed until 1941.

In service: Introduced during 1935 in Czechoslovakia. Taken over by the German Army following the occupation in 1939. Used during the campaign in France. Also in service with the Rumanian Army and an improved version was used by the Hungarian forces.

36 The Pz Kw 38(t), most important of the Czech types in German service.

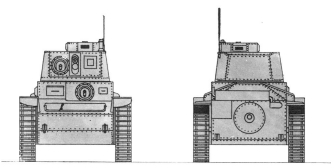

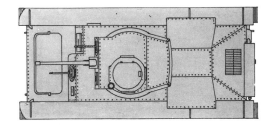

37 Panzerkampfwagen 38(t) mit 3·7 cm KwK.
L: 490 B: 206 H: 237 HP: 125 Wt: 9·725 A: 25 Cr: 4 Sp: 42.

Variant:
Aufklärungspanzer 38(t) mit 2 cm KwK 38 (Recce tank).

Pz Kw 38(t)

Distinguishing features: Four bogies, suspended in pairs on leaf springs. Angular superstructure, with vertical sides and front MG in a ball mount. Reconnaissance version was fitted with the turret of the light scout car Sd Kfz 222.

Assessment: Well-constructed vehicle with robust and reliable chassis. At the time of its introduction it was one of the most modern vehicles and superior to all other types of its class. The recce version was an emergency solution to the problem of difficult road conditions on the Eastern Front. The same type was supplied to the Swiss, Swedish and Peruvian armies.

In service: Introduced in Czechoslovakia during 1938. Taken over in 1939 by the Germans following the occupation and retained in production. Widely used until 1941 to supplement the Pz Kw III. During 1944 the reconnaissance version was issued in small numbers to recce units.

38 The Krupp prototype for the Pz Kw III series. This was not adopted, but features from it were later used in the Pz Kw IV, whose design Krupp were responsible for.

39 The Pz Kw III Ausf A, which had five medium-size road wheels and was armed with a 3·7 cm L/45 gun and co-axial machine gun.

40 The Pz Kw III Ausf B and C featured eight small bogie wheels which gave excellent riding qualities. Note the original type of "dustbin" cupola with unprotected vision slits.

41 The Pz Kw III Ausf D had eight small road wheels each side suspended by three large leaf springs. This model also had a new pattern armoured cupola, and a pivoted mount for an anti-aircraft machine gun was fitted on the left side of the superstructure.

42 In the Pz Kw III Ausf E the suspension took the final form adopted for all subsequent production models on this chassis. There were six small road wheels with conventional torsion arm suspension. The Pz Kw III Ausf E was the first major production version, its 3·7 cm gun being subsequently replaced by a short calibre 5 cm weapon. This model was in service at the time of the invasions of Poland and France, 1939–1940.

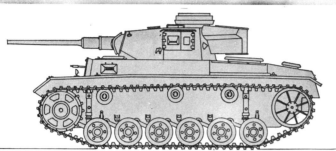

43 Panzerkampfwagen III mit 5 cm KwK 39 L/60 (Sd Kfz 141/1) Ausf J–L.
L: 552   B: 295   H: 251   HP: 300   Wt: 22·3   A: 50+20   Cr: 5   Sp: 40.

Variants:
Panzerkampfwagen III mit 3·7 cm KwK L/45 (Sd Kfz 141) Ausf A–D.
Panzerkampfwagen III mit 5 cm KwK L/42 (Sd Kfz 141) Ausf E–H.
Panzerkampfwagen III mit 5 cm KwK L/60 (Sd Kfz 141) Ausf M.
Panzerkampfwagen III (Flamm) Sd Kfz 141/3 (Flamethrower tank).
Panzerbefehlswagen III (Sd Kfz 266, 267, 168) (Commander's tank).
Panzerbeobachtungswagen III (Sd Kfz 143) (Observation post tank).
Bergepanzer III (Recovery tank).
Mun Pz III (Ammunition carrier).

Derivatives:
Panzerkampfwagen III mit 7·5 cm KwK L/24 (Sd Kfz 141/2) Ausf N.
(NB. Some of these were built as such, others were Ausf L and M re-armed.)

Pz Kw III

Distinguishing features: B, C and D models had eight bogies on leaf springs. The model A had five medium size bogies on torsion bars. From the model E onwards six slightly smaller bogies on torsion bars became standard. A to C had 15 mm thick frontal armour, and the D to G models had 30 mm. Models H to L had additional front armouring. Models A to C had 230 hp engines and Models D to O had 300 hp. Models A to C had five forward and one reverse gear and models D to H had ten forward and four reverse gears with semi-automatic transmission. Models J to O had six forward and one reverse gear. The low square superstructure had vertical sides and the square turret had a rear-mounted cupola. The Pz Kw III/IV experimental vehicles had a similar hull and turret but were distinguished by their interleaved suspension.

Assessment: Well-constructed vehicle which was superior in fire power and mobility to most tanks in the same class in service with other nations between 1939 and 1941.

In service: Introduced as a replacement for the Pz Kw I and II in 1937. From 1943 it was largely replaced by the Pz Kw IV, though special purpose variants remained in service until the end of the war.

44 This early production Pz Kw III Ausf J with 5 cm L/42 gun illustrates changes introduced on the later Pz Kw III models. Features to note are the 5 cm gun (first introduced retrospectively on Models F and G), the squatter thicker cupola (introduced from Model G), the new pattern sprocket and idler wheels and wider spaced return rollers (introduced from Model H) and the thicker hull MG ball-mount (introduced on Model J). A stowage box was fitted on the turret rear from Model F (retrospectively) and Model H.

45 The Befehlspanzer III Ausf H. This was an OP version fitted with a dummy main armament and a central ball-mounted machine gun in the mantlet. Space provided in the turret by omission of the main armament was devoted to a map table and extra radio equipment.

46 (below) The Pz Kw III Ausf J was the standard 1943 production model and was armed with the long barrel 5 cm L/60 gun which was basically the same weapon as the standard German anti-tank gun of the period. Armour basis was increased to 50 mm and the combat weight was 22·3 tons. This model introduced the escape hatches in each side, visible between the two leading return rollers. Note also the elimination of the pistol ports in the turret sides, which was most unusual in the Model J and may indicate that this is a reworked model fitted with a Model L turret.

47 (above) The Pz Kw III Ausf L had 20 mm spaced armour added across the front of the superstructure and across the mantlet front. This example retains pistol ports in the turret sides, indicating an early production vehicle. They were eliminated in later vehicles.

48 The Pz Kw III Ausf M had the same modifications as the Model L, with addition of three smoke dischargers each side of the turret. Some were also fitted with skirt armour (Schürzen) and a few had Ostketten (Eastern Front tracks) which enabled grousers to be fitted for muddy going. Side doors and pistol ports were eliminated in this model.

49 The Pz Kw III Ausf M (Flamm) carried a flamethrower in a wide mantlet in place of the main armament. The co-axial and bow machine guns were retained. Flame fuel capacity was 1000 litres carried inside the hull. Range of the flame gun was about 60 metres and combustion rate was 7·8 litres per second at 15–17 atmospheres pressure. These vehicles equipped flamethrower companies on the Eastern Front in 1943.

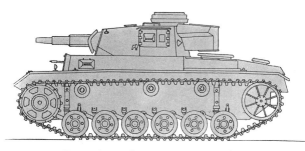

50 Panzerkampfwagen III Ausf N mit 7·5 cm KwK L/24 (Sd Kfz 141/2).
L: 552 B: 295 H: 251 HP: 300 Wt: 22·3 A: 57+20 Cr: 5 Sp: 40.

51 Pz Kw III Ausf N with the 7·5 cm L/24 gun. Note the spaced armour shield round the rear of the turret on this particular vehicle. Some Model Ns were Model Ls or Model Ms re-armed and re-designated.

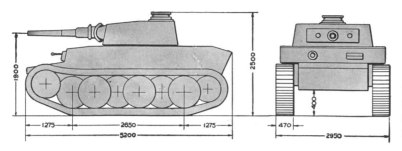

52   The VK 2001 (K) of 1935 was a fore-runner of the Pz Kw IV design. It existed only as a Krupp design project. Designed armament was a 7·5 cm KwK L/70.

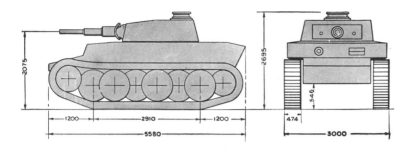

53   The VK 2002 (MAN) was a design by MAN to the same 20-ton tank specification as the Krupp VK 2001. Again it did not proceed beyond the project stage.

54   VK 2001 (Rh B) was Rheinmetall-Borsig's design to the VK 2001 specification. Its suspension of eight paired road wheels in sprung bogies (as in the contemporary Pz Kw V) was simple but out of date even at the time of its design. Of the three VK 2001 designs, Krupp's, with modifications, was subsequently accepted for production. Bataillonsführerwagen (BW) (battalion commander's vehicle) was a designation given to all three VK 2001 designs following Germany's "concealed purpose" policy for new designs at the time of her rearmament.

55   The Pz Kw IV Ausf A of 1936 was the first production model, made only in small numbers. It was a 19-ton vehicle with 230 hp engine. Suspension remained unaltered throughout the Pz Kw IV production series.

Pz Kw IV Ausf D

Distinguishing features: Eight double bogies, suspended in pairs from leaf springs. Three return rollers. Idler with narrow spokes. Tall cupola at rear of the turret. Air grilles on the engine compartment decking. Short, stubby gun. Prominent driver's compartment; from model B superstructure had a straight front. Front MG in a ball mount manned by wireless operator. Collapsible dipole aerial on the right hand side.

Assessment: Robust well-constructed type which was fully developed. Remained a standard type throughout the war and was produced in greater numbers than any other German tank.

In service: From 1937 was used as a close support tank (as the assault gun later was) in the heavy companies of tank battalions.

56 Panzerkampfwagen IV Ausf D mit 7·5 cm KwK L/24 (Sd Kfz 161)
L: 591   B: 286   H: 268   HP: 300   Wt: 20·0   A: 30   Cr: 5

Variants:
Pz Kw IV Ausf B–F 1 mit 7·5 cm KwK L/24

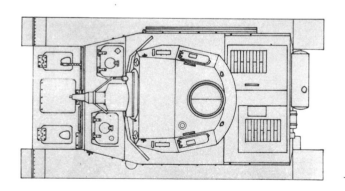

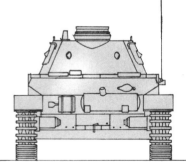

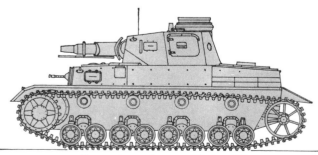

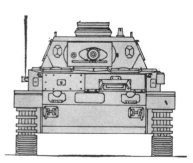

57 Panzerkampfwagen IV Ausf D.

58 The Pz Kw IV Ausf B and C were produced in 1937 and 1938 respectively. Differing only in detail, they lacked a hull machine gun, being provided with a carbine port instead in the right hull front. Compared with the Model A they had increased frontal armour and a more powerful engine, giving a power-to-weight ratio of 18·1 hp/ton (on Model A it was 13·3 hp/ton). Model C illustrated.

59 Pz Kw IV Ausf E was an interim vehicle which went into production in December 1939. Only a small number were built and some were used in the invasion of France and Flanders. Model E had a port for a hull machine gun with internal ball mount, and featured appliqué armour across hull front and on sides.

60 (below) The Pz Kw IV Ausf F, later designated FI when the F2 appeared re-armed with the long 7·5 cm L/43 gun. This was the last Pz Kw IV model with the short 7·5 cm gun.

61 Panzerkampfwagen IV mit 7·5 cm KwK L/43 Ausf F2 (Sd Kfz 161).
L: 593   B: 288   H: 268   HP: 300   Wt: 23·6   A: 50+30   Cr: 5   Sp: 42.

Variant:
Pz Kw IV mit 7·5 cm KwK L/43 Ausf G (Sd Kfz 161/1).

Pz Kw IV Ausf F2

Distinguishing features: Chassis and hull like the Models B to F1. Long gun in an improved turret with conical muzzle brake. Some additional armour plates on the superstructure front.

Assessment: With the fitting of the long 7·5 cm gun, Pz Kw IV changed from the role of a close support vehicle to being a tank able to take on the most powerful enemy tanks, and in many cases outgun them. The heavier armour and armament lowered the power/weight ratio enormously. This vehicle was known as the "Pz IV Special" to the British when first encountered in the Western Desert.

In service: From 1942 became standard equipment of armoured regiments. Later replaced by Models H–K with the 7·5 cm L/48 gun.

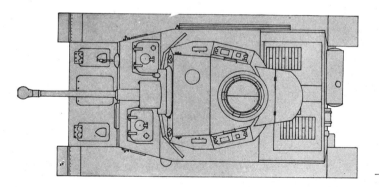

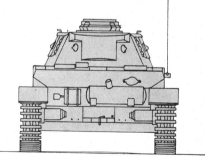

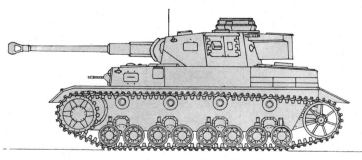

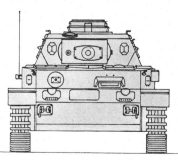

62 Panzerkampfwagen IV Ausf F2.

63 Panzerkampfwagen IV mit 7·5 cm KwK
L/48 Ausf H (Sd Kfz 161/2).
L: 589   B: 329   H: 268   HP: 300   Wt:
25   A: 80   Cr: 5   Sp: 42.

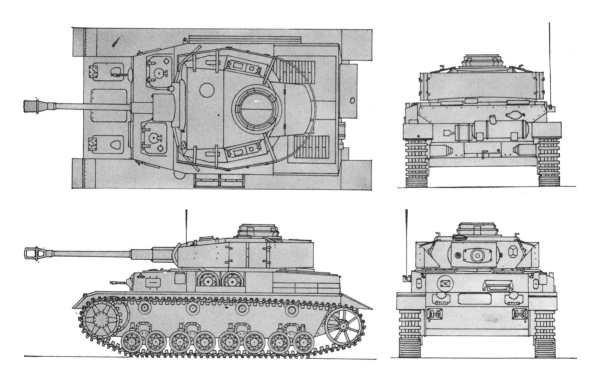

64 Panzerkampfwagen IV Ausf H.

Pz Kw IV Ausf H

Distinguishing features: Introduced the long L/48 tank gun. Gun fitted with double-baffle muzzle brake. Apron armour 5 mm thick for hull and 8 mm thick on turret to offer protection against hollow-charge and bazooka grenades. "Zimmerit" anti-magnetic paste was usually applied to these vehicles to prevent the attachment of magnetic charges.

Assessment: Last production versions of the Pz Kw IV type. Further increases in fire power and stability at the cost of mobility.

In service: From 1943 as standard equipment of tank regiments.

65 Pz Kw IV Ausf J fitted with wire mesh skirt armour, introduced on the Russian Front in 1944.

66 To overcome supply problems in Russia the Germans used trailers to tow spare fuel. Vehicle shown is a Pz Kw IV Ausf F1. Note the palings for use in "un-ditching" and the German national flag, commonly used at this period, summer 1941, as an aerial recognition sign to prevent erroneous attack by friendly aircraft.

67 A wooden model of a projected version of the Pz Kw IV with two 7·5 cm recoilless guns, proposed in 1945.

68 Pz Kw III/IV was an experimental vehicle, basically a Pz Kw III with large overlapping road wheels. Though adopted later in German tanks, this type of suspension was too complicated to mass-produce at the time the Pz Kw III was developed.

69 and 70 Developed from the Grosstraktor of 1929 were two similar vehicles, differing only in armament. These were produced under the "concealed-purpose" name of *Neubaufahrzeuge* (new construction vehicles), and were later designated Pz Kw V (*top*) and Pz Kw VI (*above*). The Pz Kw V had a 7·5 cm and 3·7 cm gun in the turret and weighed about 24 tons, while the Pz Kw VI was armed with 10·5 cm gun and 3·7 cm gun. Both vehicles had an auxiliary machine gun turret at the front and rear of the main turret. These vehicles, produced in 1935, represented the "heavy" designs of the integrated German tank programme, and followed the same sort of layout as contemporary vehicles produced by other nations, notably the British "Independent" and the Soviet T-32. German tank production was concentrated on the light and medium types, however, and the Pz Kw V and VI did not go into production, only a few pilot models being produced for trials by Rheinmetall-Borsig with armament by Krupp. Suspension was the same as Rheinmetall-Borsig's VK 2001 (Pz Kw IV prototype) design. These vehicles had an armour basis of 14·5 mm and a crew of 7. The engine was a Maybach 360 hp 12-cylinder petrol unit. The few vehicles of this type built were not used operationally in World War II but a well-known propaganda picture shows them in Oslo following the occupation of Norway in 1940. The designations Pz Kw V and Pz Kw VI were later applied to the Panther and Tiger respectively.

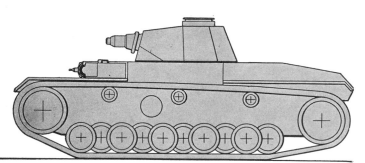

71 The VK 6501 (H) which had been built by Henschel in prototype form (two being completed) in 1938. It was also known as the *Sturmwagen* (SW) (assault vehicle) or Pz Kw VII. In the 65-ton class work on the project was cancelled before trials were complete. It was an early progenitor of the Tiger. More details are given in the notes on the Tiger development starting on page 68.

72 The VK 3001 (P), Porsche's prototype for the VK 3001 requirement of 1941. It had petrol-electric drive. Details are given in the Tiger development story.

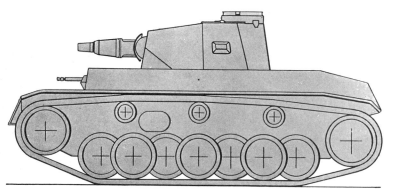

73 The VK 3001 (H) was Henschel's prototype for a tank in the 30-ton class, the entire project being dropped following the appearance of the greatly superior Russian T-34 in 1941. Two of the four Henschel chassis built were however completed as 12·8 cm SP guns and tested in service on the Russian Front. They are described elsewhere in this book.

74 Last of the 30-ton prototypes was that built by Daimler-Benz, the VK 3002 (D), at the end of 1941, which showed in its hull shape the influence of the Russian T-34.

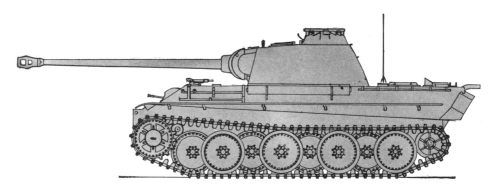

75 Panzerkampfwagen V Panther mit 7·5 KwK 42 L/70 (Sd Kfz 171) Ausf A, D.
L: 688   B: 343   H: 310   HP: 700   Wt: 45·5   A: 80   Cr: 5   Sp: 46.

Variants:
Panzerkampfwagen V Panther Ausf G.
Panzerkampfwagen V Panther Ausf F mit 7·5 cm KwK 44/1 L/70.
Befehlspanzer Panther (Commander's tank).
Beobachtungspanzer Panther (Observation Post tank).
Bergepanzer Panther (Recovery tank).

Panther

Distinguishing features: Interleaved suspension and steeply sloped superstructure similar to the T-34. Overhanging tracks. Prominent long-barrelled gun.

Assessment: Well-shaped highly mobile vehicle with good fire power.

In service: From 1943 in increasing numbers in tank regiments, supplementing and replacing the Pz Kw IV tank. Experimental vehicles were produced in 1945 with bulldozer blade and mine clearing equipment.

76 The Pz Kw V Panther Ausf D was the first Panther type in service. It is distinguished by the driver's visor, the opening for the bow MG, and the separate stowage boxes beneath the hull sponsons at the rear. Note early cupola similar to Tiger type.

77 The Pz Kw V Panther Ausf G was the last standard Panther type in service in quantity. It had a ball mount for the bow MG, episcopes for the driver instead of the visor, and straight sloping undersides to the hull sponsons. This vehicle has skirt armour on the sides concealing this feature which is better seen in plates 75 and 83.

78 Pz Kw V Panther Ausf A was the other Panther type, coming between the D and G chronologically. This had the same hull shape as the D, but a ball mount for the bow MG replaced the opening hatch. Driver's visor was retained.

79 Front and rear views of the Pz Kw V Panther Ausf A. Note the rear escape hatch on the turret, the rear stowage boxes, the MG ring on the cupola and the "Zimmerit" anti-magnetic coating.

80 Panther commander's model (an Ausf D with early type cupola) was fitted with short and medium wave radio. Note smoke projectors on turret sides.

81 The Panther OP tank was an artillery observation vehicle with fixed turret and wooden dummy gun. Note the turret machine gun in a ball mount and extra vision devices in turret roof. Vehicle is basically an Ausf D.

82 An urgent need for a heavy recovery vehicle in the weight class of the Panther and Tiger was met by the conversion of 270 early Panther Ausf D chassis to ARV configuration. This entailed removal of the turret and the fitting of a winch in the space so vacated. A spade was fitted on the rear—raised and lowered by the winch—to provide extra purchase when winching, and a demountable jib was fitted, seen erected in this view of a captured Bergepanzer Panther (Bergepanther) under test by the British.

83 The Pz Kw V Panther Ausf G showing the continuous slope of the lower edge of the hull sponsons, the stowage boxes being cast integral with the hull instead of being made separately. Note the rail for attaching Schürzen (skirt armour).

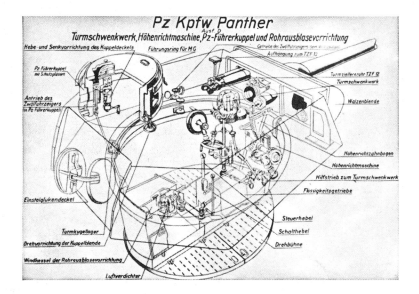

84 Cut-away diagram of Pz Kw V Panther Ausf D turret showing the early type cupola which lacked the all-round vision blocks, and the gun, sights and control installations.

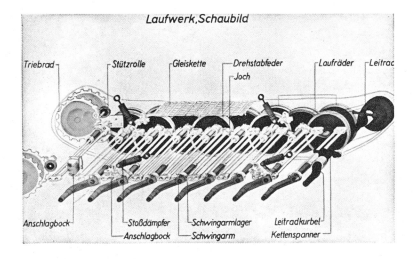

85 Exploded view of the Panther's torsion bar suspension, with road wheels omitted from the left hand side to show the staggered arrangement of the axles.

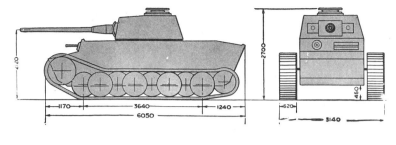

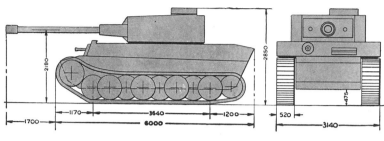

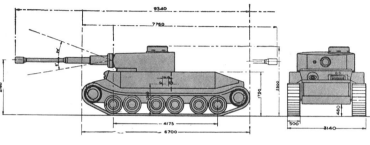

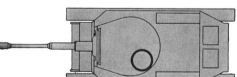

86 The VK 3601 prototype built by Henschel in March 1942, but cancelled before further development, was another of the designs which influenced the final Tiger design.

87 The VK 4501 (H) was the true Tiger (H) prototype and incorporated the best features of both the VK 3001 (H) and VK 3601 (H) (see plates 73 and 86).

88 (*left*) The VK 4501 (P) was Porsche's design to the VK 4501 requirement and featured petrol-electric drive. It was abandoned in favour of the Henschel vehicle for production, but the initial run of vehicles, laid down as a precaution against failure of the Henschel design, were converted to Ferdinand (Elefant) SP guns.

89 (*below*) The Porsche VK 4501 Tiger prototype. Though this vehicle ran trials at Rastenburg it was not proceeded with as a gun tank, and the 90 chassis laid down were completed as Ferdinand SP guns (see plate 130).

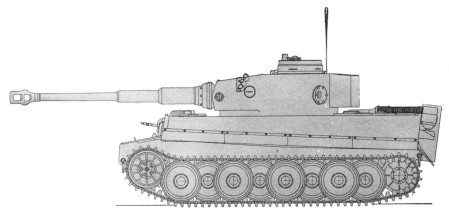

90 Panzerkampfwagen VI Tiger I, mit 8·8 cm KwK 36 L/56 (Sd Kfz 181) Ausf E.
L: 620 B: 373 H: 286 HP: 700 Wt: 55·0 A: 100 Cr: 5 Sp: 37.

Variant:
Bergepanzer Tiger I (field modification into recovery vehicle).

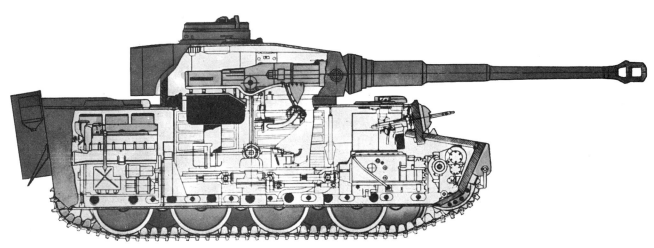

91 Cut-away view of an early production Pz Kw VI Tiger I Ausf E showing the immense thickness of the frontal armour and engine and armament installation.

Pz Kw VI Tiger I Ausf E

Distinguishing features: Interleaved suspension similar to the Panther, but squared-off super-structure and cylindrical turret.

Assessment: Heavily armoured vehicle, but poorly shaped. Limited mobility. A narrower track was necessary when being transported by rail, owing to the extreme width of the vehicle with full suspension.

In service: From 1943 with independent army tank battalions; some were also used in Waffen-SS armoured regiments.

92 Late production model of the Pz Kw VI Tiger I Ausf E. Note the absence of the Feifel air cleaning system and the later type cupola with vision blocks.

93 An early production Pz Kw VI Tiger I Ausf E, seen from several aspects and complete with Feifel air cleaning system visible on the rear decking, with equipment fully stowed.

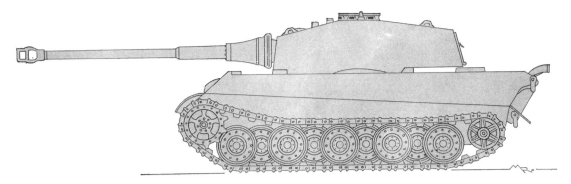

94 Panzerkampfwagen VI Tiger II, mit 8·8 cm KwK 43 L/71 (Sd Kfz 182) Ausf B.
L: 726   B: 375   H: 309   HP: 700   Wt: 69·7   A: 150   Cr: 5   Sp: 40.

Variants:
Pz Kw VI Tiger II, mit 8·8 cm KwK 43 L/71 (Sd Kfz 182) Ausf B (Porsche turret).
Befehlspanzer Tiger II (Commander's tank).

95 A production Tiger II with the Henschel-built turret.

Tiger II

Distinguishing features: Similar shape to the Panther, but chassis longer. Longer, more roomy turret and 8·8 cm gun. First 50 vehicles had the Porsche turret, which was of more rounded appearance than the Henschel turret of the remainder (see plate 96).

Assessment: Heaviest operational tank produced by any nation during World War II. Heavily armoured, but severely limited mobility and mechanically unreliable. Total number produced was 485.

In service: From May 1944, allocated as for the Tiger I.

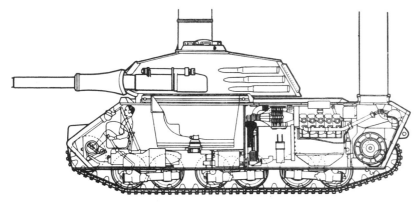

96 The projected VK 4502 (P) Porsche prototype design submitted to meet the requirement for an improved version of the Tiger, known to Porsche as the Type 180. This had petrol-electric drive like the VK 4501, and though rejected, 50 turrets for this vehicle which had already been started were fitted to the first 50 Henschel-built vehicles.

97 One of the first 50 Pz Kw VI Tiger IIs fitted with the Porsche-built turret from the VK 4502 (P). The Tiger II—known to the Allies as the "Royal Tiger" or "King Tiger" was the production version of the VK 4503 (H) prototype.

98 Wooden model of the Tiger-Maus (also known as the Lion) design to requirement VK 7001 for a 70-ton replacement for the Tiger II. Designed by Krupp, it did not proceed beyond design stage.

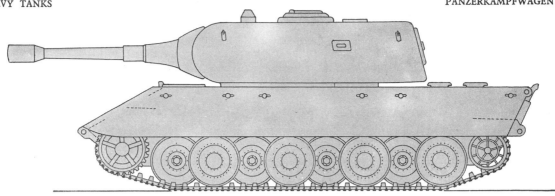

99   Panzerkampfwagen E 100 mit 15 cm KwK 44 L/38 and co-axial 7·5 cm KwK 44 L/36·5 (Prototype).
L: 869   B: 448   H: 332   HP: 1200   Wt: 140   A: 200   Cr: 6   Sp: 40.

The E 100

Distinguishing features: Eight interleaved bogies. Steel tyres with rubber insets. Sprocket at the front. The superstructure sloped and similar in shape to the Panther and Tiger II. Turret like that of the Maus.

Assessment: Heavily armoured and armed vehicle which was never fully developed. Its tactical value would have been limited.

In service: The prototype was undergoing tests in 1944. Further development was halted by the general disruption of German industry at this period.

100 (*left*)   The uncompleted E 100 proto-type gives an idea of the massive size of this "scaled-up" Tiger II type vehicle with its heavy armour and interleaved suspension. The lugs on the sides are attachment points for the side skirt armour.

101 (*below*)   The uncompleted E 100 proto-type being inspected by American troops when the Adler plant was over-run before the vehicle was completed. Note the size of the turret ring and the interleaved road wheels.

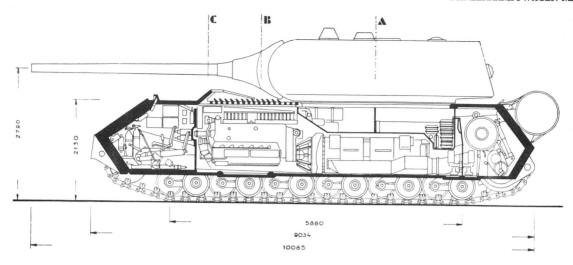

102 Panzerkampfwagen Maus mit 15 cm KwK 44 L/38 and co-axial 7·5 cm KwK 44 L/36·5 (Prototype).
L: 903   B: 366   H: 366   HP: 1200   Wt: 188   A: 200   Cr: 6   Sp: 20.

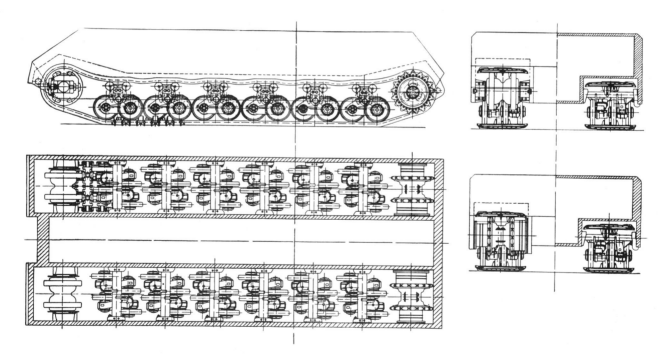

103   The Maus chassis. Front end is to the left.

The Maus

Distinguishing features: The suspension consisted of six bogies assemblies with spiral springs carried on cross bars between the hull and the armoured skirts. Vertical side walls sloped at the front and rear. Diesel or petrol-electric drive contemplated. Rear drive sprocket. Submersible to obviate river bridge limitations. 50-ton turret with sloping walls and mantlet, set well back towards the hull rear.

Assessment: A technically interesting but tactically useless vehicle. Virtually a mobile fort.

In service: Two prototypes were undergoing tests in 1944.

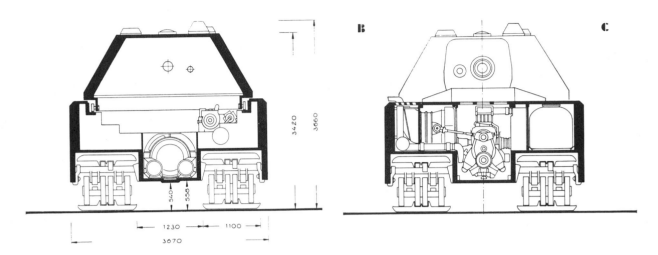

104 Front and rear cross-sections of the Maus.

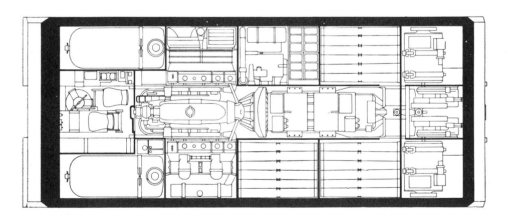

105 Plan view of the Maus. Front end is on the left. Note the engine and generator on the centre-line and the electric drive units at the rear.

106 This rare picture shows German troops repainting the prototype Maus from winter to spring camouflage after the snow melted in March 1945. Vehicle was then running trials with a simulated turret.

107 and 108 Two views of the Maus prototype—which was known as Porsche Type 205—on test. A simulated turret has been installed to depict the weight and bulk of the designed turret.

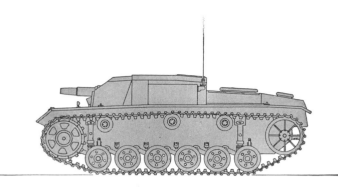

109 Sturmgeschütz III mit 7·5 cm StuK L/24 (Sd Kfz 142).
L: 549 B: 295 H: 194 HP: 300 Wt: 22 A: 50 Cr: 4 Sp: 40.

Variant:
Sturmgeschütz III mit 10.5 cm StuH 42 L/28.3 (Sd Kfz 142/2).

StuG III

Distinguishing features: Basic Pz Kw III chassis with turret replaced by low fixed superstructure. A short gun, or later a howitzer, fitted in the superstructure front with limited traverse.

Assessment: Relatively heavily armoured with very low profile. First type of turretless fighting vehicle produced for close support of the infantry. Thoroughly developed, it soon became necessary to fit a more powerful gun for combat against other tanks.

In service: From 1940 with the assault artillery battalions.

(Sturmgeschütz means "assault gun".)

110 One of the initial production series of the StuG III with 7·5 cm StuK L/24 gun. This was built on the Pz Kw III Ausf F chassis.

111 The StuG III Ausf G with 10·5 cm StuH 42 howitzer.

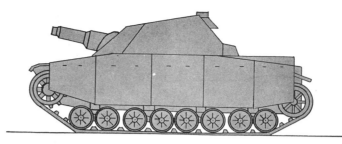

112   Sturmpanzer IV "Brummbär" mit 15 cm StuH 43 L/12 (Sd Kfz 166).
L: 589   B: 310   H: 249   HP: 300   Wt: 28·2   A: 100   Cr: 5   Sp: 40.

Brummbär

Distinguishing features: The Pz Kw IV basic tank chassis fitted with a roomy fixed superstructure and short gun in a prominent mantlet. Side aprons. Built only in small numbers. Later vehicles had a bow machine gun and cupola.

Assessment: Overloaded chassis. Effective in its intended role of infantry support for street fighting, though lack of a bow MG in the original design was a disadvantage.

In service: From 1944 with heavy infantry gun companies of Panzergrenadier Regiments and with armoured artillery battalions as well as with army tank battalions.

113   Early production Sturmpanzer IV Brummbär (Grizzly Bear). Later production vehicles had a ball mount machine gun on in the front superstructure left of the main armament, and improved driver's and commander's vision devices.

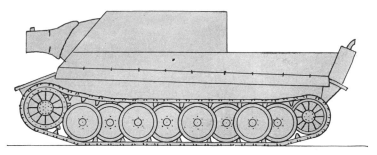

114   Sturmpanzer VI mit 38 cm Mörser RW 61, Sturmtiger.
L: 631   B: 373   H: 246   HP: 700   Wt: 68.   Cr: 5   Sp: 37.

Sturmtiger

Distinguishing features: Chassis of the Tiger I with massive squared-off superstructure, and short squat mortar barrel. Re-loading derrick prominent at rear of superstructure when rigged.

Assessment: Slow moving, strongly armoured vehicle for special tasks such as attacking individual targets at close range with high angle fire. Limited tactical value.

In service: Only a few examples were produced and these entered service during 1944.

115   A Sturmtiger captured by US forces early in 1945. Note that this is on a late-production Tiger chassis with steel disc wheels and resilient inserts.

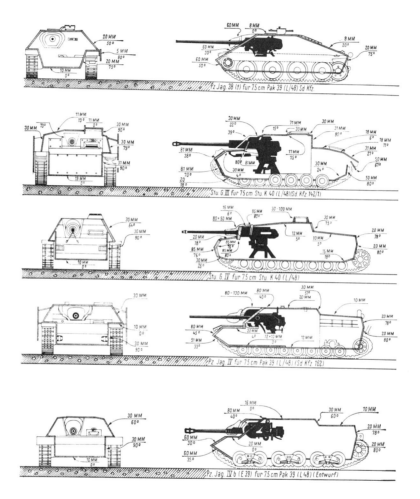

116 Comparison of armour thicknesses, and gun installations in the principal German tank destroyer types armed with the 7·5 cm KwK L/48.

117   Jagdpanzer 38 Hetzer mit 7·5 cm PaK 39 L/48.
L: 487   B: 263   H: 210   HP: 150   Wt: 16   A: 60   Cr: 4   Sp: 42.

Variant:
Flammpanzer 38(t) (Flamethrower vehicle).

Hetzer

Distinguishing features: Four large bogies. Low superstructure with all sides steeply sloped. Gun in ball mount projected a long way past the vehicle's nose.

Assessment: Effective use of the Czech Skoda-built Pz Kw 38(t) tank chassis. Adequate fire power. Protective shield on MG for local defence. Further development was the 38(d) with the 7·5 cm L/70 gun. Flame-thrower version was also produced.

In service: From 1944 with anti-tank battalions of infantry divisions. Also used post-war by the Swiss Army.

118 A standard production Jagdpanzer 38(t) Hetzer (Baiter).

119 Flammpanzer 38(t), flame-throwing version of the Baiter produced in small numbers, with protective cover removed to show flame projector.

StuG III

Distinguishing features: Low angular super-structure with cupola towards rear. From 1943 many vehicles had skirt armour.

Assessment: Later versions of the StuG III fitted with more powerful gun enabling them to be used in the anti-tank as well as the close support roles. Highly mobile and successful design.

In service: From 1943 with assault gun companies of artillery and tank battalions. Some were also used by anti-tank battalions in infantry divisions.

(Sturmgeschütz means "assault gun".)

120 Sturmgeschütz III mit 7·5 cm StuK 40 L/48 (Sd Kfz 142/1).
L: 548   B: 292   H: 230   HP: 300   Wt: 24
A: 81   Cr: 4   Sp: 40.

Variants:
Sturmgeschütz III mit 7·5 cm KwK L/33 (Sd Kfz 142).
Sturmgeschütz III mit 7·5 cm StuK 40 L/43 (Sd Kfz 142/1).
Sturmgeschütz III mit 10·5 cm StuH 42 L/28·3 (Sd Kfz 142/2).

121 (*left*) The StuG III Ausf G with the StuK L/48 gun, an example of a very late production model with Saukopf (pig's head) mantlet, cupola, and "Zimmerit" anti-magnetic coating.

122 (*below*) StuG III Ausf G with StuK 40 L/48 gun, welded mantlet and cupola, which distinguished the 1942–43 production types. Note the rails for fitting skirt armour.

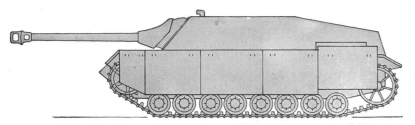

123 Jagdpanzer IV mit 7·5 cm PaK 39 L/48 (Sd Kfz 162) (Panzerjäger 39).
L: 602   B: 318   H: 186   HP: 300   Wt: 24   A: 80   Cr: 4   Sp: 40.

Variants:
Jagdpanzer IV mit 7·5 cm StuK 40 L/48 (Sd Kfz 163) (StuG IV).
Jagdpanzer IV mit 7·5 cm KwK 42 L/70 (Sd Kfz 162).
Jagdpanzer IV mit 7·5 cm StuK 42 L/70 (Sd Kfz 162/1).

Jagdpanzer IV

Distinguishing features: Very low superstructure with steeply sloping sides and L/48 gun with double-baffle muzzle-brake. A few vehicles with the L/70 (Panther) gun. Variant with the StuK 40 gun had a similar superstructure to the StuG III.

Assessment: The vehicle was somewhat nose heavy but was better protected than the original Pz Kw IV tank. The vehicles with the Panther gun were an interim type supplementing the Jagdpanther and were very nose heavy.

In service: Vehicles with the L/48 gun were used by anti-tank battalions of tank divisions from the end of 1943. Vehicles with L/70 guns were brought in towards the end of the war, and then only in small numbers (see plate 26).

124 Early production model of the Jagdpanzer IV with 7·5 cm PaK 39 L/48 gun, side skirts, and "Zimmerit" anti-magnetic coating.

125 StuG IV with the 7·5 cm L/70 gun, one of the few trials vehicles of this type built.

126 A late-production Jagdpanzer IV with 7·5 cm StuK 42 L/70 gun. Note the steel-typed wheels with resilient rubber inserts and reduced number of return rollers.

127 Sturmgeschütz IV L/48, 7·5 cm StuK 40, was a "hybrid" type which had the StuG III superstructure on the Pz Kw IV chassis. Characteristics were similar to the late model StuG III (see plates 120–122). Minor modifications were made to suit the Pz Kw IV chassis and the type was built to supplement StuG III production. 632 were built from mid-1943 onwards.

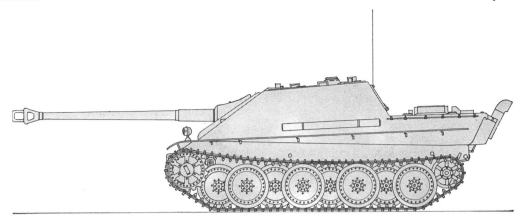

128 Jagdpanzer V Jagdpanther mit 8·8 cm PaK 43/3 L/71 (Sd Kfz 173s).
L: 687   B: 328   H: 272   HP: 700   Wt: 45·5   A: 80   Cr: 5   Sp: 45.

Jagdpanther

Distinguishing features: The same chassis as the Panther. Prominent superstructure with sloping surfaces on all sides. The long barrelled gun was fitted into a recessed mantlet well forward.

Assessment: Outstanding fire power and an ideal shape combined with sufficient mobility. The best of all German tank destroyers.

In service: With Army heavy anti-tank units from 1944.

129 A standard production Jagdpanther showing equipment stowage and rails for attachment of skirt armour.

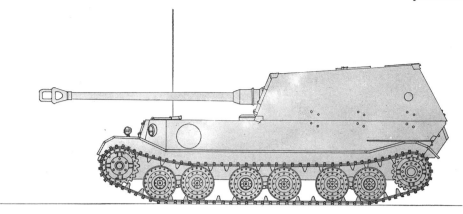

130   Jagdpanzer Tiger (P) Elefant, mit 8·8 cm PaK 43/2 L/71 (Sd Kfz 184s) Originally Ferdinand.
L: 680   B: 343   H: 297   HP: 640   Wt: 68   A: 200   Cr: 6.

Elefant

Distinguishing features: The original VK 4501 (P) (Porsche 101) Tiger chassis. Rear drive, but both sprocket and idler were cogged. High, box-like superstructure in the rear with a very prominent long gun in a large mantlet. Powered by two Maybach HL 120 engines with electric drive.

Assessment: Strongly armoured vehicle of limited mobility. The 8·8 cm gun was the same type as in the Jagdpanther and Tiger II. Size of this vehicle limited mobility and there was a spares problem with the electric drive.

In service: From 1943 with two heavy anti-tank battalions on the Eastern Front. Survivors used in Italy, 1944. A recovery version was built in very small numbers.

131   Side view of the Jagdpanzer Elefant (originally the Ferdinand) in original production form.

132 One of the modified Jagdpanzer Elefants with added frontal armour, hull machine gun aperture, and "Zimmerit" anti-magnetic coating.

133 One of the original Elefants which saw action in the Kursk offensive on the Russian Front.

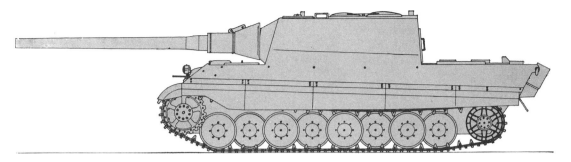

134 Jagdpanzer VI Jagdtiger mit 12·8 cm PaK 44 L/55 (Sd Kfz 186s) (Pz Jg Tiger, Ausf A, Porsche).
L: 780 B: 353 H: 292 HP: 700 Wt: 69·9 Cr: 6 Sp: 40.

135 Late production Jagdtiger with Porsche torsion bar suspension instead of the original Henschel type found on earlier production vehicles.

Jagdtiger

Distinguishing features: Same chassis as the Tiger II. Squarer and higher superstructure than the Jagdpanther.

Assessment: Heavily armoured and armed but with limited mobility.

In service: From 1944 a few vehicles were with heavy anti-tank battalions.

136 Profile of Jagdtiger (same vehicle as plate 135).

137 **and** 138 Comparison of the Henschel transverse torsion bar suspension with inter-leaved road wheels (*left*) and the much simplified Porsche longitudinal torsion bar suspension with wheels in pairs (*below left*). Early production Jagdtigers retained the original Henschel suspension, standard in the Tiger II.

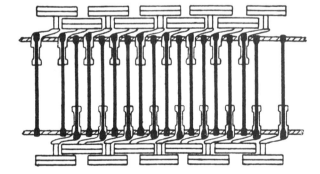

139 The Jagdtiger prototype chassis used to test the Porsche torsion bar suspension. Wheels were of smaller diameter than the Henschel type and there were only eight axles instead of nine in the original Henschel torsion bar layout. This Porsche suspension saved time, space, and materials, and simplified production.

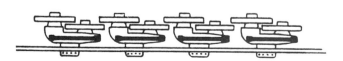

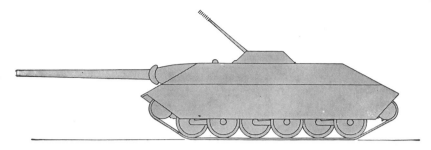

140 Jagdpanzer mit 10·5 cm KwK und 3 cm Flak (Porsche design) (E 25).
L: 490   H: (without turret) 150   B: 310   HP: 500   Wt: 27   A: 120   Cr: 4.

Jagdpanzer

Distinguishing features: Developed from the 245/00 10 and 245/00 11 designs. Very low silhouette. Medium large bogies on helical springs suspended in pairs in progression. Transverse engine, air cooled, V-12, with injection and boost. Fully automatic, hydraulic Voith operating and steering gears behind the engine. Tank cannon probably recoilless on the high and low pressure principle. A small revolving turret with AA gun for the commander.

Assessment: An example of the final stages of development in German tank construction. Heavily armoured and very mobile. Multi-purpose vehicle. Good AA protection and excellent shape. Very advanced mechanically.

In service: Project only planned as a multi-purpose vehicle, chiefly for supporting the infantry. Designed May 1944.

141 (*above*) Side view of the HL kl 4(H) showing the excellent low profile of this vehicle.

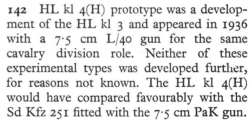

142 HL kl 4(H) prototype was a development of the HL kl 3 and appeared in 1936 with a 7·5 cm L/40 gun for the same cavalry division role. Neither of these experimental types was developed further, for reasons not known. The HL kl 4(H) would have compared favourably with the Sd Kfz 251 fitted with the 7·5 cm PaK gun.

143 HL kl 3(H) prototype with 3·7 cm KwK 37 L/24 gun in rotating turret which was evaluated for possible use with rifle regiments in light mechanised (cavalry) divisions in 1935.

144 Late production model of the Sd Kfz 250 half-track with revised superstructure (see plate 147). Vehicle shown with hoops fitted for canvas tilt.

Schützenpanzerwagen (Sd Kfz 250/1).

L: 456   B: 195   H: 198   HP: 100   Wt: 5·7   A: 12   Cr: 6   Sp: 65.

Variants:

Sd Kfz:

250/2	Fernsprechwagen	Telephone/line layer vehicle
250/3	Funkwagen	Radio car
250/4	Luftschützwagen	Air support vehicle
250/5	Beobachtungswagen	Observation post vehicle
250/6	Munitionswagen	Ammunition carrier
250/7	8 cm Gr-W-Wagen	8 cm Mortar carrier
250/8	7·5 cm KwK 37 L/24 auf le SPW	SP 7·5 cm gun
250/10	3·7 cm PaK auf le SPW	SP 3·7 cm A/T gun
250/11	s PzB 41 auf le SPW	SP 2·8 cm Panzerbüchse
250/12	le Messtrupp Pz Wg	Survey section instrument vehicle
252	le gp Mun Trspt Wg	Armoured ammunition carrier
253	le gp Beobachtungswagen	Armoured observation post vehicle

Derivative:

250/9 Panzerspähwagen	Armoured reconnaissance car

Schützenpanzerwagen (Sd Kfz 250)

Distinguishing features: Half track chassis with interleaved suspension and lubricated, rubber padded track. Sloping sides the tops of which inclined sharply inward. In later models the knuckle was horizontal. Engine was at the front driving the sprocket by semi-automatic Variorex gears. No front wheel drive. Chassis derived from the standard tractor. Distinguished from the Sd Kfz 251 type by the smaller number of road wheels and longer bonnet in relation to overall length.

Assessment: A very fast vehicle. Armour proof only against small arms ammunition and splinters. Poor cross-country performance, particularly in muddy conditions. Very good power/weight ratio.

In service: From 1942 with rifle companies of armoured reconnaissance and Panzergrenadier units. Replacement planned towards the end of the war by recce tanks adapted from the Pz Kw 38(t) chassis (see plate 37).

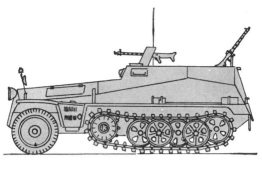

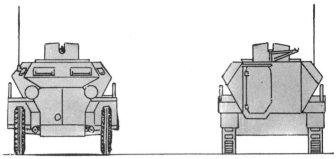

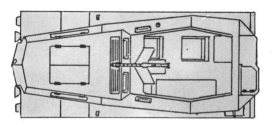

145 Leichte Schützenpanzerwagen Sd Kfz 250/1.
Early production type.

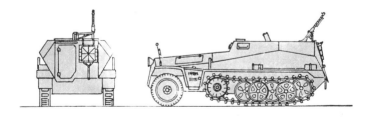

146 Sd Kfz 250/7 mit 8 cm Gr W.

147   Sd Kfz 250/8 with 7·5 cm KwK 37 L/24 gun.

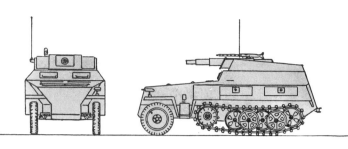

148   Sd Kfz 250/8 mit 7·5 cm KwK 37 L/24 gun.

149   Sd Kfz 250/10 with 3·7 cm gun.

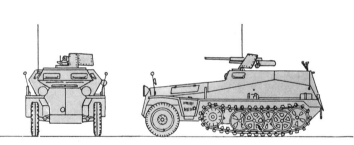

150   Sd Kfz 250/10 mit 3·7 cm PaK.

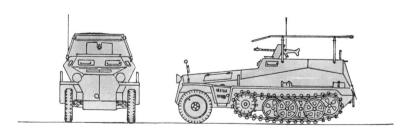

151   Sd Kfz 250/3 Funkwagen.

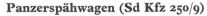

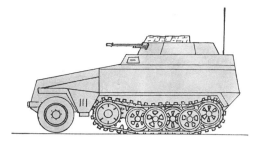

152 Panzerspähwagen (Sd Kfz 250/9) mit
2 cm KwK 38 L/55 (neuere Ausführung).
L: 460 B: 195 H: 220 HP: 100 Wt: 6
A: 12 Cr: 3 Sp: 65.

Panzerspähwagen (Sd Kfz 250/9)

Distinguishing features: The turret of the
Sd Kfz 222 on the chassis of the Sd Kfz 250
light personnel carrier.

Assessment: Mobility greater than that of
the four-wheel scout car but less than that
of the eight-wheel vehicle. An interim type
with overloaded chassis.

In service: From 1943 with companies of
some armoured reconnaissance battalions.
Classified as an armoured car in this role.

153 The Sd Kfz 250/9 which was the
standard Sd Kfz 250 half-track fitted with
the turret from the Sd Kfz 222 light
armoured car (see plate 181).

154 Sd Kfz 252 munitions carrier.

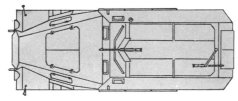

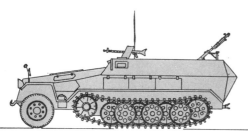

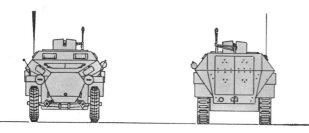

155   Schützenpanzerwagen (Sd Kfz 251/1).

156   Schützenpanzerwagen (Sd Kfz 251/1).
L: 580   B: 210   H: 210   HP: 120   Wt:
8·5   A: 12   Cr: 12   Sp: 55.

Schützenpanzerwagen (Sd Kfz 251/1)

Distinguishing features: Suspension and superstructure similar to the Sd Kfz 250 but larger, longer and more roomy. Later production vehicles had a simplified nose. Normal four-gear drive to sprocket wheel. No front wheel drive. Body open at the top. Chassis developed by Hanomag for the 3-ton tractor.

Assessment: Underpowered and difficult to handle, especially cross-country. Difficult to steer due to slope of steering wheel. Effective and useful vehicle for the armoured support role.

In service: From 1940 with Panzergrenadier units and armoured engineer companies, as well as many other units.

Variants:
Sd Kfz:

251/2	8 cm Gr W-Wagen	8 cm Mortar carrier
251/3	Funkwagen	Radio car
251/4	le IG-ZgKW	Ammunition carrier (for light infantry gun)
251/5	Pioneer SPW	Assault engineer vehicle
251/6	Kommandowagen	Command vehicle
251/7	Pi-Gerätewagen	Engineer equipment carrier
251/8	Krankenpanzerwagen	Armoured ambulance
251/9	7·5 cm StuK 37 L/24	SP 7·5 cm L/24 gun
251/10	3·7 cm PaK	SP 3·7 cm A/T gun
251/11	Fernsprechwagen	Telephone/line layer vehicle
251/12	Messtruppgerätewagen	Survey section instrument carrier
251/13	Schallaufnahmewagen	Sound recording vehicle
251/14	Schallauswertewagen	Sound ranging vehicle
251/15	Lichtauswertewagen	Shot spotting vehicle
251/16	Flammpanzerwagen	Flamethrower vehicle
251/17	2 cm Flak auf SPW	SP AA vehicle, 2 cm gun
251/18	Beobachtungswagen	Observation post vehicle
251/19	Fernsprechbetriebswagen	Telephone exchange vehicle
251/20	Infrarotscheinwerfer "UHU"	Infra-red searchlight vehicle
251/21	1·5 od 2 cm Flak-MG-Drilling 151	SP AA vehicle with triple 1·5 or 2 cm cannon
251/22	7·5 cm PaK 40 auf SPW	SP 7·5 cm A/T gun

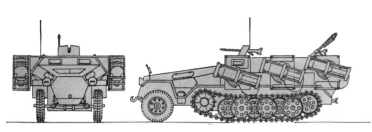

157 Sd Kfz 251/1 with 28 cm rocket launchers.

158 Sd Kfz 251/1 with 28 cm rocket launchers (Wurfrahmen).

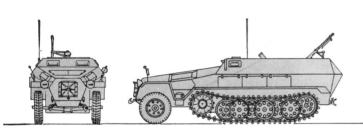

159 Sd Kfz 251/2 with 8 cm Gr W (mortar).

160 An Sd Kfz 251/1 troop carrier in standard form showing equipment and stowage boxes. Later production vehicles had straight back, sloping out towards the top, and a straight sloping front end.

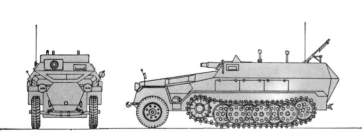

161 Sd Kfz 251/9 with 7·5 cm StuK 37 L/24.

162 Sd Kfz 251/9 with 7·5 cm L/24 gun.

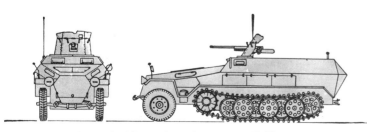

163 Sd Kfz 251/10 with 3·7 cm PaK.

164 Sd Kfz 251/10 with 3·7 cm anti-tank gun. These were mostly used by platoon commanders of Panzergrenadier battalions. Later vehicles of this type sometimes lacked the gunshield.

165 Sd Kfz 251/20 was a vehicle fitted with an infra-red 60 cm searchlight, and known as Uhu (Eagle Owl). These vehicles were intended for use in conjunction with Panthers fitted with infra-red sights.

166 The Sd Kfz 251/21 had triple 1·5 cm AA cannons (aircraft type) and was intended to equip AA platoons of Panzergrenadier battalions.

167 The Sd Kfz 251/22 was an expedient in the same class as the Sd Kfz 234/4 armoured car. It was fitted with a complete 7·5 cm PaK 40 gun on its field carriage with wheels removed.

168 The HKp 606 was a 1941 prototype vehicle with 170 hp engine and larger road wheels. It did not go into production.

169 This Leichter Wehrmachtschlepper (light army tractor) was a 1943 prototype for a design intended to replace the Sd Kfz 250 and 251. It had wider longer tracks intended to give better off-road mobility. It did not enter production.

Early experimental armoured cars

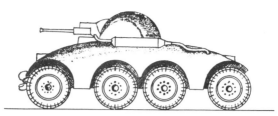

170 Daimler-Benz ARW/MTW 1 prototype, 1927–29.

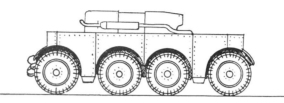

171 The same vehicle with dummy superstructure to "disguise" its military role.

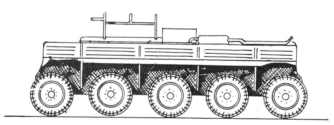

172 Büssing-NAG ZRW prototype, 1927–
29.

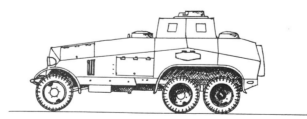

173 Daimler-Benz G3(p) prototype, 1930–
32, on a commercial type chassis which
eventually was developed into the standard
type produced in the thirties.

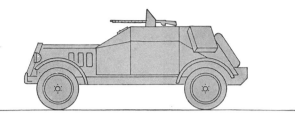

174   Maschinengewehr-Kraftwagen mit MG (Kfz 13).
L: 420   B: 170   H: 150   HP: 60   Wt: 2·25   A: 8   Cr: 2   Sp: 50.

Variant:
Funkraftwagen (Kfz 14).

175   MGKw mit MG (Kfz 13).

Maschinengewehr-Kraftwagen (Kfz 13/14)

Distinguishing features: Light open-topped armoured superstructure on commercial four-wheel chassis. Engine at the front. MG on a pintle with protective shield. The wireless car had a frame-type radio antenna.

Assessment: An interim type with inadequate cross-country performance.

In service: From 1933 with cavalry regiments. During the war with the heavy squadrons of the infantry divisions' reconnaissance battalions.

176 Panzerspähwagen (MG) (Sd Kfz 221).
Ausf A and B.
L: 472 B: 200 H: 180 HP: 75 Wt: 4
A: 8–14·5 Cr: 2 Sp: 72.

Variants:

Pz Spw (Fu) (Sd Kfz 223)
kleiner Pz Funkwagen (Sd Kfz 260 and
261).

Panzerspähwagen (Sd Kfz 221)

Distinguishing features: Four-wheel drive, four-wheel steering. Steeply sloping superstructure. Flat sloping open-topped turret with an MG. Two hundred and twenty-three vehicles had additional frame-type radio antennae.

Assessment: Fast manoeuvrable recce vehicle with an inadequate cross-country performance.

In service: From 1937 with the armoured scout companies of armoured recce battalions.

177 Standard Sd Kfz 221 armoured car.

178 The Sd Kfz 261 was the radio-equipped version of the Sd Kfz 221 light armoured car. It had a folding antenna.

179 The Sd Kfz 223 showing the radio aerial erected. This was later replaced by whip aerials.

180   A standard Sd Kfz 222 light armoured car.

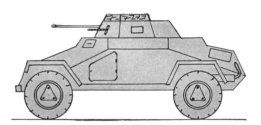

181   Panzerspähwagen (Sd Kfz 222) mit
2 cm KwK 38 L/55 Ausf A and B.
L: 472 B: 200 H: 206 HP: 75 Wt: 4·8
A: 8–14·5 Cr: 3 Sp: 72.

Variant:
Pz Spw (Sd Kfz 222) mit 2·8 cm s Panzerbüchse.

Panzerspähwagen (Sd Kfz 222)

Distinguishing features: Four-wheel drive
and four-wheel steering. The superstructure
was steeply sloped, with a knuckle along the
sides. Flat, sloping, open-topped turret with
protective guard. The armament was
mounted for AA defence. Variants without
the 2 cm gun had wireless equipment.

Assessment: Fast manoeuvrable vehicle
with a poor cross-country performance.
Chassis overloaded by the heavier gun
mount.

In service: From 1938 with armoured car
companies of armoured reconnaissance
battalions.

182   The Sd Kfz 222 with the 2·8 cm
tapered bore anti-tank rifle (Panzerbüchse).

183 The Pz Spw (6 Rad) Sd Kfz 231 heavy armoured car shown on prewar Army manoeuvres.

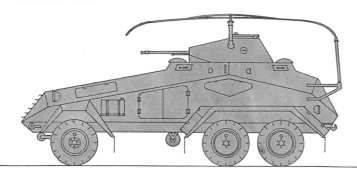

184 Panzerspähwagen (6 Rad) (Sd Kfz 232) (Fu) mit 2 cm KwK.
L: 561 B: 185 H: 224 HP: 65 Wt: 5·0
A: 14·5 Cr: 4 Sp: 60.

Variants:
Panzerspähwagen mit 2 cm KwK (6 Rad) (Sd Kfz 231).
Panzerfunkwagen (6 Rad) (Sd Kfz 263).

Panzerspähwagen (Sd Kfz 232)

Distinguishing features: Based on commercial six-wheel chassis. Front axle not driven. Rear axles double wheeled. Steeply sloping, very long coffin-like superstructure. The wireless car variant had a tall "bedstead" frame antenna. Could be driven forward and reverse, but could only be steered from the front axle.

Assessment: Interim type of heavy armoured car whose shape and design were influential on the later eight-wheel types. Limited cross-country performance.

In service: From 1933 with armoured reconnaissance companies of armoured reconnaissance battalions. Replaced by the eight-wheel vehicle.

185 The Pz Spw (6 Rad) Sd Kfz 232 (Fu) was the radio-equipped variant with rotating turret and co-axial 2 cm gun and MG 34. Note the "unditching" rollers.

186 The Sd Kfz 263 was a similar vehicle but with a fixed turret and extra equipment for staff officers.

187   The Sd Kfz 231. Note stowage bin at front.

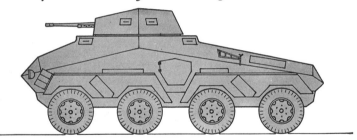

188   Panzerspähwagen (Sd Kfz 231) mit
2 cm KwK 38.
L: 580   B: 221   H: 234   HP: 150   Wt: 4
A: 8–14·5   Cr: 4   Sp: 85.

Variants:
Panzerspähwagen (Fu) (Sd Kfz 232) mit 2
cm KwK 38.
Panzerspähwagen (Sd Kfz 233) mit 7·5 cm
StuK L/24.
Panzerfunkwagen (Sd Kfz 263).

Panzerspähwagen (Sd Kfz 231)

Distinguishing features: Eight-wheel drive and steering. Could be steered and driven fast in forward and reverse. Twin mudguards. Steeply sloping sides. The wireless car variants had fixed turret and superstructures. The vehicles fitted with the assault gun were open topped. Wireless vehicles had frame antennae until 1942, but were later fitted with dipole antennae.

Assessment: A fast vehicle with good cross-country performance. Complicated chassis. Relatively high profile particularly in the vehicles fitted with frame antennae.

In service: From 1938 with the armoured recce companies of armoured reconnaissance battalions and (motorised) recce battalions. The Sd Kfz 233 was used in an armoured role support from 1941. The Sd Kfz 263 type equipped the signal sections of armoured recce battalions and armoured signals battalions.

189 The Sd Kfz 233 had a 7·5 cm L/24 gun in an open-topped superstructure.

190 The Sd Kfz 231, distinguished by its rotating turret, here traversed aft.

191 The Sd Kfz 232 (Funk) had turret and radio antennae.

192 The Sd Kfz 263 had a fixed superstructure and radio aerials for staff and HQ use.

Note that all these eight-wheel vehicles carried similar designations to the six-wheelers, normally distinguished by including "(6 Rad)" in their designations.

193 Panzerspähwagen (Sd Kfz 234/1) mit 2 cm KwK.
L: 602 B: 236 H: 210 HP: 220 Wt: 10·5 A: 30 Cr. 4 Sp: 85.

Variants:
Panzerspähwagen (Sd Kfz 234/2) mit 5 cm KwK L/60 ("Puma").
Panzerspähwagen (Sd Kfz 234/3) mit 7·5 cm StuK L/24.
Panzerspähwagen (Sd Kfz 234/4) mit 7·5 cm PaK L/48.

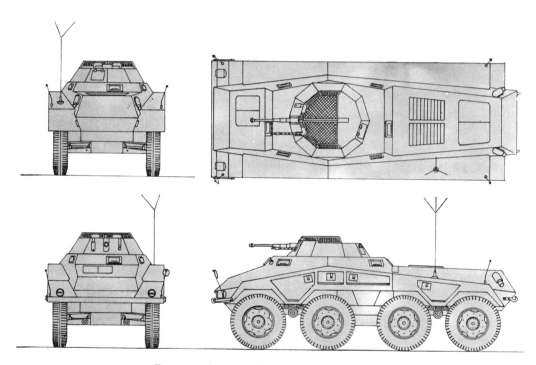

194 Panzerspähwagen (Sd Kfz 234/1) mit 2 cm KwK.

Panzerspähwagen (Sd Kfz 234/1)

Distinguishing features: Eight-wheel steering and eight-wheel drive. Fast forward and reverse with steering from either end. Large balloon-tyred wheels. One-piece mudguards, in contrast to Sd Kfz 231 type. Superstructure similar to the 231 type but less slope on engine cover. Flat open-topped turret like the Sd Kfz 222 type. The armament was capable of AA defence. Air-cooled diesel engine. Radius of action was 600 km. Variants with turret and 5 cm gun (Puma), and short and long 7·5 cm guns.

Assessment: Improved cross-country mobility compared to the Sd Kfz 231. Very good power/ weight ratio. Better radius of action due to fitting of a diesel engine. Well shaped, but armament was weak. Design incorporated the lessons of desert warfare. Rather complicated chassis.

In service: From 1944 with armoured recce battalions. About 2300 vehicles of this type were built.

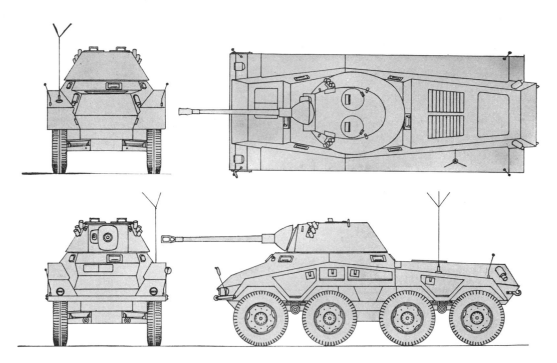

195   Panzerspähwagen (Sd Kfz 234/2) mit 5 cm KwK L/60 (Puma).

196   The Sd Kfz 234/2 with 5 cm L/60 gun in a rotating turret was known as the Puma.

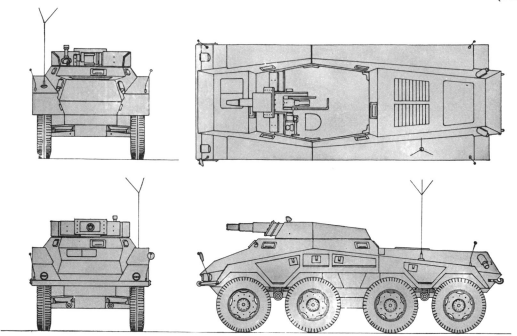

197   Panzerspähwagen (Sd Kfz 234/3) mit 7·5 cm StuK L/24.

198   The Sd Kfz 234/4 with 7·5 cm gun PaK 40, which had the complete field mount with wheels removed.

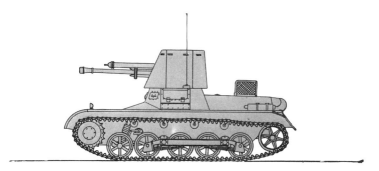

199 Panzerjäger 4·7 cm PaK(t) auf Pz
Kw I (Ausf B) L: 442 B: 185 H: 225
HP: 100 Wt: 6·4 A: 13 Cr: 3 Sp: 40.

200 Standard Panzerjäger 47 cm PaK(t) auf Pz Kw I (Ausf B) was the first German SP weapon
and was a conversion on the existing Pz Kw I tank chassis.

Panzerjäger (4.7 cm PaK (t) auf Pz Kw I (Ausf B))

Distinguishing features: The chassis of the Pz Kw I Ausf B, with the turret removed and replaced
by a tall defensive shield and Czech gun.

Assessment: The first version of an SP carriage on an obsolete tank chassis. Very high and awkward,
but showed the way for future developments of SP carriages.

In service: In limited numbers with anti-tank units of infantry divisions from the spring of 1940.

Captured Vehicles

Germany made greater use of captured equipment than any other nation during World War II. Some items were obtained by occupation, notably the Czech chassis and guns, prior to the outbreak of the war. Following the invasion of France and the Dunkirk evacuation, thousands of French tanks and some British vehicles were also acquired. Similarly the invasion of Russia yielded quantities of Soviet guns and tanks.

Of the French armoured vehicles acquired, only the Lorraine met German requirements and became a standardised type. This is illustrated and described separately. Most other French tanks were held in reserve, but the progressive shortage of first-line equipment caused by disruptive bombing of German industry and the attrition on the Russian Front, led to the adaptation of French chassis into SP equipment of various kinds, examples of which are illustrated. In addition some French tanks were put back into service for German occupation forces and some typical of these are shown here. Most were used only in France, releasing first-line equipment for use elsewhere, though some French types were also used in Russia. Others were used for training and, with turrets removed, as tractors and ammunition carriers.

Few British or American types were used, except locally, since only small numbers of any one type were captured. On the Russian Front, however, some units were wholly equipped with the excellent T-34 and SU-85 types, and smaller numbers of KV types were also used by the Germans.

201 (*top*) British Universal Carrier fitted with German 3·7 cm PaK 35 gun. These vehicles were also used in standard form as munitions carriers.

202 (*above left*) Somua 35 in service with a German unit patrolling an airfield in France. German designation: Pz Kw 35 S (f).

203 Hotchkiss H 39/40 in German service. German designation for this vehicle was Pz Kw 39 H (f).

204 4·7 cm PaK (t) auf Gw Renault R 35 (f).

This was the French Renault R35 tank with turret replaced with new superstructure and 4·7 cm Czech gun as also used on the Panzerjäger 4·7 cm (t) auf Pz Kw I.

205 7·5 cm PaK 40 L/48 auf Gw Lr S (f).

This was the PaK 40 mounted on the French Tracteur Blinde 38L (Lorraine Tractor). This equipment was comparable in performance and characteristics to the Marder II and Marder III (see plates 210–218) and was in fact known as the Marder I. 184 Lorraines were converted to take this gun and were used in France 1943–44.

206 3·7 cm PaK 35/35 auf Inf-Schlepper UE (f).

This was the standard 3·7 cm anti-tank gun on the French UE infantry carrier. This equipment was of very limited tactical value.

207 4·7 cm PaK (f) auf Gw Lr S (Pz Jg Lr S) (f).

This was the French 4·7 cm gun mounted on the basic Lorraine chassis. Only a few were so converted.

208 7·5 cm PaK 40 L/48 auf Gw Hotchkiss (f).

24 French Hotchkiss H 39 tanks (see plate 203) were converted in 1943–44 to mount the standard PaK 40 gun, which was fitted to the platform extending forward over the driver's position.

209 7·5 cm PaK 40 L/48 auf Gw FCM (f).

This was the FCM 36 tank converted to take the PaK 40 similarly to the Hotchkiss H 39 chassis shown in plate 208. Only ten were completed.

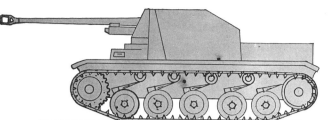

210 7·5 cm PaK 40/2 L/46 "Marder II" auf Gw II Ausf A–C and F (Sd Kfz 131). L: 462 B: 227 H: 220 HP: 140 Wt: 10·8 A: 15 Cr: 4.
Variants:
7·5 cm PaK 40/2 L/46 "Marder II" auf Gw II Ausf D, E (Sd Kfz 132).
7·62 cm PaK 36(r) L/54 auf Gw II Ausf A, C, D, E, F (Sd Kfz 132).

211 and 212 The 7·5 cm PaK 39 auf Gw II, Marder II was built on the Pz Kw II, Ausf A, B, C and F chassis.

Marder II

Distinguishing features: Chassis of the Pz Kw II, Models A, C and F with five medium large bogies on leaf springs. The 7·5 cm anti-tank gun and shield was fitted into the front of a superstructure which was open at the top and at the back.

Assessment: This was the first effective anti-tank SP carriage, utilising the standard Pz Kw II chassis. A quick interim solution to meet the urgent demands of the Eastern Front. 1217 were built.

In service: With anti-tank battalions of infantry divisions from mid-1942.

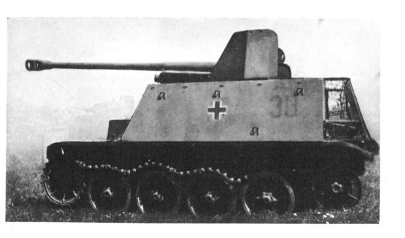

213 Similar vehicle to the Marder II was the Sd Kfz 132, built on the Pz Kw Ausf D and E chassis (qv) which had Christie-type suspension. This was fitted with the captured Russian 7·62 cm anti-tank gun re-chambered to take German PaK 40 ammunition. Full designation was 7·62 cm PaK 36(r) auf Gw II Ausf D (or E), Sd Kfz 132. Vehicle illustrated had damaged track. Appearance was quite different from that of the Marder II on the standard Pz Kw II chassis. Some vehicles of this type had the 7·5 cm PaK 40/2 fitted instead of the PaK 36(r). These vehicles with the Russian gun were built pending availability of the PaK 40.

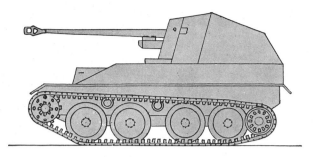

214 Marder III Ausf M with front-mounted engine and near-mounted gun. 7·5 cm PaK 40/3 L/46 "Marder III" auf Gw 38 (Sd Kfz 138) Ausf M.
L: 465 B: 216 H: 248 HP: 125 Wt: 10·5 A: 10–25 Cr: 4 Sp: 42.

Variants:
7·62 cm PaK (r) L/54 auf Gw 38 (Sd Kfz 139) "Marder III".
Bergepanzer 38 (Recovery vehicle).
Munitionspanzer 38 (Ammunition carrier).

215 A Marder III Ausf H with the front-mounted gun and rear-mounted engine.

Marder III

Distinguishing features: Engine mounted in the front of the Pz Kw 38(t) chassis and high superstructure at the rear. Early vehicles retained engine at the rear as in the original tank with the fighting compartment at the front since the specially modified chassis with the engine moved forward was not ready in time.

Assessment: Another interim makeshift anti-tank SP vehicle which gave good service until the introduction of the Jagdpanzer 38 on the same chassis. Limited mobility, and high profile, but effective in service.

In service: With Panzergrenadier and anti-tank units from 1942, used in both North Africa and on the Russian Front.

Note: For Marder I (on Lorraine chassis) see plate 205.

216 and 217 Two views of the Marder III Ausf M which had the engine sited forward and the gun aft. This was the final and major production type, 799 being built from 1943 on. Total production of the earlier Marder III Ausf H was 418, May 1942 to March 1943.

218 Earliest Marder III variant was the Sd Kfz 139, which consisted of the 7·62 cm PaK 36(r) mounted on the Pz Kw 38(t) chassis as an interim measure pending availability of the PaK 40; the first 344 Marder III vehicles built (in Spring 1942) were of this type.

Panzerjäger prototypes

Final group of Panzerjäger illustrated were all based on the Pz Kw 38(d) chassis which was a German-built refinement of the Czech-designed Pz Kw 38(t) chassis which had provided the carriage for so many earlier types of German SP equipment. Ardelt were responsible for the development of most of these, though none got beyond the prototype stage. A selection from the series is illustrated. All appeared in late 1944 or 1945.

219   The 8·8 cm PaK 43 auf Panzerjäger 38(t) served as the pilot vehicle for a proposed type based on an adapted Pz Kw 38(t) chassis.

220   The 8·8 cm PaK 43 auf Rheinmetall-Borsig/Ardelt Selbstfahrlaffette 38(d) had all round traverse. Note the front-mounted engine and the folded travelling lock for the gun.

221 (*below*)   The 8·8 cm PaK 43 auf Krupp/Steyr Sfl 38(d) was a similar type to the Ardelt design except that the chassis incorporated the suspension units of the Raupenschlepper Ost (Eastern Front tractor). Alternative armaments were proposed.

222 8·8 cm PaK 43/1 L/71 auf Gw III/IV "Nashorn" (Sd Kfz 164) (earlier "Hornisse").
L: 580 B: 295 H: 265 HP: 300 Wt: 24 A: 30 Cr: 5 Sp: 40.

Nashorn

Distinguishing features: SP carriage with 8·8 cm gun and fighting compartment sited at the rear on the chassis of the Pz Kw IV.

Assessment: Relatively mobile vehicle with tall distinctive superstructure, but lightly armoured for its size.

In service: With the heavy anti-tank units from 1943. Four hundred and seventy-three built. Replaced by the Jagdpanther.

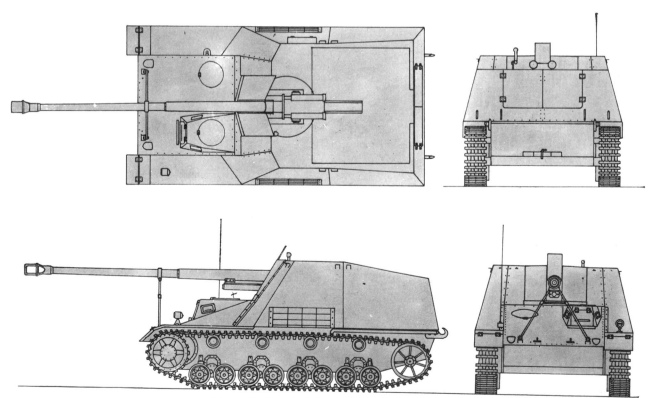

223 8·8 cm PaK 43/1 L/71 auf Gw III/IV "Nashorn".

224   The VK 3001 (H) chassis (see plate 73) shown after conversion to an SP vehicle (Panzerjäger) with 12·8 cm gun.

Panzerjäger (12·8 cm Kanone Sf VK 3001 (H))

Distinguishing features: Fighting compartment sited at rear. Raised driver's and wireless operator's roofs. Long overhanging gun.

Assessment: Experimental vehicles to test the feasibility of SP vehicles of this large calibre. Unwieldy.

In service: Two of these vehicles (converted from the four VK 3001 (H) chassis built) were tested with the heavy anti-tank units during 1943 on the Russian Front.

225   Another view of the VK 3001 (H) after conversion to SP 12·8 cm gun configuration. Only two of these were built.

226   15 cm Schweres Infanteriegeschütz 33 auf Pz Kw I (Ausf B). Data for this chassis is as for Pz Kw I Ausf B (see plate 14).

15 cm Schweres Infanteriegeschütz 33 auf Pz Kw I (Ausf B)

Distinguishing features: Very tall box-shaped superstructure on the chassis of the Pz Kw I Ausf B. Open at the top and rear.

Assessment: Top heavy and heavily overloaded chassis, but a quick way of producing an infantry support weapon.

In service: The first infantry gun to be mounted on an SP carriage. Was in service during the Polish and Flanders campaigns.

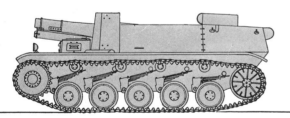

227   15 cm Schweres Infanteriegeschütz 33 auf Sf II.
L: 475   B: 224   H: 160   HP: 140   Wt: 12   A: 10–20   Cr: 5   Sp: 40.

228   The 15 cm Schweres Infanteriegeschütz 33 auf Sf II utilised the standard Pz Kw II chassis.

15 cm Schweres Infanteriegeschütz 33 auf Sf II

Distinguishing features: Very low superstructure on chassis of the Pz Kw II. Driver's and wireless operator's compartment ahead of the fighting compartment. Ammunition stowed above the engine decking. Open-topped fighting compartment with the heavy infantry gun sIG 33. Some vehicles had the standard chassis, and in others the chassis was extended by one extra axle's lngeth.

Assessment: One of the most successful of all the SPs built on obsolete chassis. This vehicle was nearest to the assault tank type.

In service: Used in small numbers by the heavy infantry gun companies of Panzergrenadierregiments from 1942, in both North Africa and Russia.

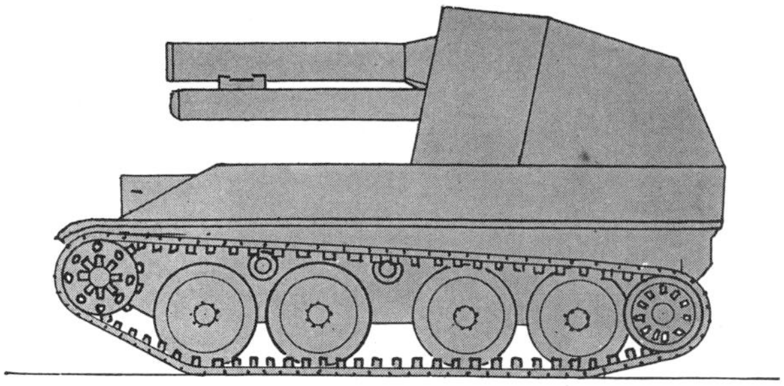

229 15 cm Schweres Infanteriegeschütz 33/1 auf Gw 38 (Ausf M) (Sd Kfz 138/1).
L: 495 B: 215 H: 247 HP: 125 Wt: 12 A: 25+25 Cr: 4 Sp: 40.
Variant:
15 cm sIG 33/1 auf Gw 38 (Ausf H, Sd Kfz 138/1).

230 15 cm sIG 33/1 auf Gw 38(t) Ausf M which had the fighting compartment aft and the engine forward.

231 15 cm sIG 33/1 auf Gw 38(t) Ausf H which had the engine aft and the fighting compartment forward. This vehicle in both the Ausf M and Ausf H variants, was sometimes known as the Bison. As in the Panzerjäger Marder III (plates 214, 216 and 217) the early vehicles, Ausf H, were built on the unaltered Pz Kw 38(t) chassis. From May 1943 the modified chassis with engine moved forward became available specially for SP mounts, the variant on this modified chassis being designated Ausf M.

Schweres Infanteriegeschütz 33/1 auf Gw 38 (t)

Distinguishing features: The chassis of the Pz Kw 38(t) tank. The Ausf M had the engine at the front while the Ausf H had it in the original position at the rear. The fighting compartment was then either fitted at the rear or at the front. High box-like superstructure with vertical walls, sloping towards the front. The gun had a heavy, projecting cradle. Some vehicles were not fitted with main armament and were used in the role of ammunition carriers designated Munitionspanzer Gw 38(t).

Assessment: Heavily loaded chassis but the vehicle had a good cross-country performance due to the excellent inherent qualities of the Pz Kw 38(t).

In service: From 1943 with heavy infantry gun companies of Panzergrenadier regiments, supplementing the version on the Pz Kw II chassis. Three hundred and seventy were built.

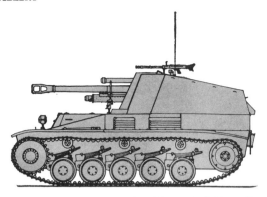

232 10·5 cm Panzerhaubitze 18 "Wespe" auf Gw II (Sd Kfz 124).
L: 479 B: 224 H: 232 HP: 140 Wt: 11·5 A: 10–20 Cr: 5 Sp: 48.

Wespe

Distinguishing features: The chassis of the Pz Kw II series. Five medium large bogies on leaf springs. Sloping front plate incorporating driver's cab roof. The fighting compartment, mounted on the top of the chassis, was open at the top and at the rear. It was fitted with the 10·5 cm light field gun with muzzle brake. Several small detail differences in individual vehicles. Some had a slightly lengthened chassis. Munition carrier version was built, lacking the gun.

Assessment: One of the most important German SP armoured artillery types. An effective adaptation of an obsolete chassis. A very tall silhouette, and somewhat unstable. Also suffered from lack of stowage space on the vehicle, which necessitated the use of timber vehicles to carry extra ammunition.

In service: From 1942 with the light batteries of armoured artillery battalions of armoured artillery regiments in Panzer divisions. Six hundred and eighty-three built. In production until 1944, when the factory in Poland (Famo) was overrun.

233 The 10·5 cm Panzerhaubitze 18/3 Wespe auf Gw II was another important piece of SP equipment built on the Pz Kw II chassis. Picture shows a vehicle with normal chassis, while the drawing shows a vehicle with slightly extended chassis. The Wespe munitions carrier was of similar appearance but without the gun and with the embrasure plated over.

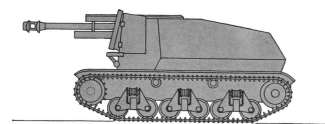

234 10·5 cm Panzerhaubitze 18 auf Sf 39 H (f).

L: 528   B: 187   H: 208   HP: 80   Wt: 9
A: 12   Cr: 5   Sp: 40.

Variants:
10·5 cm Panzerhaubitze 18 auf Gw LrS (f).
10·5 cm Panzerhaubitze 18 auf Sf 35 R (f).
10·5 cm Panzerhaubitze 18 auf Sf B 2 (f).
15 cm Panzerhaubitze 13/1 auf Gw LrS (f) (Sd Kfz 135/1).

235 (*right*) **and 236** (*below right*) These two views show howitzers mounted on two different types of captured French chassis, the Hotchkiss H 39 (also shown in the drawing), with the 10·5 cm leFH 18 and the 10·5 cm leFH 16 fitted to the FCM chassis. Only 24 of the latter were produced.

Panzerhaubitze 18 auf Sf 39 Hotchkiss (f) and FCM

Distinguishing features: Guns mounted on the chassis of former French tanks (Renault, Hotchkiss and Lorraine). Usually very tall fighting compartments, open topped.

Assessment: Extemporised adaptations, usually with overloaded chassis and very low power/weight ratios. They were captured French vehicles converted during 1943–44 chiefly by the Alfred Becker Company in Krefeld to mount various types of gun.

In service: Used in limited numbers mainly by occupation troops in France in 1944 when attrition elsewhere (e.g. Russia) had put heavy strains on the supply of first-line equipment.

237 Most important of the SP types built on captured French chassis was the 15 cm sFH 13 auf Gw Lorraine Schlepper (LrS) (f). The gun was of World War I vintage and could be fitted with little modification to the rear cargo compartment of the Lorraine Schlepper (carrier). Unlike other SP conversions on captured French chassis, which were considered as second line equipment due to their inherent unsuitability for the purpose, the Lorraine with its open rear compartment made an excellent chassis for adaptation to the SP gun role. The 15 cm sFH 13/1 auf LrS was widely used in North Africa, Russia, and France. Another type on the Lorraine chassis was the 7·5 cm PaK 40 (7·5 cm PaK 40/1 auf Gw Lorraine Schlepper (f)) (see plate 205). A few had the 10·5 cm leFH 18 fitted in a similar style to the mounting on the Hotchkiss chassis (plate 235).

238 An early experimental type on the Pz Kw IV chassis was the 10 cm K 18 au Pz Sfl IV A. Krupp built two of these in 1941 on Pz Kw IV Ausf A chassis and they were used operationally on the Russian Front, though the weapon was not considered good enough to merit production of the type. The gun was adapted from the 10 cm sFK 18 field gun.

239 An excellent view of the Heuschrecke showing the folded gantry equipment which was raised and swung aft to lift the turret for emplacement.

Heuschrecke (Sd Kfz 165/1)

Distinguishing features: Pz Kw IV chassis with heavy, sloping turret and prominent mantlet. Lifting arms on the track covers enabled the whole turret to be moved to the rear and lifted off the vehicle. The turret could then be fitted with two wheels, and towed into position, or emplaced as desired.

Assessment: First experimental type of weapon carrier (Waffenträger) with demountable armament. Simple design.

In service: Prototype appeared in 1942. Eight vehicles built. Not taken into general service but served as basis for further developments.

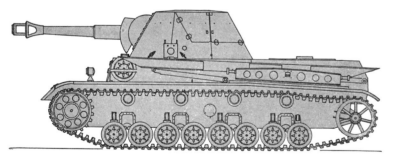

240 10·5 cm leFH 18/40 auf Gw IVb "Heuschrecke" (Sd Kfz 165/1) (Prototype). L: 655 B: 295 H: 233 HP: 300 Wt: 17·3 A: 20 Cr: 5 Sp: 40.

241 The leFH 18/1 (Sf) auf Gw IVb (Sd Kfz 165/1) was a new Panzerartillerie vehicle built in an experimental batch of eight by Krupp at about the same time (1942) as the Heuschrecke. This type was on a shortened Pz Kw IV chassis (six wheels instead of eight). The shortened chassis was to have become a standard type but production was abandoned. These eight vehicles were subsequently used operationally in Russia.

Hummel

Distinguishing features: SP carriages on a chassis utilising parts of both Pz Kw III and IV. Fighting compartment at rear with high sides incorporating engine grilles. Sloping driver's cab front. Early models with muzzle brake. Later models lacked this and had an improved driver's cab front.

Assessment: Very successful and powerful SP armoured weapons, although being a makeshift solution, used in large numbers.

In service: From 1943 with tank battalions of tank divisions. Six hundred and sixty-six built.

242 15 cm Panzerhaubitze 18 (M) auf Gw III/IV "Hummel" (Sd Kfz 165).
L: 580 B: 292 H: 281 HP: 300 Wt: 23·5 A: 30 Cr: 6 Sp: 40.

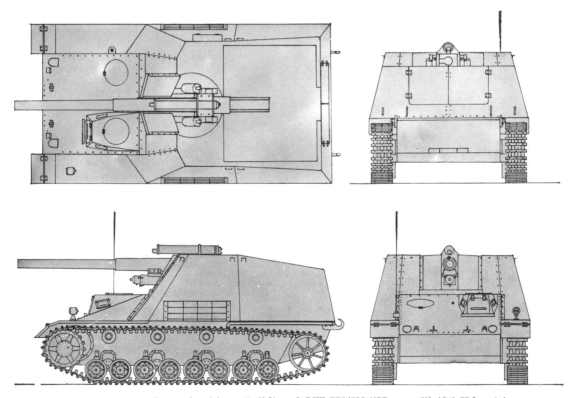

243 15 cm Panzerhaubitze 18 (M) auf GW III/IV "Hummel" (Sd Kfz 165).

244 Wooden model of the Grille 10, designed by Krupp. Though not completed in this form, the Grille 10 chassis was built and formed the basis of the experimental 8·8 cm Flak 41 SP equipment drawn and illustrated in the Flakpanzer section.

Grille Series

The Grille (Cricket) family of SP chassis built by Krupp were a logical advance on the Waffenträger series, with the same basic idea much refined. The chassis were to have standardised parts, and much heavier calibres were to be used. This ambitious programme was beyond the strained resources of the Germany of 1943–45, and none reached production status. Here are the three projected vehicles from the series.

245 Wooden model of the Grille 15 designed by Krupp. This was to be fitted with a 12·8 cm K 43 gun which was demountable in Waffenträger fashion.

246 Wooden model of the Grille 17/21 by Krupp. This was designed to mount either a 17 cm gun or a 21 cm mortar. Prototype vehicle was commenced, though it was not finished by the time hostilities ceased.

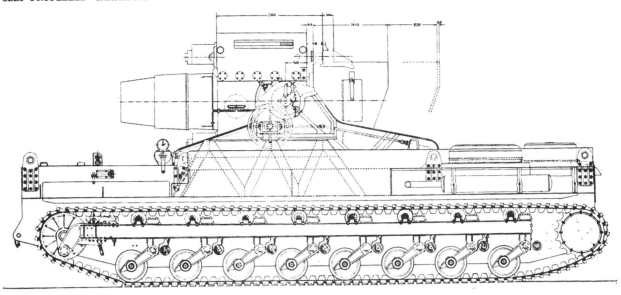

247 60 cm Mörser Karl.

The massive Karl (or Gerät 040) was designed as a heavy bombardment weapon for seige operations. Initially they had been designed to bombard strongpoints in the Maginot Line, but after the fall of France they were mainly used in operations on the Russian Front, notably the seige of Sevastopol and Brest-Litovsk. Karl (Gerät 041) was a later vehicle with 54 cm mortar instead of the 60 cm of the Gerät 040. The hull was of 12 mm armour plate. Six Gerät 041 vehicles were built in 1943–44.

L: 1115   B: 315   H: 478   HP: 580   Wt: 120   Sp: 10.

Variant:
54 cm Mörser (Gerät "041").

248 54 cm Mörser "Karl" (Gerät "041") showing the Munitionspanzer IV (see plate 251) alongside about to transfer a round of ammunition.

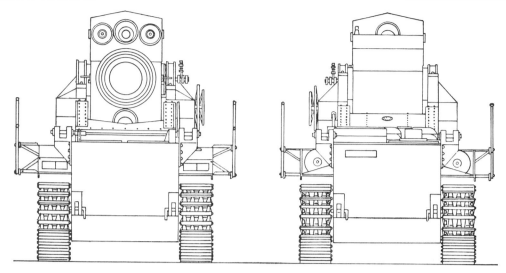

249 60 cm Mörser "Karl".

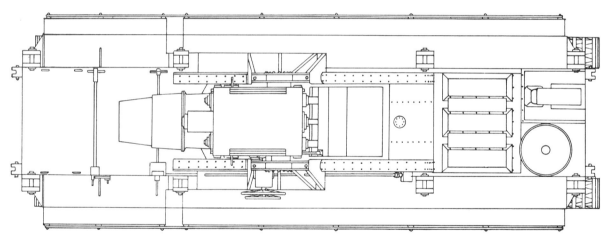

250 Plan view of 60 cm Mörser "Karl".

251 Munitionspanzerwagen IV. This was a Pz Kw IV fitted with a crane to carry ammunition rounds for these giant mortars. The mode of operation is seen in plate 248.

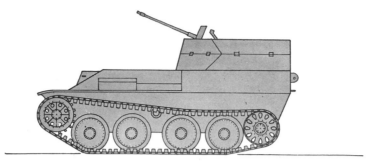

252 2 cm Flakpanzer 38(t) L/55 auf Sf 38(t) (Sd Kfz 140).
L: 461   B: 214   H: 225   HP: 150   Wt: 9·8   A: 10–50   Cr: 5   Sp: 42.

253 Flakpanzer 38(t). The basis of this vehicle was the Pz Kw 38(t) chassis modified for SP conversion with the engine moved forward.

Flakpanzer 38(t)

Distinguishing features: SP carriage with open-topped superstructure at rear mounting an anti-aircraft gun with all-round traverse.

Assessment: Transitional and simple adaptation using the chassis of the Pz Kw 38(t) to provide an AA tank. Replaced by the Flakpanzer IV models. Limited armoured protection for the anti-aircraft gun crew.

In service: Anti-aircraft tank used in small numbers in 1943 with AA platoons of tank battalions. One hundred and sixty-two built.

Further development: An anti-aircraft tank with twin 3 cm cannon 103/38 and coupled 2 cm twin AA guns 151/20 (both types were aircraft guns) produced by Daimler-Benz on the chassis of the 38(d) remained in the development stages during 1944.

254 Flakpanzer IV (2 cm) "Wirbelwind"
auf Fgst Pz IV/3.
L: 592 B: 292 H: 276 HP: 272 Wt:
22 Cr: 5 Sp: 42.

Variants:
3·7 cm Flak 43 L/60 "Ostwind" auf Sf IV.
3·7 cm Flak 43 L/60 auf Fgst Pz IV "Möbelwagen".
2 cm Vierlingsflak 38 L/55 auf Sf IV.

Flakpanzer IV

Distinguishing features: Möbelwagen was
an SP AA carriage with four hinged armoured sides and an AA mount replacing the
turret. Wirbelwind and Ostwind had open-
topped, multi-faced sloping turrets. All were
on the basic Pz Kw IV chassis.

Assessment: SP carriages with insufficient
armour protection for the crew when in
action, Wirbelwind and Ostwind were effective transitional designs, whose weapons
could also be used against ground targets.

In service: With anti-aircraft platoons in
tank regiments from 1944. One hundred and
fifty Wirbelwind were with anti-aircraft
platoons of tank battalions from 1944. Forty
Ostwind with anti-aircraft platoons of tank
regiments from 1945.

Further developments: A prototype Zer-
storer 45 built by Ostbau with 3 cm quadruple MK 103/38 and an SP with 3·7 cm
twin Flak 43 anti-aircraft guns, from
Alkett were projected during 1944 but not
developed. A 3·7 cm twin Flak 44 Ostwind II
from Ostbau, as well as an 8·8 cm AA gun
on the chassis of a Pz Kw V and the Coelian
AA tank with a 3·7 cm AA, twin 341 flak
gun, on a Pz Kw V tank chassis remained in
the development stage. The Kugelblitz was
on troop trials during 1945 and is described
separately.

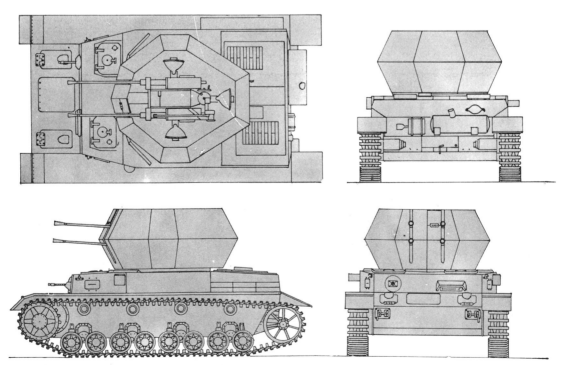

255 Flakpanzer IV (2 cm) (Wirbelwind).

256   3·7 cm Flak 43 L/60 auf Sf IV "Ostwind".

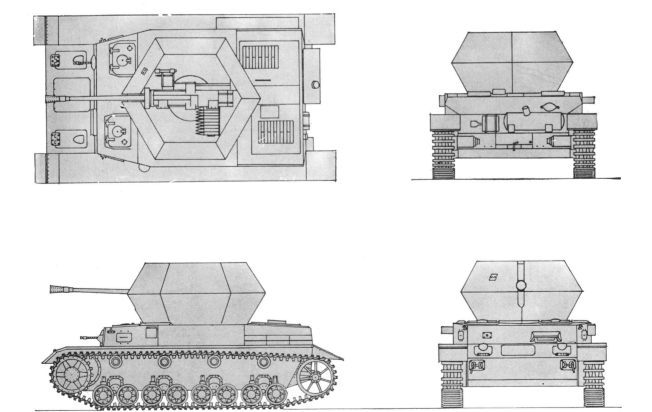

257   Flakpanzer IV (3·7 cm) auf Fgst Pz Kw IV Ostwind.

258   2 cm Vierlingsflak 38 L/55 auf Sf IV.

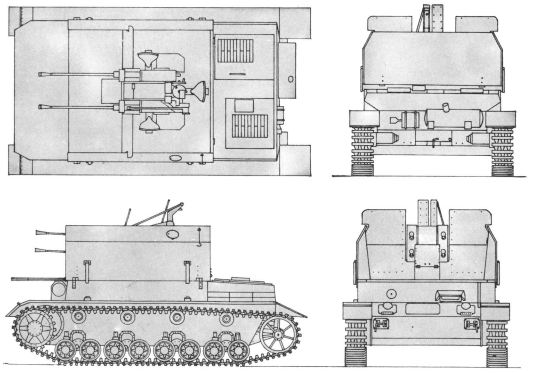

259   Flakpanzer IV (2 cm) auf Fgst Pz Kw IV.

260   3·7 cm Flak 43 L/60 auf Sf IV (Möbelwagen).

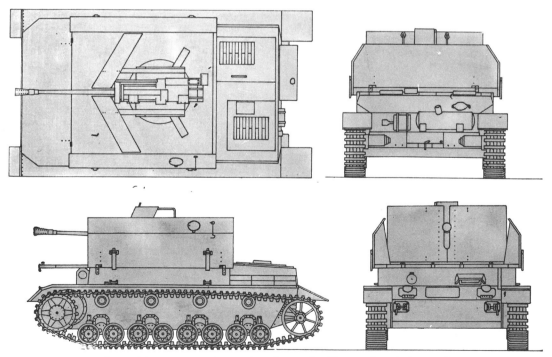

261   Flakpanzer IV (3·7 cm) auf Fgst Pz Kw IV "Mobelwagen".

262 The 3·7 cm Flak 43 auf SWS was a simple modification of the Schwerer Wehrmachtsschlepper (SWS) half-track (qv) in which the gun was mounted in the cargo space. There was no protection for the crew.

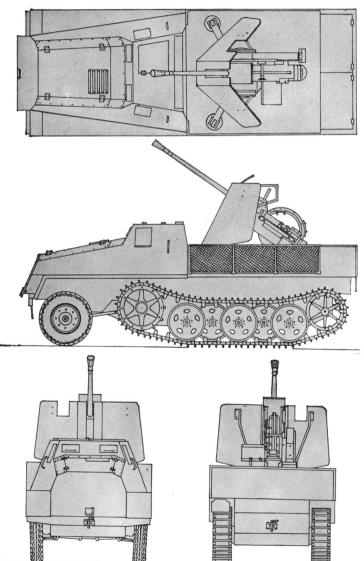

263 3·7 cm Flak 43 auf SWS (not to scale).

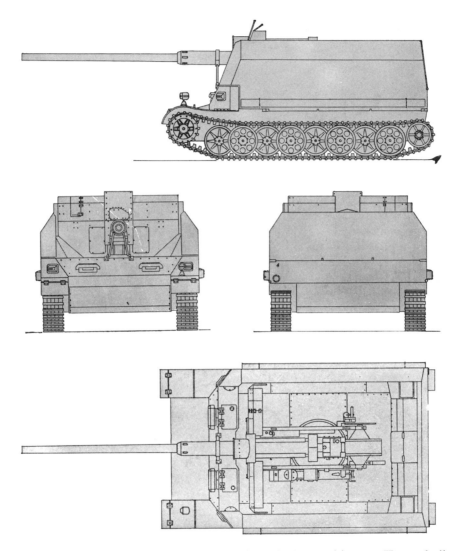

264 The 8·8 cm Flak 41 auf Sonderfahrgestell (purpose-built chassis) was a Krupp-built prototype utilising the Grille 10 chassis (qv) for a heavy self-propelled AA gun. The vehicle was produced in 1944. It did not enter production.

265 The 8·8 cm Flak 37 auf Sonderfahrgestell was an earlier type prototype (1943)
on the same Krupp chassis. Front view with
side screens lowered to show stowage of
crew's personal equipment. Distinguished
from Flak 41 vehicle by higher narrower
Flak 37 mount.

266 and 267 Two further views of the
Krupp 8·8 cm Flak 41 auf Sonderfahrgestell,
shown in the scale drawing in plate 264.

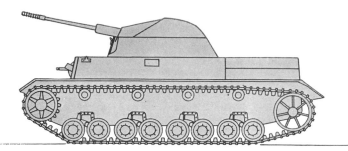

268   Flakpanzer IV "Kugelblitz" mit 3 cm Zwillingsflak 103/38 (Daimler-Benz prototype).

Flakpanzer "Kugelblitz"

Distinguishing features: Hemi-spherical turret with twin aircraft-type cannon. Rate of fire 450 rounds per minute. Chassis and basic superstructure of the Pz Kw IV.

Assessment: The only German anti-aircraft tank with an enclosed turret and overhead protection. Very serviceable weapon. An expensive special design as the final answer to the AA tank problem.

In service: Only six vehicles produced towards the end of the war.

269   The Flakpanzer IV Kugelblitz, shown as a drawing in plate 268.

270   Wooden model of a projected Flakpanzer V which would have mounted a 8·8 cm Flak gun on a Panther chassis.

"Maultier" Panzerwerfer

Distinguishing features: Armoured version of the Maultier chassis (a standard truck) with Carden-Lloyd suspension. Flat sloping rear with a Nebelwerfer gun which could be traversed and elevated remotely. The Nebelwerfer had 2×5 rocket tubes.

Assessment: A mobile SP carriage with good cross-country performance. The armour was similar to that of the Sd Kfz 251 half-track.

In service: From 1944 with Panzerwerfer battalions. Used to bring down heavy concentrations of fire.

271 15 cm NbW 42 auf 2 t "Maultier" (Opel) (Sd Kfz 4/1).

272 The 15 cm NbW 42 auf 2 ton "Maultier" was an improved rocket-firing vehicle which had to be loaded from outside the vehicle as shown here.

273 An extemporised rocket-launcher installation mounted on the modified chassis of a captured French Somua half-track. This was not a standardised type. A few Somua half-track chassis were fitted with 7·5 cm PaK 40 guns at the rear, firing forward over the cab.

274 The 15 cm Panzerwerfer 42 auf SWS was an improved self-propelled rocket launcher on the Schwerer Wehrmachtsschlepper. Characteristics were similar to the Maultier-based version, but mobility was improved and there was stowage for more re-load rockets in the armoured body.

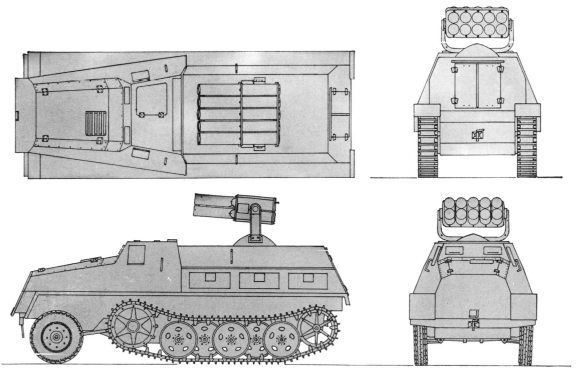

275 15 cm Panzerwerfer 42 auf SWS.

276 An experimental mounting of a 10·5 cm recoilless gun on the chassis of the Borgward VK 302 munitions carrier. This conversion was carried out in 1941–42 by Rheinmetall-Borsig and was designated 10·5 cm LG 2540 Rh Sfl. The chassis was also used for the Funklenkpanzer B IV radio-controlled demolition tank (see plate 285).

277 The 7·5 cm PaK 40/1 auf Sf RSO was built in 1943–44 on the chassis of the Raupenschlepper Ost (i.e. RSO) or "Eastern Front tractor", which was basically a tracked carrier for service on the Russian Front. Eighty-three of these light SP vehicles were built, and the type was designed to give better mobility to infantry anti-tank platoons.

278 Beobachtungspanzer RK 7 (Sd Kfz 254).
This was an Austrian wheel-track design by Saurer, put into limited service as an OP vehicle with a few armoured artillery units. It was a complicated vehicle, difficult to steer and handle.

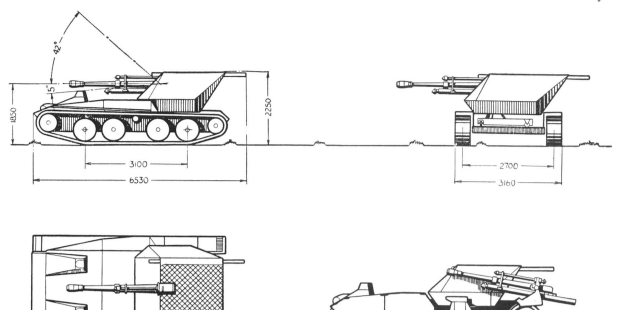

279 Waffenträger Grösse I (large weapons carrier). Designed towards the end of 1944, this incorporated the 10·5 cm leFJ 18/40 L/28 light field howitzer. The gun could be removed from the chassis and placed on its normal field mount. It was intended to greatly increase the mobility of the artillery of infantry divisions. Combat weight was 14 tons.

280 Waffenträger Grösse II. Developed in 1944 to take the 12·8 cm L/55 gun. Note the extremely low profile. Combat weight (including 30 rounds of stowed ammunition) was 17·8 tons. Gun was of limited traverse only. Chassis is a lengthened version of the Sfl 38(d).

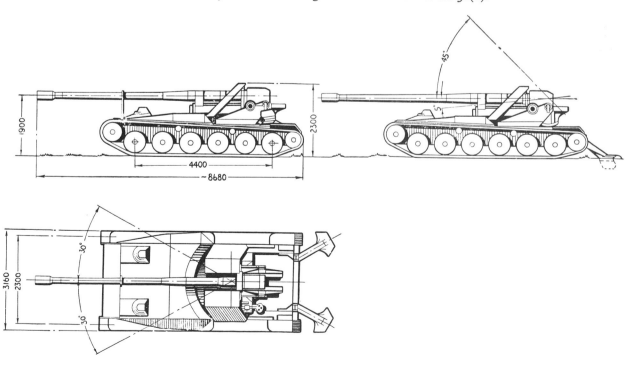

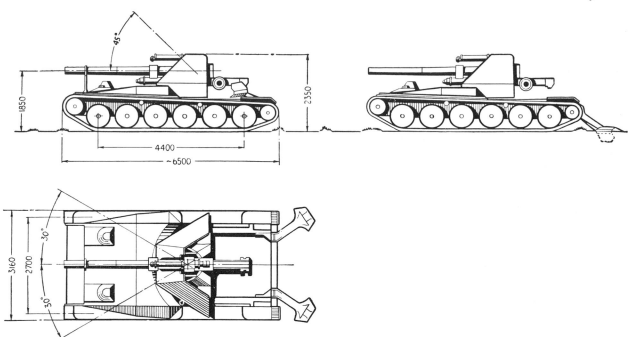

281 Waffenträger Grösse II. Seen here fitted with an alternative weapon, the 15 cm sFH 18 L/29·5 field howitzer. A further alternative gun for this chassis was the 8·8 cm PaK 43 L/71 anti-tank gun. Chassis is a lengthened version of the Sfl 38(d).

Waffenträger Grösse

The Waffenträger Grösse I and II were further developments from the Panzerartillerie prototypes produced on the modified Pz Kw 38(d) chassis (see plates 219, 220 and 221), but these types existed only as projects and by the end of the war had still not been fully developed.

282 and 283   The Minenräumpanzer Räumer was a prototype mine-clearing vehicle. It was a giant articulated armoured vehicle with heavy solid wheels, intended to detonate mines by its great weight. The front section was 2·6 metres wide, the rear section 3·27 metres wide, the height was 3·93 metres and overall length 15·63 metres. The wheels were 2·7 metres in diameter and the rims were 53 cm wide. This vehicle was not put into production. US soldier standing alongside the cab after the vehicle had been captured gives a good idea of its size. Weight was approximately 130 tons.

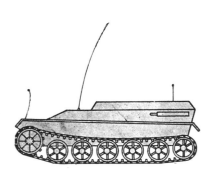

284   Funklenkpanzer B IV (Sd Kfz 301) Ausf A, B and C.
L: 335   B: 180   H: 125   Wt: 3·6   A: 150.

285   A Funklenkpanzer B IV shown dropping its explosive charge, which was carried at the front end.

Funklenkpanzer B IV

Distinguishing features: Small low vehicle with radio control fittings. Either gas decontamination equipment or a 450 kg explosive charge was fitted on the front which could be released by radio control. The radio control was effective for distances up to 2 km.

Assessment: Fast and mobile. Limited in service to special tasks (the destruction of strong field fortifications, demolition of obstacles or mine detection).

In service: From 1944 with a few heavy (Tiger) tank battalions. A further development was the radio-controlled NSU Springer.

286 and 287 The Schwerer Wermachtsschlepper (heavy army tractor) was a vehicle with armoured cab designed as a general replacement for earlier half-track designs (i.e. the Sd Kfz 250 and 251 series). Simplicity of production and maintenance were aimed for in the design. Panzerwerfer and 3·7 cm Flak variants were also produced (see plates 262, 263, 264 and 275).

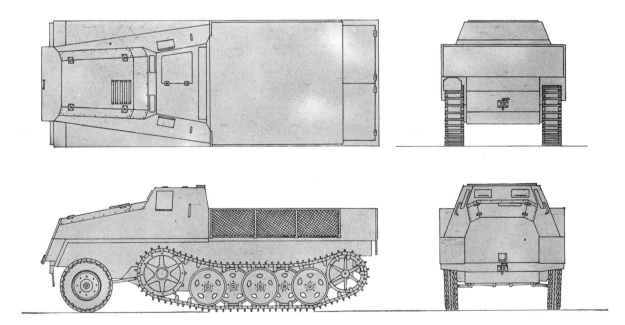

Appendix 1

Metric Weights and Measures and their British and American equivalents

1 millimetre (mm)	=	0·039 in
1 centimetre (cm)	=	0·394 in
1 metre (m)	=	1·094 yd
1 kilogram (kg)	=	2·205 lb
1 metric ton (tonne)	=	0·984 British ton*
	=	1·1 US ton†
1 litre	=	0·22 Imperial gal
	=	0·26 US gal

*British ton = 2240 pounds
†US ton = 2000 pounds

Appendix 2

Numerical Tank Strength 1940–42
(based on official German Army figures)

Model	May 1940	June	July	Aug	Sept	Oct	Nov	Dec	Jan 1941	Feb	Mar	Apr	May	June	July	Aug	Sept	Oct	Nov	Dec	Jan 1942
Pz Kw I (MG)	1077	943	919	942	·	1026	1047*	1079	1028	1044	786	829	·	843	917	959	1005				
Pz Kw I (sIG)	38	38	38	38	·	38	38	38	38	38	38	38	38	38	38	38	38	38	38	38	38
Pz Kw I (4·7 cm)	100	100	100	100	·	100	100	100	100	100	100	100	100	100	100	100	100	100	100	100	38
Pz Kw I (Mun Schl)	51	51	51	51	·	51	51	51	51	51	51	51	51	51	51	51	51	51	51	51	51
Pz Kw R 35 (4·7 cm)	—	—	—	51	·	51	51	51	51	51	51	51	51	51	51	51	51	51	51	51	51
Pz Kw II (2 cm)	1092	963	887	908	·	935	947	955	984	994	1019	1019	·	1067	1023	1018	1043	·	·	1114	1161
Pz Kw II (F)	·	17	23	31	·	45	61	85	87	87	85	85	·	85	85	85	86	87	87	87	89
Pz Kw II (Brücklg)	—	1	1	1	·	1	6	—	—	—	—	—	—	—	—	—	—	—	—	—	—
Pz Kw II (sIG)	—	—	—	—	—	—	—	—	—	—	—	—	—	—	—	—	—	—	—	—	—
Pz Kw III (3·7 cm)	38	325	381	459	·	·	475	483	484	489	493	418	379	350	327	268	243	227	216	203	174
Pz Kw III (5 cm)	·	·	33	17	·	167	263	347	434	526	617	782	944	1090	1174	1307	1490	1683	1870	2080	2299
StuG III (7·5 cm)	·	23	55	90	136	234	197	250	282	227	256	292	318	377	416	454	483	520	601	643	689
Pz Kw IV (7·5 cm)	290	236	241	274	·	300	353	386	418	453	476	514	554	586	625	669	705	719	769	829	
Pz Kw 35(t)	143	105	110	123	·	124	126	131	153	169	171	175	181	182	184	189	189	190	191	192	197
Pz Kw 38(t)	·	238	233	253	277	·	320	401	432	476	520	570	636	686	763	843	908	974	1040	1095	1144
Pz Bw (gr and kl)	244	206	180	180	·	202	244	232	260	286	308	330	331	349	365	375	376	385	385	402	402
Pz BeobW auf RK 7												128	128	128	128	128	128	128	128	128	128
Pz SpW	800	753	754	757	769	·	817	840	861	893	929	951	1008	928	947	1061	1121	1149	1181	1247	1295
Pz SpW	333	305	313	319	·	328	331	343	349	365	·	377	380	390	390	398	420	432	444	458	479
gep MunSchl (VK 302)																				18	22

* 57 vehicles delivered for conversion to 4·7 PaK (t) (Sfl).

Appendix 3

The sign = appears frequently in these tables and serves as a horizontal ditto mark. It thus refers to figures or characters immediately *on its left.*
The sign . means "not known"; the sign — means "not applicable".

(a) Panzerkampfwagen

Designation / Ausführung	Pz Kw I Sd Kfz 101 — A	Pz Kw I Sd Kfz 101 — B	Kl Pz Bw Sd Kfz 265	Pz Kw II Sd Kfz 121 — D–E	Pz Kw II Sd Kfz 121 — F–J	"Luchs" Sd Kfz 123 — L	Pz Kw III Sd Kfz 141 — A	Pz Kw III Sd Kfz 141 — B, C	Pz Kw III Sd Kfz 141 — D	Pz Kw III Sd Kfz 141 — E
Combat weight in tons	5·4	6·0	5·88	10·0	9·5	11·8	15·0	=	19·3	19·5
Turret weight in tons	·	·	—	·	·	·	·	·	·	·
Maximum speed in kph — by road	37	40	=	55	40	60	32	=	40	40
across country	·	·	=	19	=	·	·	·	·	18
Active range in km — by road	145	140	170	200	200	250	150	=	165	175
across country	97	115	115	130	100	150	95	=	95	97
Fuel consumption in litres per 100 km of road	100	103	85	100	85	95	200	=	182	183
Fuel supply in litres	145	=	=	200	170	236	300	=	=	320
Length overall in cm	402	442	=	464	481	463	569	=	541	=
Length without barrel in cm	402	442	=	464	481	463	569	=	541	·
Barrel overhang in cm	0	·	=	·	·	·	281	=	291	=
Width overall in cm	206	=	=	230	228	249	·	=	·	·
Turret ring in cm	·	·	=	·	·	·	234	254	·	=
Height in cm	172	·	199	202	·	213	·	·	244	·
Axis height of gun in cm	·	·	·	159	159	·	234	·	189	·
Engine No/cylinders/type	1/4/B/O	1/6/R/O	=	1/6/R/O	=	=	1/12/V/O	=	=	=
Type	Krupp M 305	Maybach NL 38 TR	=	HL 62 TRM	=	HL 66 P	HL 108 TR	=	HL 120 TR	HL 120 TRM*
HP/HP:Kg	57/·	100/4·30	=	140/4·35	=	180/2·67	230/4·01	=	320/2·88	300/3·07
Cooling/cylinder capacity (litres)	A/3·46	W/3·79	=	W/6·19	=	W/6·75	W/10·84	=	W/11·87	=
Rpm	2500	3000	=	2600	=	3200	2600	=	3000	=
Type of transmission	Sliding pinion ZF FG 35	ZF FG 31	=	Synchron SSG 46	=	=	ZF SFG 75	·	Variorex ZF SSG 76	=
Gears	5 F 1 R	=	=	6 F 1 R	=	=	5 F 1 R	=	10 F 1 R	=
Type of steering	Clutch	=	=	=	=	=	=	=	Single radius	Clutch
Turning at the halt	·	=	·	No	=	=	=	=	=	=
Smallest radius (metres)	2·1	2·1	2·1	·	4·8	·	·	5·8	=	=
Drive from	Front	=	=	=	=	=	=	=	=	=
Length of track in contact with the ground in cm	247	=	=	220	240	220	286	=	=	=
Track width in cm	28	=	=	30	=	36	=	=	=	=
Wheel base in cm	167	=	=	192	=	207	249	=	=	=
Steering ratio 1:s	1·48	1·45	·	1·17	1·27	1·06	1·15	=	·	=
Track type	84 links	=	=	·	·	Lubricated	Dry	=	=	=
Track spacing	100	100	·	106	=	96	99	=	·	=
Bogie breadth in cm	·	·	·	·	·	·	·	Bogie/½	·	·
Type of suspension/springs per roller	Bogie/1·1/4	=	=	Torsion rods	Leaf springs	Torsion/1	Indep/1	=	Torsion/1	Torsion/1
Weight/power ratio (ton/HP)	19·5	16·7	17·0	14·0	14·7	15·2	15·3	=	16·6	15·4
Ground pressure kg/sq cm	0·40	0·42	0·43	0·8	0·66	0·75	0·73	=	0·93	0·95
Ground clearance in cm	29	=	=	34	34	=	38	=	=	=
Gap crossing ability in cm	140	=	=	175	170	=	260	230	=	=
Vertical climb in cm	36	=	=	30	30	30	60	=	=	35

Designation / Ausführung	Pz Kw I Sd Kfz 101 A	Pz Kw I Sd Kfz 101 B	Kl Pz Bw Sd Kfz 265	Pz Kw II Sd Kfz 121 D-E	Pz Kw II Sd Kfz 121 F-J	"Luchs" Sd Kfz 123 L	Pz Kw III Sd Kfz 141 A	Pz Kw III Sd Kfz 141 B, C	Pz Kw III Sd Kfz 141 D	Pz Kw III Sd Kfz 141 E
Gun calibre in cm/type	—	—	—	2/KwK 30 od.38	=	2/KwK 30	3·7/KwK	=	=	5/KwK
Length in calibres	—	—	—	55	=	=	45	=	=	42
Muzzle velocity Armour-piercing shell m/sec	—	—	—	800–990	=	=	762–1030	=	=	685
Muzzle velocity HE shell m/sec	—	—	—	800	=	=	·	·	·	·
Turret MGs number/calibre in mm	2/7·92	=	1/7·92	=	=	=	2/7·92	=	=	1/7·92
Anti-aircraft MGs number/cal in mm	—	—	—	—	—	—	—	—	—	=
Bow MGs number/calibre in mm	—	—	—	—	—	—	1/7·92	=	=	=
Sub-machine guns number/calibre in mm	·	·	·	·	·	·	·	·	·	·
Weapons for local defence	·	·	·	·	·	·	·	·	·	·
Sighting equipment	TZF 2	=	=	TZF 4	TZF 4/36 o. 38	TZF 6 o. 6/38	TZF 5a	=	=	=
Number of rounds carried for main armament	—	—	—	180		330	150	=	=	99
MG ammunition	1525	—	900	1425	2550	2250	4500	=	=	2000
SMG ammunition	·	·	·	·	·	·	·	·	·	·
Crew	2	=	3	3	3	4	5	=	=	=
Turret traverse	Hand	=	—	Hand	=	=	Hand	=	=	=
Hull armour type	F	=				=	F+H	=	=	=
Bow armour in mm/°	13/63	=	14·5+17/65	30/58*	35/77	30/65	14·5/69	=	30/69	=
Driver plate armour mm/°	13/68	=	14·5+17/67	30/87*	30/80	20/90	14·5/81	=	30/81	=
Side armour bottom mm/°	13/90	=		15/90	20/90	=	14·5/90	=	30/90	=
Side armour top mm/°	13/73–82	=	14·5/67–72	14·5/90	20/90	30/85	14·5/90	=	30/90	=
Stern armour mm/°	13/50–75	=	14·5/35–70	14·5/83	=	20/60	14·5/77–80	=	30/77–80	=
Roof armour mm/°	6/0–58	=	7/15	14·5/0	=	13/0	18/0	=	30/0	=
Floor armour mm/°	6/0	=	=	5/0	=	10/0	14·5/0	=	=	=
Turret armour type						·	F+H	·		=
Mantlet maximum mm/°										
Front mm/°	13/80	=	14·5+17/67	30/gew	30/gew	30/80	14·5/75	=	30/75	=
Side mm/°	13/68	=	14·5/67–72	14·5/67	15/68	15/70	14·5/65	=	30/65	=
Stern mm/°	13/68	=	14·5/70	14·5/68	=	20/70	14·5/78	=	30/78	=
Roof mm/°	8/0–18	=	8/0	10/0–16	10/0–13	13/0–10	10/0–7	=	=	=
Remarks				*20 more later						* Some with HL 120 TR

(a) Panzerkampfwagen—*continuation*

Designation / Ausführung	Pz Kw III — Sd Kfz 141 F, G	Sd Kfz 141 H	Sd Kfz 141 J, L	Sd Kfz 141/1 M, N (Sd Kfz 141/2)	Pz Kw IV A	B	Sd Kfz 161 C	D	Sd Kfz 161 E	Sd Kfz 161 F I	Sd Kfz 161 F 2
Combat weight in tons	20·3	21·6	22·3	·	17·3	17·7	20·0	·	21	22·3	23·6
Turret weight in tons	·	·	·	·	·	·	·	·	·	·	·
Maximum speed in kph — by road	40	=	=	=	30	40	=	=	42	=	40
— across country	18	=	19	=	17	20	=	=	=	=	16
Active range in km — by road	175	=	=	=	150	200	=	=	=	=	=
— across country	97	=	=	=	100	130	=	130	=	=	=
Fuel consumption in litres per 100 km of road	183	=	=	=	313	235	=	=	=	=	=
Fuel supply in litres	320	=	=	=	470	=	=	=	=	=	=
Length overall in cm	541	552	641	=*	560	587	=	591	=	593	663
Length without barrel in cm	541	552	=	=**	560	587	=	591	=	593	593
Barrel overhang in cm	0	=	89	=	0	=	=	286	0	=	70
Width overall in cm	292	295	=	=	285	=	=	=	=	288	=
Turret ring in cm			251	·	165	=	=	=	=	=	=
Height in cm	244	250	=	=	259	=	=	268	=	=	=
Axis height of gun in cm	·	·	190	=	·	195	=	=	=	196	·
Engine No/cylinders/type	1/12/V/O Maybach	=	=	=	=	=	=	=	=	=	=
Type	HL 120 TRM	=	=	=	HL 108 TR	HL 120 TR	HL 120 TRM	=	=	=	=
HP/HP:Kg	300/3·07	=	=	=	250/4·01	320/2·88	300/3·07	=	=	=	=
Cooling/cyl capacity (litres)	W/11·87	=	=	=	W/10·84	W/11·87	=	=	=	=	=
Rpm	3000	=	=	=	=	=	=	=	=	=	=
Type of transmission	Variorex SGR 328.145	ZF SSG 77	Synchron	=	ZF SFG 75	ZF SSG 76	=	=	=	=	=
Gears	10 F 1 R	6 F 1 R	=	=	5 F 1 R	6 F 1 R	=	=	=	=	=
Type of steering	Clutch	=	=	=		=	=	=	=	=	=
Turning at the halt	No	=	=	=	No	=	=	=	=	=	=
Smallest radius (metres)	5·8	=	=	=	5·92	=	=	=	=	=	=
Drive from	Front	=	=	=		=	=	=	=	=	=
Length of track in contact with the ground in cm	286	=	286	=	352	=	=	=	=	=	=
Track width in cm	36	40	=	=	38	=	=	=	40	=	=
Wheel base in cm	249	251	=	=	239	=	=	=	245	=	=
Steering ratio 1:s	1·14	1·14	=	=	1·47	=	=	=	1·44	=	=
Track type	Dry	=	=	=		=	=	=	=	=	=
Track spacing	99 Links	=	=	=	101 Links	=	=	=	=	99	=
Bogie breadth in cm	·	·	·	=		·	=	=	=	=	·
Type of suspension/springs per roller	Torsion/1	=	=	=	Bogie/1/2	=	=	=	=	=	=
Weight/power ratio (ton/HP)	14·8	13·9	13·5	=	14·4	18·1	15·0	=	14·3	13·4	12·7
Ground pressure kg/sq cm	0·99	0·95	0·94	=	0·65	0·66	0·75	=	0·79	0·79	0·84
Ground clearance in cm	38	=	41	=	40	=	=	=	=	=	=
Gap crossing ability in cm	230	259	=	=	230	=	=	=	220	=	=
Vertical climb in cm	60	=	=	=	60	=	=	=	=	=	=
Gradients	30°	=	=	=	35°	30°	=	=	=	=	=
Wading depth in cm	80	=	=	130***	80	=	=	100	=	=	=

Designation / Ausführung	Pz Kw III				Pz Kw IV						
	Sd Kfz 141 F, G	Sd Kfz 141 H	Sd Kfz 141/1 J, L	Sd Kfz 141/2 M, N	Sd Kfz 161 A	Sd Kfz 161 B	Sd Kfz 161 C	Sd Kfz 161 D	Sd Kfz 161 E	Sd Kfz 161 F1	Sd Kfz 161 F2
Gun calibre in cm/type	5/KwK	=	5/KwK 39*	7·5/KwK	=	=	=	=	=	=	7·5/KwK 40
Length in calibres	42	=	60	24†	24	=	=	=	=	=	43
Muzzle velocity Armour-piercing shell m/sec	685	=	823–1198	385	=	=	=	=	=	=	740–990
Muzzle velocity HE shell m/sec	·	·	549	420	=	=	=	=	=	=	=
Turret MGs number/calibre in mm	1/7·92	=	=	=	=	=	=	1/7·92	=	=	=
Anti-aircraft MGs number/cal in mm	—	—	—	—	—	—	—	—	—	—*	—*
Bow MGs number/calibre in mm	1/7·92	=	=	=	=	=	=	1/7·92	=	=	=
Sub-machine guns number/calibre in mm	·	·	1/9	·	·	·	·	·	·	·	·
Weapons for local defence	·	·	·	·	·	·	·	·	·	·	·
Sighting equipment	TZF 5 d	=	TZF 5 d, e	TZF 5 b	TZF 5 b o. / TZF 5 b/36	=	=	=	TZF 5 b od / TZF 5 b/36	=	TZF 5 f
Number of rounds carried for main armament	99	=	78	64	80	=	=	=	=	=	87
MG ammunition	2000	=	2000**	3450	2700	=	=	2700	=	3150	=
SMG ammunition	·	·	=	=	=	·	=	·	=	=	=
Crew	5	=	=	=	=	=	=	=	=	=	=
Turret traverse	Hand	=	=	=	Hand-El	=	=	=	=	=	=
Hull armour type	F	=	=	=	=	=	=	=	=	=	=
Bow armour in mm/°	30/69	30+30/69	50/69	50+20/81	14·5/78	30/78	=	=	50/78	=	=
Driver plate armour mm/°	30/81	30+30/81	50/81***	=	14·5/80	30/80	=	=	30+30/80	50/80*	=
Side armour bottom mm/°	30/90	=	=	=	14·5/90	=	=	20/90	20+20/90	=	=
Side armour top mm/°	30/90	=	=	=	14·5/90	=	=	20/90	20+20/90	=	=
Stern armour mm/°	30/77–80	30+30/77–80	53/77–80***	50/77–80	15/78–90	=	14·5/78–90	20/78–90	=	=	=
Roof armour mm/°	18/0	=	=	=	11/0	=	=	10/0	=	=	=
Floor armour mm/°	30/0	=	=	=	8/0	=	=	=	=	=	=
Turret armour type	F+H	=	=	=	=	=	=	=	=	=	=
Mantlet maximum mm/°	30/75	·	***	57/·	20/79	=	30/79	=	=	50/79	=
Front mm/°	30/65	=	30/75***	57+20/75	20/64	=	=	=	=	50/64	=
Side mm/°	30/78	=	=	=	20/74	=	=	=	=	30/74	=
Stern mm/°	=	=	=	=	=	=	=	=	=	=	=
Roof mm/°	10/0–7	30/0–7	10/0–7	=	10/0–6	=	=	=	=	=	=
Remarks										*Some vehicles with an additional 30 mm	*Some vehicles with an additional 30 mm

Some Ausf J with 5 cm KwK L/42 and 99 rounds
**L=4950
***L=as M
Ausf L were similar

*N=552
**N=0
***N=89
†M=Some

(a) Panzerkampfwagen—*continuation*

Designation / Ausführung	Pz Kw IV Sd Kfz 161/1 G	Pz Kw IV Sd Kfz 161/2 H	Pz Kw IV Sd Kfz 161/2 J	Pz Kw V "Panther" Sd Kfz 171 A	Pz Kw V "Panther" Sd Kfz 171 D	Pz Kw V "Panther" Sd Kfz 171 G	Pz Kw V "Panther" Sd Kfz 179 Berge Pz	Pz Kw V "Panther" Sd Kfz 179 Beob Pz
Combat weight in tons	23·6	25·0	=	45·5	43·0	44·8	42·7	41·0
Turret weight in tons	.	.	.	7·5	=	=	.	.
Maximum speed in kph								
by road	40	38	=	46	=	=	=	=
across country	16	=	=	24	=	=	20	24
Active range in km								
by road	200	=	300	177	169	177	310	210
across country	130	=	180	89	85	89	150	100
Fuel consumption in litres per 100 km of road	235	=	227	412	432	412	347	343
Fuel supply in litres	470	=	680	730	=	=	1075	720
Length overall in cm	663	702	=	886	=	=	808	688
Length without barrel in cm	591	589	=	688	=	=	808	688
Barrel overhang in cm	72	113	=	198	=	=	0	0
Width overall in cm	288	329*	=	343	=	=	328	343
Turret ring in cm	165	=	=	165	=	=	—	—
Height in cm	268	=	=	310	=	=	274	295
Axis height of gun in cm	196	=	=	226	295	300	.	.
Engine No/cylinders/type	1/12/V/O Maybach	=	=	=	=	=	=	=
Type	HL 120 TRM	=	=	HL 230 P 30	HL 210 P 30	HL 230 P 30	=	=
HP/HP:Kg	300/3·07	=	=	700/1·86	650/.	700/1·86	=	=
Cooling/cylinder capacity (litres)	W/11·87	=	=	W/23·88	W/21·35	W/23·88	=	=
Rpm	3000	=	=	=	=	=	=	=
Type of transmission	Synchron ZF SSG 77	=	=	All-claw AK 7-200 7 F 1 R	=	=	AK 7-400	AK 7-200
Gears	6 F 1 R	=	=		=	=	=	=
Type of steering	Clutch	=	=	Super-imposed	=	=	=	=
Turning at the halt	No	=	=	=	=	=	=	=
Smallest radius (metres)	5·92	.	.	10·0	=	=	=	=
Drive from	Front	=	=	=	=	=	=	=
Length of track in contact with the ground in cm	352	=	*	391	=	=	=	=
Track width in cm	40	=	**	65	=	=	=	=
Wheel base in cm	245	=	=	262	=	=	=	=
Steering ratios 1:s	1·44	=	=	1·49	=	=	=	=
Track type	Dry	=	=	=	=	=	=	=
Track spacing	99 Links	=	=	86	=	=	=	=
Bogie breadth in cm	.	.	.	86/.	=	=	=	=
Type of suspension/springs per roller	Bogie/1/2	.	.	Torsion/2	=	=	=	=
Weight/power ratio (HP/ton)	12·7	12·0	=	15·4	15·1	15·6	16·4	·
Ground pressure kg/sq cm	0·84	0·89	=	0·90	0·85	0·88	0·84	·
Ground clearance in cm	40	=	=	56	=	=	=	=
Gap crossing ability in cm	220	235	=	191	=	=	=	=
Vertical climb in cm	60	=	=	91	=	=	=	=
Gradients	30°	=	=	35°	=	=	=	=
Wading depth in cm	100	120	=	170	=	=	190	=

Designation / Ausführung	Pz Kw IV Sd Kfz 161/1 G	Pz Kw IV Sd Kfz 161/1 H	Pz Kw IV Sd Kfz 161/2 J	Pz Kw V "Panther" Sd Kfz 171 A	Pz Kw V "Panther" Sd Kfz 171 D	Pz Kw V "Panther" Sd Kfz 171 G	Pz Kw V "Panther" Sd Kfz 179 Berge Pz	Pz Kw V "Panther" Sd Kfz 179 Beob Pz
Gun calibre in cm/type	7·5/KwK 40	7·5/KwK 40	=	7·5/KwK 42	=	=	2/KwK 38	—
Length in calibres	43	48	=	70	=	=	55	—
Muzzle velocity Armour-piercing shell m/sec	740–990	750–930	=	935–1120	=	=	800–990	—
Muzzle velocity HE shell m/sec	.	550	=	700	=	=	800	—
Turret MGs number/calibre in mm	1/7·92	—**	—	1/7·92	—	1/7·92	—	1/7·92
Anti-aircraft MGs number/cal in mm	—			1/7·92	—	1/7·92	=	=
Bow MGs number/calibre in mm	1/7·92	1/9	1/9	=	=	=	—	=
Sub-machine guns number/calibre in mm							=	.
Weapons for local defence				NbW	=	=		.
Sighting equipment	TZF 5 f od. TZF 5 f 1	TZF 5 f o. TZF 5 f/1	TZF 5 f/1 o. TZF 5 f/2	TZF 12a	TZF 12	TZF 12a	KZF 2	—
Number of rounds carried for main armament	87			79		82		
MG ammunition	2250	3150		4200	4104	4200		4500
SMG ammunition		.					.	
Crew	5	=	=	=	=	=	4	4
Turret traverse	Hand-El	Hand-El	Hand	Hand-Hydr	=	=	.	.
Hull armour type	F			F				
Bow armour in mm/°	50/78*	80/78	=	80/35	=	=	=	=
Driver plate armour mm/°	50/80	80/80	=	80/35	=	=	80/40	80/35
Side armour bottom mm/°	30/90	=	†	40/90	=	=	=	=
Side armour top mm/°	30/90	=	=	40/50	=	50/60	40/50	=
Stern armour mm/°	20/78–90	=	=	40/60	=	40/0	15/0	=
Roof armour mm/°	15/0	=	16/0	15/0	=	=	=	=
Floor armour mm/°	10/0	16–30/0–6	=	20+13/0	=	=	=	=
Turret armour type mm/°	F+H			F				
Mantlet maximum mm/°				120/gew	=	=		=
Front mm/°	50/79	80/.	=	110/80	80/80	100/80	=	=
Side mm/°	30/64	=	=	45/65	=	=	—	=
Stern mm/°	30/74	†	=	45/62	=	=	—	=
Roof mm/°	10/0–6	16–30/0–6	=	15/2–7	=	=	—	=
Remarks	* Some vehicles with an additional 30 mm	* With 5 mm skirt armour ** Some with 1×7·92 † Skirt armour +8 mm	* "East Tracks" 56 ** With "East Tracks" 262 † Skirt armour 5–8 mm	Pz Bw Sd Kfz 267 m 64 rounds 7·5 MG-SAA 4800		Pz Bw Sd Kfz 268 64 rounds 7·5 MG-SAA 5100	Some with the HL 210 P 30 engine	Range finder

(a) **Panzerkampfwagen**—*continuation*

Designation / Ausführung	Pz Kw "Tiger I" Sd Kfz 181 / E	Pz Kw "Tiger II" Sd Kfz 182 / B	Pz Kw "Tiger II" Sd Kfz 182 / B*	Pz Kw "Maus" / I*	Pz Kw E 100 / B*
Combat weight in tons	55·0	69·7	69·4	188	140
Turret weight in tons	.	.	.	50	=
Maximum speed in kph					
by road	38	38	=	20	40
across country	20	17	=	.	.
Active range in km					
by road	100	110	=	190	.
across country	60	85	=		.
Fuel consumption in litres per 100 km of road	535	782	=	2525	.
Fuel supply in litres	534	860	=	4800	.
Length overall in cm	824	1026	=	1008	1025
Length without barrel in cm	620	726	=	903	869
Barrel overhang in cm	204	300	=	105	156
Width overall in cm	373 Country 315 Loaded	375 Country 327 Loaded	=	367	448
Turret ring in cm	179	.	=	300	.
Height in cm	286	309	=	366	332
Axis height of gun in cm	219	.	=	279	.
Engine No/cylinders/type	1/12/V/o	=	=		=
Type	Maybach HL 230 P 45*	HL 230 P 30	=	Daimler-Benz MB 509	Maybach HL 234
HP/HP:Kg	700/1·86		=	1200/.	1200/.
Cooling/cylinder capacity (litres)	W/21·35	W/23·88	=		W/23·4
Rpm	3000		=	2400	3000
Type of transmission	Preselector Olvar 401216 8 F 4 R	Olvar 401216 B	=	2 Electric engines	mech. hydr. combined Schalt-Lenkgetriebe "Mekydro"
Gears	.	.	=	2	
Type of steering	Double-radius	=	=	Electric	
Turning at the halt	No	=	=	—	
Smallest radius (metres)	7·0	4·8	=		
Drive from	Front	=	=	Rear	Front
Length of track in contact with the ground in cm	361	413	=	588	490
Track width in cm	72·5	80	=	110	100
Wheel base in cm	283	279	=	233	318
Steering ratio l:s	1·35	1·48	=	2·52	1·54
Track type	Dry	=	=	=	=
Track spacing	96 Links	.	=	.	
Bogie breadth in cm	.	.	=	55/10	
Type of suspension/springs per roller	Torsion bar/2	.	=	Independent/1	Interleaved/1
Weight/power ratio (HP/ton)	12·3	10·1	=	6·35	8·5
Ground pressure kg/sq cm	1·04	1·07	=	1·45	1·43
Ground clearance in cm	43	50	=	54	57
Gap crossing ability in cm	180	250	=	450	.
Vertical climb in cm	79	85	=	72	.
Gradients	35°	=	=	30°	.
Wading depth in cm	120**	160	=	200**	.

Designation / Ausführung	Pz Kw "Tiger I" Sd Kfz 181 E	Pz Kw "Tiger II" Sd Kfz 182 B	Pz Kw "Tiger II" Sd Kfz 182 B*	Pz Kw "Maus" I*	Pz Kw E 100 B*
Gun calibre in cm/type	8·8/KwK 36	8·8/KwK 43	=	15/KwK 44***	=
Length in calibres	56	71	=	38	.
Muzzle velocity — Armour-piercing shell m/sec	810	1000-1130	=	.	
Muzzle velocity — HE shell m/sec	780	700-750			.
Turret MGs number/calibre in mm	1/7·92	=	=	=	=
Anti-aircraft MGs number/cal in mm	—	1/7·92	=	=	=
Bow MGs number/calibre in mm	1/7·92	=	=	.	.
Sub-machine guns number/calibre in mm	1/9	.	.	.	.
Weapons for local defence	6 NbW	NbW	.	.	.
Sighting equipment	TZF 9 b	TZF 9 d	TZF 9 b I	.	.
Number of rounds carried for main armament	92	84	78	50	.
MG ammunition	3920	5850	.	1000	
SMG ammunition	.	.			
Crew	5	=	=	6	=
Turret traverse	Hand-Hydr	=	=	El	.
Hull armour type	F	=	=	=	=
Bow armour in mm/°	100/66	100/40	=	200/60	200/30
Driver plate armour mm/°	100/80	150/40	=	200/35	
Side armour bottom mm/°	60/90	80/90	=	80+100/90	120/.
Side armour top mm/°	80/90	80/65	=	180/90	150/60
Stern armour mm/°	82/82	80/60	=	160-165/50-60	.
Roof armour mm/°	26/0	40/0	=	100/0	.
Floor armour mm/°	26/0-9	25-40/0	=	40/0	
Turret armour type	F	.	.	F+H	=
Mantlet maximum mm/°	110/.	80/.	100/gew.	240/.	.
Front mm/°	100/80	185/80	80/60	200/60	=
Side mm/°	80/90	80/69	80/60	200/60	=
Stern mm/°	80/90	80/70	80/60	60/0	=
Roof mm/°	26/0-9	44/0-10	40/0-12		.
Remarks	* Some with the HL 210 P 45 engine ** First 495 vehicles 396 cm	* With Porsche turret		* II = MB 517 Diesel motor ** 800 cm *** In addition 7·5 cm K44 gun L/36·5 with 200 rounds instead of K15 also 12·8 cm gun with 68 rounds	* A = Motor as for "Tiger II"

(b) Sturmpanzer

(c) Jagdpanzer

Designation / Ausführung	StuG III Sd Kfz 142 B	Sd Kfz 142/2 G	Stu Pz 43 Sd Kfz 166	Stu Pz VI	Jgd Pz 38 t "Hetzer"	Jgd Pz IV Sd Kfz 162/1	Jgd Pz V "Jagdpanther" Sd Kfz 173	Jgd Pz VI "Jagdtiger" Sd Kfz 186 Henschel	Jgd Pz VI "Jagdtiger" Sd Kfz 186 Porsche	Jgd Pz Tiger (P) "Elefant" Sd Kfz 184s
Combat weight in tons	22	23·9	28·2	68	16	25·8	45·5	71·7	69·9	68
Maximum speed in kph — by road	40	=	=	=	=	=	46	38	=	20
across country	24	·	·	·	14	16	24	17	=	·
Active range in km — by road	164	169	210	120	180	200	210	170	=	150
across country	95	90	130	85	130	=	140	121	=	90
Fuel consumption in litres per 100 km of road	195	184	225	450	178	235	333	515	=	833
Fuel supply in litres	320	310	470	540	320	470	700	865	=	950
Length overall in cm	549	614	589	631	627	860	986	1066	1037	814
Length without barrel in cm	549	559	589	631	487	602	687	780	·	680
Barrel overhang in cm	0	55	0	0	140	258	299	286	·	134
Width overall in cm	295	296	310	373	263	318	328	363	359	343
Height in cm	194	215	249	346*	210	185	272	282	292	297
Axis height of gun in cm	150	·	182	·	·		196		·	
Engine No/cylinders/type	1/12/V/O Maybach	=	=	=	1/6/R/O Praga EPA AC	1/12/V/O Maybach	=	=	=	2/12/V/O
Type	HL 120 TRM	=	=	HL 230 P 45		HL 120 TRM	HL 230 P 30	=	=	HL 120 TR
HP/HP:Kg	300/3·07	=	=	700/1·86	150/·	300/3·07	700/1·86	=	=	2×320/2·88
Cooling/cyl capacity (litres)	W/11·87	=	=	W/23/88	W/7·75	W/11·87	W/23·88	=	=	W/11·9
Rpm	3000	=	=	3000	2600	3000		3000	=	
Type of transmission	Synchron ZF SSG 77	=	= ZF SSG 76	Preselector Olvar 40 12 16	=	Synchron ZF SSG 76	All-claw AK 7-400	Preselector Olvar 40 12 16 B	=	Electric Siemens
Gears	6 F 1 R	=	=	8 F 4 R	5 F 1 R	6 F 1 R	7 F 1 R	8 F 4 R	=	Continuous
Type of steering	Single-radius	=	Clutch	Double-radius	Clutch	=	Superimposed	Double-radius	=	Electric
Turning at the halt	No	=	·			No		No	=	
Smallest radius (metres)	5·8	=	5·92	7·0	4·5	5·92	10·0	4·8	=	2·15
Drive from	Front	=	=	=	=	=	=	=	=	Rear
Length of track in contact with the ground in cm	286	·	352	381	269	357	391	424	434	419
Track width in cm	40	·	40	72	35	40	65	79	65	65
Wheel base in cm	250	·	246	283	214	·	262	283	279	268
Steering ratio 1:s	1·14	·	1·43	1·35	1·25	·	1·49	1·5	1·56	1·56
Track type	Dry	=	=	=	=					
Track spacing	90 Links	=	98	96	96 Links	99	86/.			
Bogie breadth in cm										
Type of suspension/springs per roller	Torsion/1	=	Bogie/⅓	Torsion/1	Bogie/1/2	=	Torsion/2	Torsion/1	Torsion/1/2	Torsion/1/2
Weight/power ratio (ton/HP)	14·9	12·6	11·6	10·3	9·4	11·6	15·4	9·8	10·2	9·4
Ground pressure kg/sq cm	0·96	1·04	1·0	1·24	0·85	0·90	0·90	1·07	1·02	1·24
Ground clearance in cm	36	39	40	47	38	40	55	46	56	48
Gap crossing ability in cm	230	259	220	230	130	220	245	249	=	264
Vertical climb in cm	60	60	60	79	64	60	91	85	=	78
Gradients	30°	27°	30°	35°	25°	30°	35°	35°	=	22°
Wading depth in cm	80*	80	95	120	90	95	155	180	=	100

Designation / Ausführung	StuG III Sd Kfz 142 B	StuG III Sd Kfz 142/2 G	Stu Pz 43 Sd Kfz 166	Stu Pz VI	Jgd Pz 38 t "Hetzer"	Jgd Pz IV Sd Kfz 162/1	Jgd Pz V "Jagdpanther" Sd Kfz 173	Jgd Pz VI "Jagdtiger" Sd Kfz 186 Henschel	Jgd Pz VI "Jagdtiger" Sd Kfz 186 Porsche	Jgd Pz Tiger (P) "Elefant" Sd Kfz 148s
Gun calibre in cm/type	7·5/StuK 37	10·5/StuH 42	15/StuH 43	38/RW 61	7·5/PaK 39	7·5/StuK 42	8·8/PaK 43/3	12·8/PaK 44*	=	8·8/PaK 43/2
Length in calibres	24	28		5·4	48	70	71	55	=	71
Muzzle velocity Armour-piercing shell m/sec	385	—	—	—	750–930	935–1120	1000–1130	920	=	1000–1130
Muzzle velocity HE shell m/sec	420	540	241	91	550	700	700–750	920	=	700–750
Turret MGs number/calibre in mm								—	—	—
Anti-aircraft MGs number/cal in mm	—							—	—	—
Bow MGs number/calibre in mm	—	1/7·92*	1/7·92*	1/7·92	1/7·92*	1/7·92	1/7·92	=	=	—
Sub-machine guns number/calibre in mm	·	·	·	·	·	·	·	—	—	·
Weapons for local defence	·	·	·	·	·	·	·	—	—	
Sighting equipment	Sfl ZF 1	Sfl ZF 1a	Sfl ZF 1a	PaK 3×8°	Sfl ZF 1a	·	Sfl ZF 1a	WZF 2/1	=	·
Number of rounds carried for main armament	44	36	38	13	40	55	60	38	=	50
MG ammunition	—	600	=	·	600	·	600	2925	=	—
SMG ammunition		·	·	·	·	·	·	—	—	—
Crew	4	=	5	=	4	4	5	6	=	=
Elevation in degrees	+20 −10	+20 −6	+30 −8·5	+85 −0	+12 −6	+15 −5	+14 −8	+15 −7·5	=	+14 −6
Traverse in degrees	12·5 R 12·5 L	10 R 10 L	8 R 8 L	10 R 10 L	11 R 5 L	10 R 10 L	11 R 11 L	10 R 10 L	=	14 R 14 L
Hull armour type	F	=	=	=	=	=	=	=	=	=
Bow armour in mm/°	50/69	50/.	50+50/75	150/66	60/50	80/45	60/35	100/40	=	100+100/.
Driver plate armour mm/°	50/80	50/.	80/78	150/80	60/30	80/45	80/35	150/40	=	200/.
Side armour mm/°	30/90	=	20+80/90	80/90	20/75	30/90	40/90	80/90	=	80/90
Stern armour mm/°	30/60–80	50/.	20/80–82	80/82	20/75	20/60	40/60	80/60	=	80/90
Roof armour mm/°	17/5–15	30/.	10–25/0	26/0	—	—	—	—	·	
Floor armour mm/°	16/0	16–30/0	10/0	26/0	10/0	·	15–20+13/0	80/0	=	
Armoured superstructure Mantlet maximum mm/°	F	=	=	=	=	=	=	250/gew	=	
Front mm/°	50/75	50+30/.	100/50	150/45	60/gew	80/45	80/35	250/75	=	185/.
Side mm/°	30/90**	30/.	20–60/65–88	80/70	60/30	40/60	50/60	80/65	=	200/60
Stern mm/°	30/60	30/.	30/64–90	80/80	20/50	20/0	40/60	80/80	=	80/60
Roof mm/°	11/0–12	20/.	20/6	40/0	8/0		17/5	30/0	=	·
Remarks	* Later models 100 ** In addition 8/59–70	* Only on roof in later models	* Only partly available	* Including crane	* All-round traversing MG			* Or PaK 80 (same performance) some with 8·8/PaK 43/3	=	

(d) Scout Cars

Designation / Ausführung	lePz Spw Sd Kfz 222	sPz Spw Sd Kfz 231 6-wheel	sPz Spw Sd Kfz 231 8-wheel	sPz Spw Sd Kfz 234/1	sPz Spw Sd Kfz 234/2
Combat weight in tons	4·8	5·0	8·2	10·5	11·0
Turret weight in tons	·	·	·	·	·
Maximum speed in kph					
by road	80	60	85	=	=
across country		·	31	=	=
Active range in km					
by road	320	250	300	600	= ·
across country	200	150	170	·	=
Fuel consumption in litres per 100 km of road	34		46	40	=
Fuel supply in litres	110		138	240	=
Length overall in cm	472	561	580	602	=
Length without barrel in cm	472	561	580	602	=
Barrel overhang in cm	0	0	0	0	0
Width overall in cm	200	185	221	236	236
Turret (ring) in cm		·	·	·	·
Height in cm	206	224	234	210	229
Axis height of gun in cm					·
Engine No/cylinders/type					
Type	1/8/V/O Horch	1/4/R/O Büssing NAG	1/8/V/O	1/12/V/D Tatra	=
HP/HP:Kg	75/.	65/.	150/. *	220/.	=
Cooling/cylinder capacity (litres)	W/|3·51	W/3·92	W/7·91	L/14·83	=
Rpm	3600	2000	3000	2250	=
Type of transmission	Sliding pinion	6 F 6 R	Claw	6 F 6 R	=
Gears	5 F I R				=
Type of steering	All-wheel	Front-wheel	All-wheel	=	=
Smallest radius (metres)	7·9	13·5	10·5	14·9	=
Drive	All-wheel	Rear-wheel	All-wheel	=	=
Wheel base cm	282	270/95	135/140/135	130/140/130	=
Track width cm	165	154	160	194	=
Wheel diameter/width	./19	./19	./19	=	=
Suspension/number of springs per wheel	Independent/2	Bogie/I, ½	Bogie/½	=	=
Weight/power ratio (ton/HP)	15·6	13·0	18·3	21	20
Ground pressure kg/sq cm	·	·	·	·	·
Ground clearance in cm	25		28	36	=
Gap crossing ability in cm	0	·	124	·	·
Vertical climb in cm	25	·	48	·	·
Gradients	19°	20°	27°	30°	=
Wading depth in cm	60	=	100	120	=

Designation / Ausführung	lePz Spw Sd Kfz 222	sPz Spw Sd Kfz 231 6-wheel	sPz Spw Sd Kfz 231 8-wheel	sPz Spw Sd Kfz 234/1	sPz Spw Sd Kfz 234/2
Gun calibre in cm/type	2/KwK 30 o. 38	2/KwK 30	2/KwK 30 o. 38	2/KwK 38	5/KwK 39/1
Length in calibres	55	=	=	=	60
Muzzle velocity Armour-piercing shell m/sec	800–990	=	=	=	823–1198
Muzzle velocity HE shell m/sec	800	=	=	=	549
Turret MGs number/calibre in mm	1/7·92	*	=	=	=
Anti-aircraft MGs number/calibre in mm	—	—	—	—	—
Bow MGs number/calibre in mm	—	—	1/9	—	—
Sub-machine guns number/calibre in mm	1/9	—	8 NbW	—	—
Weapons for local defence	2 NbW	—			—
Sighting equipment	TZF 3a Fli Vi 38	.	TZF 6	.	TZF 46
Number of rounds carried for main armament	180	200	180	280	55
MG ammunition	1100	1500	2100	2400	1980
SMG ammunition	.		192	.	.
Crew	3	4	=	=	=
Elevation in degrees	+87 −4	.	+26 −10	+75 −0	+25 −7
Hull armour type	F	=	=	W	=
Bow armour in mm/°	14·5/.	14·5/.	14·5/62**	30/.	=
Driver plate armour mm/°	14·5/.	14·5/.	14·5/.**	30/.	=
Side armour mm/°	8/.	8/.	8/50–53	8/.	=
Stern armour mm/°	8/.	8/.	8/62	14·5/.	=
Roof armour mm/°	6/.	.	5/7–19	.	=
Floor armour mm/°			.		.
Turret armour type	F	=	=	=	40–100/gew
Mantlet maximum mm/°	—			—	.
Front mm/°	8/55	14·5/.	8/65	30/.	30/70
Side mm/°	8/55	8/.	8/62	14·5/.	10/70
Stern mm/°	8/55	8/.	8/60	14·5/.	10/70
Roof mm/°	—		5/2–12	—	10/0

Remarks

lePz Spw Sd Kfz 222: Sd Kfz 221, 2 tons, 2-man, height 180 cm, without gun. Sd Kfz 223, 4·4 tons, 3-man, height 183 cm, without gun, 1200 rounds. MG Sd Kfz 260/61, 4·3 tons, 4-man, height 178 cm, without armament

sPz Spw Sd Kfz 231 6-wheel: * Designated Sd Kfz 232, 5·2 tons, height 290 cm with antennae

sPz Spw Sd Kfz 231 8-wheel: Sd Kfz 232, height 290 cm with antennae. Sd Kfz 263, 8·1 tons, height 290 cm with antennae. 1 MG, 1000 rounds, 5-man
* Later increased to 180
** Later 30

(e) Self-Propelled Carriages

(f) Captured Types

Designation	4·7 cm PaK (t) auf Pz Kw I Sd Kfz 101 Ausf B	7·5 cm PaK 40/3 auf Sf 38 Sd Kfz 138 Motor vorne	8·8 cm PaK 43/1 auf Gw III/IV Sd Kfz 164	10·5 cm Pz FH auf Sf II Sd Kfz 124	15 cm sFH auf Gw LrS (f) Sd Kfz 135/1	60 cm Mörser Gerät 040	Pz Kw 35(t) LTM 35	Pz Kw 38(t) TNHP-S Ausf A-G	Pz Spw Panhard 178 P 204 (f)
Combat weight in tons	6·4	10·5	24·0	11·5	8·1	120	10·5	9·725	8·2
Maximum speed in kph — by road	40	42	40	=	34	10	40	42	80
across country	·	·	24	20	·	·	·	15	·
Active range in km — by road	140	185	200	140	135	·	190	230	350
across country	95	140	130	95	·	·	115	165	·
Fuel consumption in litres per 100 km of road	105	118	235	121	82		81	95	40
Fuel supply in litres	148	218	470	170	111	1200	153	218	140
Length overall in cm	442	·	844	479	531	1115	445	490	460
Length without barrel in cm	442	465	580	·	479	1115	445	490	460
Barrel overhang in cm	0	0	264	·	52	0	0	0	0
Width overall in cm	185	216	295	224	188	315	214	206	200
Height in cm	225	248	265	232	208	478	220	237	237
Axis height of gun in cm	172	·	226	194	·	305	171	167	·
Engine No/cylinders/type	I/6/R/O	=	I/12/V/O	I/6/R/O	=	I/12/V/D	I/4/R/O	I/6/R/O	I/4/R/O
Type	Maybach NL 38 TR	Praga E.P.A.*	Maybach HL 120 TRM	HL 62 TR	Delahaye 103 TT	Daimler-Benz MB 507	Skoda T II	Praga EPA*	Panhard SS
HP/HP:kg	100/4·30	125/.	300/3·07	140/4·35	80/.	1250	120/.	125/.	115/.
Cooling/cylinder capacity (litres)	W/3·79	W/7·75	W/11·87	W/6·19	W/3·55	W/44·2	Water/8·52	Water/7·75	Water/6·33
Rpm	3000	2200	3000	2600	2800	2300	1800	2200	·
Type of transmission	Sliding pinion ZF FG 31	Preselector Wilson	Synchron ZF SSG 76	SSG/46	Sliding pinion	Ardelt hydraul	·	Praga-Wilson	Inversion
Gears	5 F I R	=	6 F I R	=	5 F I R	4 F	6 F 6 R	5 F I R	4 F 4 R
Type of steering	Clutch	=	=	Single-radius	Cletrac	·	Epicyclic	Clutch	No
Turning at the halt	—	—	—	·	·	·	·	·	·
Smallest radius (metres)	—	—	—	4·8	·	·	4·9	4·5	·
Drive from	Front	=	=	·	=	·	Rear	Linked	All-wheel
Length of track in contact with the ground in cm	244	292	352	240	274	700	314	292	—
Track width in cm	28	29·3	40	28	24	50	32	29·3	—
Wheel base in cm	168	177	245	188	134	265	166	178	—
Steering ratio 1:s	1·45	1·65	1·46	1·28	2·05	2·65	1·9	1·64	—
Track type	100 Links	·	·	·	·	Dry	·	·	—
Track spacing		89	98	106	·	·	·	89	—
Type of suspension/springs per roller	Indep/I	Bogie/½	=	Bogie/I	Bogie/½	Torsion/I	Bogie/½	Bogie/½	Leaf springs
Weight/power ratio (HP/ton)	15·6	11·9	12·5	12·6	9·9	1·77	11·4	12·9	14·0
Ground pressure kg/sq cm	0·47	0·61	0·85	0·82	0·65	35	0·52	0·57	·
Ground clearance in cm	29	40	40	36	18	·	=	40	26
Gap crossing ability in cm	140	208	230	170	180	·	·	·	·
Vertical climb in cm	36	84	60	42	56	·	·	·	·
Gradients	30°	=	=	30°	24	·	28·6°	28·6°	·
Wading depth in cm	58	90	100	80	85	·	80	90	90

Designation	4·7 cm PaK (t) auf Pz Kw I Ausf B Sd Kfz 101	7·5 cm PaK 40/3 auf Sf 38 Sd Kfz 138 Motor vorne	8·8 cm PaK 43/1 auf Gw III/IV Sd Kfz 164	10·5 cm Pz FH auf Sf II Sd Kfz 124	15 cm sFH auf GW LrS (f) Sd Kfz 135/1	60 cm Mörser Gerät 040	Pz Kw 35(t) LTM 35	Pz Kw 38(t) TNHP-S Ausf A–G	Pz Spw Panhard 178 P 204 (f)
Gun calibre in cm/type	4·7/PaK (t)	7·5/PaK 40/3	8·8/PaK 43/1	10·5/leFH 18/2	15/sFH 13	60	3·7/KwK A3	3·7/KwK A7**	2·5/·
Length in calibres	43·4	46	71	28	17	8·44	40	40	73
Muzzle velocity Armour-piercing shell m/sec	775	792–933	1000–1130	—	—	—	600	600	900
Muzzle velocity HE shell m/sec	·	550	700–750	540	381	264	—	—	—
Turret MGs number/calibre in mm	—	—	—	—	—	—	1/7·92(t)	1/7·92(t)	1/7·5 (f)
Anti-aircraft MGs number/cal in mm	—	—	—	—	—	—	—	—	—
Bow MGs number/calibre in mm	·	·	·	1/7·92	·	·	1/7·92(t)	1/7·92(t)	—
Sub-machine guns number/calibre in mm	—	·	·	2/9	·	·	—	—	—
Weapons for local defence	·	·	·	·	·	·	·	·	·
Sighting equipment	·	·	Sfl ZF 1a	Sfl ZF 1	=	·	·	=	=
Number of rounds carried for main armament	86	38	40	32	8	—	72	90	150
MG ammunition	—	—	—	—	—	—	1800	2700	3150
SMG ammunition	·	·	·	·	·	·	—	—	—
Crew	3	4	5	=	=	·	4	=	=
Elevation in degrees	+12 −8	+25 −10	+20 −5	+42 −5	+40 −1·25	+75 −10	—	—	=
Traverse in degrees	15 R 15 L	30 R 30 L	15 R 15 L	17 R 17 L	7 R 7 L	2·5 R 2·5 L	—	—	=
Hull armour type	F	=	=	=	=	F	=	=	=
Bow armour in mm/°	13	20	30/78	20/75	8/gew	15	25	=	20·7
Driver plate armour mm/°	13	25	20/90	20/60–75	9/55	15	25	=	
Side armour mm/°	·	15	20/·	15/90	9/90	15	16	17·5	
Stern armour mm/°	8	·	·	8–15/80–90	9/54–79	·	·	·	
Roof armour mm/°	8	·		10/0	6/0	·	·	·	
Floor armour mm/°		·		5/0	5/0				
Turret armour type	F	F	=	=	=	—	F	=	=
Mantlet maximum mm/°	14·5	·		10/66	10/72	—	·	·	20·7
Front mm/°	14·5	25	10/60	12/69	9/78–80	—	25	25	
Side mm/°	·	10	10/74	10/73	7–9/78–79	—	15	25	
Stern mm/°	—	·	10/·	8/74	—	—	·	·	
Roof mm/°			—	—	—	—	·	·	
Remarks		With rear engine, weight 10·8 tons, length 577 cm, height 251 cm, armour 25–10 * Some 150 hp at 2600 rpm							* Later 150 hp at 2600 rpm ** Some with the German 3·7 cm KwK L/45 gun

(g) Personnel Carriers

Designation	leSPW Sd Kfz 250	mSPW Sd Kfz 251	leWS	sWS	HKp 606	HL Kl 3 (H)	HL Kl 4 (H)
Combat weight	5·7	8·5	6·9	13·5	7	6·5	6·5
Maximum speed in kph	60	50	23	27	71	50	50
Active range in km	320	300	.	300	.	.	.
Length in cm	456	580	520	667	485	510	520
Width in cm	195	210	212	250	198	200	200
Height in cm	166*	175*	200	283	185	.	.
Horse power	100	120	95	100	170	70	100
Transmission	Variorex	Schub	ZF Adler	ZF Kb 40 D	Olvar	ZF	Borgward
Gears	7 F 3 R	4 F 1 R	2×4 F 2 R	2×4 F 2 R	8 F 1 R	2×4 F 2 R	2×4 F 2 R
Steering	Cletrac	=	=	=	=	=	=
Smallest radius (metres)	9	13·5	.	.	.	.	.
Wheel base in cm	250	278	250	347	260	160	180
Track in contact with the ground in cm	120	180	135	204	150	.	.
Wheel width in cm	19	19	.	20	.	.	.
Track width in cm	24	28	.	50	.	.	.
Track base in cm	163/158	165/160	180	210/195	170	165	165
Power/weight ratio (HP/ton)	17·5	14·1	13·8	13·4	25·6	10·8	15·2
Axle load in kg	1160	1300	.	.	.	.	.
Track pressure in kg	4540	7200	.	.	.	.	.
Ground clearance in cm	28	30	.	47	.	.	.
Vertical climb in cm	24°	24°	.	24°	.	.	.
Wading depth in cm	70	50	.	1000	.	.	.
Armoured hull in front mm	12	12	.	.	.	.	26
Armoured hull at the sides in mm	7	7	.	.	.	.	11
Crew	6	12	.	.	.	.	.

* Without shield

(h) Automatic Weapons

Designation	MG 13 K	MG 34	Flak MG 151/15	Flak MG 151/20	KwK	KwK Flak	Flak MK 103	Flak
Type	MG	MG	Flak	Flak	KwK	KwK Flak	Flak	Flak
Calibre mm	7·92	7·92	15	20	20	20	30	37
Model	13 K	34	MG 151/15	MG 151/20	30	38	MK 103	43
Length in calibres	.	.	.	.	55	55	38	60
Weight of shell (gram)	12·8	12·8	72	136	115–148	115–148	330	623–658
Rpm	500–625	800–900	750	750	280	480	450	180
MV m/sec	770	770	880	760	800–900	800–900	800–900	770–820
Cooling	Air	Air	Air	Air	Air	Air	Gas pressure	Air
Model	Recoilless	Recoilless	Recoilless	Recoilless	Recoilless	Recoilless	.	Gas pressure
Type of ammunition	s S	s S	.	HE AP	HE AP AP 40	HE AP AP 40	HE AP	HE Incendiary AP
Ammunition feed	Magazines 25 or 100 Drum 50	Belt 150 Magazine 100 Belt/drum 50	.	.	Magazine 10	Magazine 10	Belt	Clip 8

(i) Tank and Anti-tank Cannon

	s Pz B	KwK	PaK	PaK	KwK	KwK	PaK	KwK
Calibre cm	2·8	3·7		4·7	5	5		7·5
Model	41		35/36	t		39	38	37
Length in calibres	61·3	45		43·4	42			24
AP shell model	41		40			38	40	
Weight kg	0·1305	0·68	0·354	1·67	2·18	2·25	0·975	6·8
MV m/sec	1402	762	1030	775	685	823	1198	385
Penetration 90°								
mm at 0 m	66	48	51			99	165	
mm at 457 m						78	120	
mm at 915 m						61	84	
mm at 1372 m						47		
mm at 1829 m								
mm at 2286 m								
Penetration 60°								
mm at 0 m	52	36	43	55		73	143	41
mm at 457 m				47	56	61	86	
mm at 915 m						50	55	
mm at 1372 m						40		
mm at 1829 m								
mm at 2286 m								
Type of shell	HE	HE	Hollow	HE	HE	HE		HE
Model	41					38		
Weight kg	0·085	0·625				1·96		5·7
MV m/sec	1400	745				549		420
	Hollow							
Remarks	Also smoke and canister shells							Also smoke and canister shells

	StuK	KwK	PaK	KwK StuK PaK	KwK	StuK	PaK
Calibre cm	7·5	7·5	7·5	7·5	7·5	7·5	7·62 (r)
Model	37	40	40	40 / 39	42	42	36
Length in calibres	24	43	46	48	70	70	54
AP shell model		39	40	39		40	39
Weight kg	6·8	6·8	3·2	6·8	6·8	4·8	7·54
MV m/sec	740	740	933	750	935	1120	740
Penetration 90°							
mm at 0 m			176	149			133
mm at 457 m			154	135			120
mm at 915 m			133	121			108
mm at 1372 m			115	109			97
mm at 1829 m			98	98			87
mm at 2286 m			83	83			78
Penetration 60°							
mm at 0 m	89	90	137	121	141		108
mm at 457 m		80	115	106	121		98
mm at 915 m			96	94			88
mm at 1372 m			80	83			79
mm at 1829 m			66	73			71
mm at 2286 m			53				64
Type of shell	HE	HE	Hollow	HE	HE		HE
Model				34			39
Weight kg				5·74	5·7		6·2
MV m/sec				550	700		550
	Hollow	Hollow					
Remarks	Also smoke and canister shells	Also smoke shells		Also smoke shells			

(i) Tank and Anti-tank Cannon—continuation

	PaK 7·62 (r)	KwK 8·8	KwK 8·8	PaK 8·8	PaK 12·8
Type	PaK	KwK	KwK	PaK	PaK
Calibre cm	7·62	8·8	8·8	8·8	12·8
Model	36 (r)	36	43	43	44
Length in calibres	54	56	71	71	55 80
AP shell model	40	·	39/43	40/43	43
Weight kg	4·05	9·4	10·16	7·3	28·3
MV m/sec	990	810	1000	1130	920
Penetration 90°					
mm at 0 m	190	·	225	311	
mm at 457 m	158	·	207	274	
mm at 915 m	130	·	190	241	215 (500 m)
mm at 1372 m	106	·	174	211	202 (1000 m)
mm at 1829 m	84	·	159	184	·
mm at 2286 m	65	·	145	159	·
Penetration 60°					
mm at 0 m	152	110	198	265	
mm at 457 m	118	·	182	226	
mm at 915 m	92	·	167	192	
mm at 1372 m	71	·	153	162	
mm at 1829 m	55	·	139	136	
mm at 2286 m	43	·	127	114	
Type of shell		HE Hollow	HE Hollow	Hollow Hollow HE	HE
Model		· ·	· 39	39/43 39 L/4·5	L/5
Weight kg		· ·	9·4 7·65	7·65 7·65 26·3	28
MV m/sec		780 ·	750 600	600 600 920	920
Remarks					

(j) High-angle Weapons

	leFH	StuH	StuH	sIG	sFH	RW
Type	leFH	StuH	StuH	sIG	sFH	RW
Calibre cm	10·5	10·5	15	15	15	38
Model	18/2	42	43	33	13	61
Length in calibres	26	28	12	12	17	54
Type of shell	HE Hollow Red	HE Smoke Hollow Red	HE Hollow	Smoke Hollow	HE Smoke	HE Hollow
Model	· ·	38·39 38 ·	33·38 38 Hl/A	38 39	14 ·	· ·
Weight kg	14·8 ·	14·8 · ·	37·8 25·0	38·8 7·65	43·4 ·	345·2 ·
MV m/sec	540 ·	540 · ·	240 275	240 600	380 ·	91 ·

Appendix 4

Production Statistics 1939–44

Panzerkampfwagen

Model	Manufacturer	Armament	Weight		Production						Total
			Net Vehicle	Gross Material	1939	1940	1941	1942	1943	1944 (45)	
II	MAN, Famo, Alkett	2 cm und 5 cm	11	22	15	9	233	306	77	7	647
38(t)	BMM Prag		11	28	—	275	698	195	—	—	1168
III	Alkett more than 50%, Henschel, MNH, Famo, MIAG, MAN, Krupp, Daimler-Benz, Wegmann	3·7 cm KwK	20	37	157	392	—	—	—	—	549
		5 cm KwK L/42	20	37	—	470	1673	251	—	—	2394
		5 cm KwK L/60	20	37	—	—	40	1907	22	—	1969
		7·5 cm KwK L/24	20	37	—	—	—	447	213	—	660
		Flammenwerfer	20	37	—	—	—	—	100	—	100
		Pz Bergewagen	20	37	32	34	132	50	14	—	262
IV	Krupp, Nibelungenwerke, Deutsche Eisenwerke, Vomag	7·5 cm KwK L/24	25	40	45	280	480	127	—	—	932
		7·5 cm KwK L/24 und spater L/48			—	—	—	837	3073	3161	7071
		Flak 3·7 cm			—	—	—	—	—	205	205
Panther	Henschel, MAN, Daimler-Benz,	7·5 cm KwK 42, L/70	45	82	—	—	—	—	1768	3740	5508
	MNH, Demag	Pz Bergewagen	40	82	—	—	—	—	82	215	297
Tiger I	Henschel	8·8 cm KwK 36 L/56	54	105	—	—	—	78	647	623	1348
Tiger II	Henschel	8·8 cm KwK 42 L/71	68	105	—	—	—	—	—	377 (108)	377 (108)
				Total	249	1460	3256	4198	5996	8328	23487

Self-propelled Carriages

Model	Manufacturer	Armament	Weight		Production						Total
			Net Vehicle	Gross Material	1939	1940	1941	1942	1943	1944	
II	Famo, Alkett	7·62 cm PaK (r)	11	20	—	—	—	185	—	—	185
		7·5 cm PaK 40			—	—	—	327	204	—	531
		le Feldhaub (Wespe)			—	—	—	—	518	164	682
		Mun Fahrz			—	—	—	—	103	55	158
38(t)	BMM	7·5 cm PaK 40	22	40	—	—	—	110	799	308	1217
		7·62 cm PaK (r)			—	—	—	344	224	146	344
		sIG			—	—	—	—	224	146	370
		Mun Fahrz			—	—	—	—	—	102	102
III/IV	Deutsche Eisenwerke	8·8 cm PaK 43			—	—	—	—	345	128	473
		sFH (Hummel)			—	—	—	9	368	289	666
		Mun Fahrz			—	—	—	—	96	54	150
				Total	—	—	—	975	2657	1246	4878

Production Statistics 1939-44—continuation

StuG Panzer and Jagdpanzer

Model	Manufacturer	Armament	Weight Net Vehicle	Weight Gross Material	1939	1940	1941	1942	1943	1944	Total
III/IV	Alkett, MIAG, Krupp	7·5 cm StuK L/24, 43 & 48	24	37	—	184	548	791	3041	4850	9414
		10·5 cm Stu-Haub			—	—	—	9	204	901	1114
StuG		Total			—	184	548	800	3245	5751	10528
38(t)	BMM Vomag, Alkett	7·5 cm PaK 39, L/48 7·5 cm	15·5	30	—	—	—	—	—	1577	1577
IV		7·5 cm Pz Jgk L/48 & 70	25	41	—	—	—	—	—	1531	1531
IV long gun	Deutsche Eisen 80%, Alkett 20%	7·5 cm KwK 42 L/70	29	40	—	—	—	24	74	215	313
Sturmtiger	Alkett	Sturm-Mörs, 38 cm	65	120	—	—	—	—	—	18	18
Jagdpanther	MIAG, MNH	8·8 cm KwK 43 L/71	46	85	—	—	—	—	2	228	230
Jagdtiger	Nibelungenwerk	12·8 cm Pjk 44 L/55	75	120	—	—	—	—	—	48	48
Elefant	Nibelungenwerk	8·8 cm PaK 43/2 L/71	68	110	—	—	—	—	90	—	90
		Jagdpanzer Total			—	—	—	24	166	3617	3807
		Total			—	184	548	824	3411	9368	14335

Others

Model	Manufacturer	Armament	Weight Net Vehicle	Weight Gross Material	1939	1940	1941	1942	1943	1944	Total
38(t)	BMM	2 cm Flak Sf	12	24	—	—	—	—	87	75	162
		Aufklärungspanzer			—	—	—	—	—	70	70
		Total			—	—	—	—	87	145	232

Total Production

1939	1940	1941	1942	1943	1944	Total
249	1644	3804	5997	12151	19087	42932

Bibliography

ANDRONIKOV, I. G. AND MOSTOWENKO, W. D. *Die roten Panzer. Geschichte der sowjet. Panzertruppen 1920–1960.* Munich, 1963.

BAUER, E. *La Guerre des Blindées.* Paris, 1947.

BOUCHER, J. *L'Arme Blindée dans la Guerre.* Paris, 1953.

BRADFORD, G. *Armoured Vehicles from their conception to the present time.* Bracknell, England, 1965.

CHAMBERLAIN, P. *A summary of German Self-propelled Weapons 1939–1945.* Bracknell, England, 1965.

—— *German Self-propelled Weapons 1939–1945.* Bracknell, England, 1966.

—— *German Half-track Vehicles 1939–1945.* Bracknell, England, 1968.

DUVIGNAC, A. *Histoire de l'Armée Motorisée.* Paris, 1947.

EINMANNSBERGER, L. *Der Kampfwagenkrieg.* Munich, 1934.

"FACTUS" (Editor). *Tanks at War.* London, 1943.

FEIST, U. AND NOWARRA, H. J. *The German Panzers from Mark I to the Mark V, Panther.* Fallbrook, California, 1966.

—— *Panzer helfen dir. Was der Panzergrenadier von den gepanzerten Kampffahrzeug wissen muss.* Germany, 1944.

FEY, W. *Panzer im Brennpunkt der Fronten.* Munich, 1960.

FULLER, J. F. C. *Armoured Warfare.* London, 1943.

GUDERIAN, H. *Achtung Panzer.* Germany, 1937.

—— *Panzer Marsch.* Munich, 1956.

—— *Die Panzertruppen und ihr Zusammenwirken mit der anderen Waffen.* Berlin, 1940.

—— *Panzer Leader.* London, 1952.

ICKS, R. J. *Tanks and Armoured Vehicles.* New York, 1945.

MELLENTHIN, F. W. VON. *Panzer Battles, 1939–1945.* London, 1955.

MINISTRY OF INFORMATION. *Britain's Fighting Vehicles.* London, 1942.

MURLAND, J. R. W. *The Royal Armoured Corps.* London, 1943.

OGORKIEWICZ, R. M. *Armour. The Development of Mechanised Forces and Their Equipment.* London, 1960.

ROGERS, H. C. B. *Tanks in Battle.* London, 1965.

ROYAL ARMOURED CORPS. *Movement and Fire Power. A Survey of the Engines, Gearboxes and Guns on Display at the R.A.C. Tank Museum.* Bovington, England, 1965.

—— *Comparative Table of Tanks used by the Tank Corps. RTC and RTR, 1916–1951.* London, 1952.

—— Tank Museum Guide Series. Part 1, *Tank 1915–1918—the First World War;* Part 2, *Tanks 1919–1939—the inter-war period;* *Part 3, *Tanks 1940–1946—the Second World War;* Part 4, *Armoured Cars 1900–1945;* Part 5, *Tanks of Other Nations.* Bovington, England, 1964; *1965.

SCHULTZ AND DEYCKE. *Das Panzer Merkbuch.* Berlin, 1937.

SENGER UND ETTERLIN. *Taschenbuch und Panzer, 1943–1957.*

F. M. VON. Munich, 1958.

S.H.A.E.F. *Summary of German Tanks.* London, 1944.

SPANNENKREBS, W. *Angriff mit Kampfwagen.* Oldenburg, 1939.

THEISS, R. *Panzer.* London, 1944.

U.S. WAR DEPARTMENT. *Handbook on German Military Forces.* Washington, 1945.

VICKERS-ARMSTRONG. *Mechanisation.* Chertsey, 1930.

DIRECTOR OF MILITARY INTELLIGENCE, WAR OFFICE. "Illustrated Record of German
   Army Equipment, 1939–1945," Vol. III. *Armoured Fighting Vehicles.* London, 1947.

WHITE, B. T. *German Tanks and Armoured Vehicles,* 1914–1945. Shepperton, England,
   1966.

WILLSON, G. B. *Tanks Advance.* London, 1942.

WILSON, A. *Flame Thrower.* London, 1956.